HUMAN NUTRITION
HISTORIC AND SCIENTIFIC

HUMAN NUTRITION
HISTORIC AND SCIENTIFIC

Monograph III

INSTITUTE OF SOCIAL AND
HISTORICAL MEDICINE

THE NEW YORK ACADEMY OF MEDICINE

Iago Galdston, M.D., Editor

INTERNATIONAL UNIVERSITIES PRESS, INC.

NEW YORK

CONTENTS

FOREWORD

The science of nutrition and the application of that science to human living has become, in common with other health professions, a matter of more than parochial professional interest. The knowledge acquired during recent decades in respect to the processes of metabolism and the intrinsic factors involved in animal metabolism have, to a great degree, raised our concepts of nutrition from the slough of empiricism to a fairly precise science. Granted that much is yet to be learned and understood in the fields of pure science, it is equally patent that, even in the light of our present knowledge, the science of nutrition today faces responsibilities and problems in the areas of the behavioral sciences, in agriculture, in ecology, in anthropology, in economics, in industry, that were little envisaged only a few short years ago. All of this and more demands review and reorientation of our thinking and our points of view. Hence this Conference and this volume.

Many of the factors involved in this change of conceptualization have not had their origin in the narrow field of the science of nutrition. They have been extrinsic rather than intrinsic. The effects of wars are hardly to be overestimated. An increasing knowledge of conditions in lands beyond the seas, food habits, customs and traditions, agriculture, local or national economies, governmental attitudes—all these and more are extrinsic factors that bring to bear their influence on the nutritional status and the health and well-being of all the peoples of the earth. In our own American economy, as well as in other nations of comparable material development, there are similar operating factors, plus the problems raised by food procurement, food processing, food storage and food distribution.

This volume suggests the enormity of these problems as they have developed and as they exist in this modern world. Physicians, as health maintenance personnel and as individuals dedicated to efforts to restore health, should be the first to grasp the importance of knowing the valid facts of nutrition as they are today. But physicians are beset by a confusion of public pressures, lay journalism, fraudulent or, to be charitable, unscientific high-pressure advertising. It becomes well-nigh impossible for the average practitioner to separate the wheat from the chaff. It is the opinion of this observer that, except in a few isolated instances, the medical school curricula have done far too little to emphasize the importance of applied nutrition as a science. High fat, low fat, high protein, are terms bandied about in clinical conference and bedside teaching. Nutrition as such, however, has in general been an accessory to the fact. It is high time for nutrition to take its rightful and valid place as a clinical as well as a purely scientific entity.

The scope of this volume, taken as a whole, attempts to present in kaleidoscope fashion the breadth and depth of the field of nutrition in the light of our present knowledge, the status of our world economy and our prospects for the future.

HOWARD REID CRAIG, M.D.

INTRODUCTION

Each new discovery in the science of nutrition permits genuine and sometimes dramatic advances in the production and use of food, as witnessed by the practical elimination of deficiency diseases, such as starvation, rickets, and scurvy from all the technologically advanced areas of the world. The benefits made possible by these research accomplishments are retarded, however, by a tendency for changed circumstances to create waves of confusion, fashion and fear that are costly to society—costly in terms of lowered health, needless sacrifices in enjoyment of living, and an enormous financial loss. Seeking health and the normal enjoyment of good meals, the public finds it difficult to be confident of what constitutes an excellent diet. The wealthy and the poor share in the same dilemma.

The health professions too, do not escape entirely from the confusion and the whirls of enthusiasm or fright that are set going by ill-advised reports to scientific journals and to the press, or more often, by disguised propaganda in advertising and in the claims of faddists.

Even the person who is alert to the hazards that beset the pathways of progress has need for the kind of judgment that is supported by a knowledge of history and anthropology when appraising food practices. The pressure of time in conventional education leaves little opportunity for cultivating this depth of interest and scholarship. Hence we are greatly indebted to the New York Academy of Medicine for an unusual breadth of viewpoint in suggesting and in organizing the Conference.

We are indebted also to Columbia University for the hospitality and the excellent facilities made available at Arden House.

For financial assistance, we are indebted equally to the Williams-Waterman Fund, the Wenner-Gren Foundation for Anthropological Research, E. R. Squibb and Sons, and the Nutrition Foundation, Inc.

The origins of nutrition as a science and the research that is currently of greatest interest are so closely interwoven with the history of medicine and with the foremost problems in public health today, that the papers scheduled for the program have a unique value.

Just as scurvy, rickets, beri beri, goiter and starvation presented staggering challenges to mankind until the third decade in the twentieth century, today, when infectious diseases are coming under control rapidly, half the world's children are still in dire need of an adequate supply of good-quality protein foods to permit normal growth and health. For them, increased consumption of such foods as milk, meat, fish or poultry (or scientifically blended proteins from plant sources) spells the difference between life and death. Among the most favored half of the world's population, malnutrition plagues those in the upper age brackets with its challenge to lower the high incidence of death and crippling diseases that are characterized by disturbances in fat metabolism; and these diseases are largely of unknown origin except as related to "eating too much" of total calories. Atherosclerosis ("hardening of the arteries"), cerebral "strokes," diabetes, and many forms of heart, liver and kidney disease undoubtedly will yield steadily to the new knowledge that derives from research and its applications in the science of nutrition. Eating as an art is very old, but as a science, very young.

C. G. KING

CONFERENCE ORIENTATION

Iago Galdston, M.D.

IN HIS very significant book, *Man and Crisis*, José Ortega y Gasset laments the anhistoricity of our age. He describes it as anhistorical, that is, not merely without an appreciation for and knowledge of history, but patently resistant and antagonistic to the framing of its knowledge and understanding in the perspectives of historical derivations and relations.

The anhistorical bias appears in its most malignant form in the dictum, "history is but the record of man's follies and failures." Even if this were true—which indeed it is not—is it not the height of blind arrogance to assume that follies and failures offer less of instruction to the open mind than do the sagacious triumphs?

Indeed, it is more than likely that an analytical study of man's failures and follies would reveal that they in no small measure derive from that *very* order of blind wilfulness that is disdainful of what "the past can teach us."

I suspect that the sage who wrote, "where there is no vision the people perish," had precisely this in mind. As Ortega so pointedly affirms, "The past is the only arsenal where we can find the means of making our future real. Man makes history because, faced with a future which is not in his hands, he finds that the only thing he has, that he possesses, is his past. Of this alone can he make use, this is the small ship in which he sets sail toward the unquiet future that lies ahead."

Confessedly, it is not easy to establish *what* exactly the past can teach us. But then it is not the "ease of" but the "need for" historical orientation that is being underscored and urged.

All about us, in the anxieties, confusions, and distempers of our contemporary world, we witness the painful yield of that anhistorical era, which, according to Ortega, began at the turn of the seventeenth century. That painful yield is most patent in the political and economic spheres of our divided world. But it is to be witnessed also in the biological realm, for example, in the explosive increase of the world's population, and the concomitant spectre of slow and corrosive famine.

Does it seem improper to have begun my introduction with some strictures on the utility of history? If so, may I affirm that this is more than a Conference on Nutrition. It is our aim to comprehend nutrition in the perspectives of history, and in that comprehension to forecast and anticipate its future.

This Conference is the third of the conferences organized by the Institute of Social and Historical Medicine of The New York Academy of Medicine. This Institute, which bears so impressive a title, has no corporate form, but like the Academy of Plato, has its locus in the faith and persuasion of its partisans. That persuasion affirms that issues and problems in contemporary medicine can best be understood when viewed in the perspective of their historical derivations.

Our understanding of the embrace of history is neither parochial nor doctrinaire; it is rather catholic and all-embracing. It is receptive to all phases of chronicled experience—in anthropology, in economics, in agricultural and animal husbandry, in clinical medicine, in laboratory research, in demography—in where and what you will. And I hope you will will to will. We do have a "spelled out program," but it is intended to be the groundwork for discussion and for the free exchange of judgment and opinion.

I know I speak for all who have shared in the planning of this Conference when I affirm that above all we wish not only to know, but also to understand. Knowing is the more narrow, understanding the broader exercise of human intelligence. But understanding calls for wide scanning and is the derivative of a relatedness established among a variety of knowledges. Requisite to the attainment of understanding are imagination and audacious venturesomeness.

Pray construe this then as an invitation to plumb the depths, and to range the breadths of the possible and the probable in the historical and social comprehension of nutrition.

FOOD HABITS IN LATIN AMERICA: A PRELIMINARY HISTORICAL SURVEY

Richard N. Adams, Ph.D.

LATIN AMERICA today presents a varied picture of food habits. Within brief geographical spans one finds wide differences in foods consumed, mode of preparation, and allotment within a population. An adequate and comprehensive history of these habits during the past half millenium is obviously out of the question here. In the first place, the term "food habits" covers a wide range of distinct, although related, phenomena. A glance at the table of contents of the National Research Council's *Manual for the Study of Food Habits* (14) suggests that the breadth of the anthropological approach has invaded the field. Not only does it include types of production, preservation, distribution, preparation, consumption and "postconsumption" practices, but it goes into the areas of division of labor, etiquette, food ideology, food technology, etc. In tracing this broad series of variables in Latin America, we are confounded by extreme differences in social types, ranging from self-contained tribal societies of the Amazonian forests to the complex urban aggregates of modern cities such as Buenos Aires, Rio, San Paulo, and Mexico City. And, finally, in the historical perspective, we must recognize a variety of aboriginal, European, Asiatic, and Creole societies that have preceded the present populations.

This essay will be limited to only two phases of food habits and to a brief review of what has happened to them in the past four hundred years. The first of these is the distribution of food preference patterns, specifically, those concerning staples and important secondary foods. The second is the nature of the social organization that influences the channeling of the available food to the people.

Food Habit Areas at the Time of First Contact

In terms of these two phases of food habits, the aboriginal Latin-American cultures at the time of first European contact may be divided into four types. The first is that based on an intensive cereal agriculture subsistence pattern, or a mixed dependence upon grains and tubers. These extended from the North American Southwest down the west side of northern Mexico, through all of central Mexico and Central America, and then down the west coast of South America to approximately the forty-second parallel south. This Isthmian-Andean area held the major high cultures of aboriginal America, together with numerous lowland tribes that, under their influence, developed to a degree that distinguished them from other less advanced societies.

Common to these high culture centers, Meso-America (Central Mexico, Yucatan, and highland Guatemala) and the Central Andes, was a series of expanding nations of tribal origin, with social classes that played a role in the differential distribution of food stuffs. The Aztecs demanded tribute in food from their conquered tribes, especially hard-to-come-by items such as salt. Salt, thus gained, was distributed principally among the nobility. The intensive cultivation of and dependence upon corn in the Meso-American area accompanied a depletion of wild fauna so that protein from that source was limited. Domesticated animals in this region were restricted to the turkey and the dog, both of which were of limited importance in the diet.

The dominant food complex of Meso-America was the famous corn and bean combination that is still the basic subsistence pattern today. The preparation of corn involved soaking it in limewater or wood-ash water in order to break down the grain so that it could be easily ground and prepared into the fine, flat corn cakes (*tortillas*) that still form the core of the Meso-American diet. As one moves out of the Meso-American area, corn continues to be a basic food of the agricultural populations, but both its processing and relative importance change. In modern Panama we can see the distinguishing character of the South American use of corn. Instead of being chemically broken down, the grain is simply crushed in a wooden mortar or on a stone. The stone was and is standard in Meso-America, but it is a tool for grinding rather than crushing. Also, in the Andes, corn is more commonly eaten green, whereas dried corn is standard in Meso-America.

The differences between Andean and Meso-American patterns in the use of corn have led Carl Sauer (63) to postulate maize as intrusive to the Andes, and hold that tubers, principally the potato, are the major crops indigenous to the region. It is true that corn did not grow at the highest altitudes, and that potatoes and the native Andean grain, quinoa, were the staples. But, archaeologically, corn appeared in the early periods of coastal Peru and was early a staple in the intermountain valleys, where major segments of the Andean population lived. At the time of contact there is no question as to the importance of corn. Rather, the Andean pattern included a variety of highland tubers (potatoes, *oca, ulluco, mashwa*) and grain crops.

The social structure of the Andean area was also highly segmented and classified. The prohibition of wild land game to all but the Inca nobility reflected a depletion similar to that occurring in Meso-America and is suggestive of the nature of the differential distribution of food that was an intrinsic part of Incaic organization. While corn was common to the Isthmian and Andean food regions, and both regions had redistribution through central authorities, the Andeans had a much more highly systematized food control system at the time of the first contacts. The justly famous Incaic system provided that two thirds of the produce of the entire empire be turned over to the state and the church; but, much of this was set aside in granaries for supply to needy populations within the empire during times of local famine. Thus did the Incas build their state on the sufficient distribution of food.

The next major area can be called the "eastern farmers." This region extends roughly from longitude 60 west to the Atlantic coast, and includes also the Caribbean coast of northern South America. Here, the northern and southern extremities are broken up by a third type of area, the collecting, to be discussed below. The eastern farmers differed from the Isthmian-Andean peoples both in terms of staples and social organization. Here the so-called poisonous or bitter manioc was the staple, and hunting, fishing, and gathering played a highly significant role in both economy and diet. These forms of collection, however, were still secondary to agriculture. While manioc was the staple, other plants were domesticated throughout this area; important among these were the sweet manioc, or yuca, and maize.

The eastern farmers lived in tribal and band organizations, moving every few years as they wore out their cultivation grounds. While they had chiefs, who were responsible in some cases for holding the bands together, there was no social stratification such as characterized the Isthmian-Andean area, and therefore no such channeling of food distribution through limited segments of the total population. The redistribution pattern in which gifts were given to the chief also required an equal or greater return on his part. Despotism was probably not characteristic of these tribal chiefs, nor was a palpable differentiation in food distribution due to segmentation of the society.

Our third area is that of the collectors. This is not a single, contiguous region, but rather a type of region that was found both at the northern and southern extremes of Latin America and in some internal regions as well. Although collectors, including gathering, hunting, and fishing peoples, appear to exercise less control over their food supply than do farming societies, they still have a good deal to say about what they consume. From the wide variety of foods available to collectors of the forest regions, selections and restrictions were made through taboos, traditions, and preferences. Thus Holmberg (34) reports that a Siriono family, although many days without food, would not eat meat since it had no fire with which to cook it. Levi-Strauss has noted in this respect that "no fundamental culture trait depended directly upon the botanical environment" (41).

Nevertheless, collectors collected only from what was available, and this in itself is enough to distinguish widely differing food habit patterns. In the north of Mexico the food gatherers subsisted in what was essentially an arid or desert area. They depended upon "tuna, mesquite, rabbits, deer, ducks, and other small animals; seeds were of slight importance" (46). As in the case of most such collecting societies, they utilized methods of extraction and preparation that have in some part been lost to us now. In the far south there were two general types of collectors, the hunters and gatherers of the pampas of Patagonia, and the Fuegian tribes of south Chile and Tierra del Fuego. The former were hunters and gatherers, depending upon the guanaco and ostrich and a variety of other smaller game, roots, seeds, berries, and fruits. The Fuegian tribes were principally coastal and depended upon sea hunting and fishing.

In the area of the Orinoco and along the southeastern Brazilian coast were other collecting tribes, groups that occupied regions unsuited to agriculture or that traditionally depended upon hunting and riverine resources. Such groups were and are to be found scattered through the tropical lowlands of South America.

The final area here distinguished is the interior of South America, stretching from the Andes on the west to the eastern farmers. This region is distinguished because it is a mixture of the major elements that characterize the areas surrounding it. Although there is dependence on lowland farming, bitter manioc is not the characteristic staple in much of it. Also, agriculture is generally secondary to hunting, fishing, and gathering. Some tribes move from agricultural plots to hunting areas, and many divide their labor so that the men are concerned mainly with collecting activities and the women are responsible for the agriculture. Along the base of the Andes, in the Peruvian and Ecuadorian *montãna,* there is a notable influence of the Andean highlands in many aspects of the culture.

Typical of the collecting and interior areas is a complete

lack of social stratification along class lines. Food distribution is made along familial and kin relationships on the one hand, and on residential propinquity on the other. In one of the few careful studies of food distribution among these tribes, Henry (32) has shown that generosity with food was a major way for a headman to keep his group together and, if anything, the weaker tended to receive more gifts than the stronger. While periods of scarcity affected the group, they were felt equally by all. There was no systematic storage such as developed in the Andes, so reciprocal exchange played a much larger role than did redistribution of food.

Changes in Food Habits Since the First Contacts

Archaeology indicates that there had been a regular shifting in food habit emphasis during the centuries preceding the arrival of the Europeans in the New World. In areas long used to the yoke of conquest and increasing population, the arrival of the Spaniards was merely a new development. Urbanization started on the Peruvian coast by the thirteenth century and, under both the Meso-American and Andean empires, hunting had ceased to play any role in subsistence.

In Meso-America the growth of the Spanish colonial system did not alter the traditional subsistence habits of the majority of the population. It did, as elsewhere, have a startling effect on the general welfare of the people and in Central Mexico the population dropped from about ten million in 1520 to two and one half million a hundred years later. The basic food habits that are to be found in the countryside of Meso-America today, however, are clearly carry-overs from the pre-contact period. Corn and beans remain dominant in the higher regions, and the special lime or wood-ash chemical breakdown of the corn for grinding and ultimate conversion into the tortilla is still found from Mexico to Costa Rica. The most significant innovation in this diet is the appearance of sorghum in areas of soil depletion. This crop continues to give a good yield where corn weakens, and, what is more important, it can be handled in the domestic economy in the same manner as corn.

This central complex of food is supplemented today by animal products, especially meat, whenever possible. In the populations maintaining an indigenous tradition, the food making the greatest inroad has been the plantain. There has also been regional acceptance of certain crops due to their peculiar adaptability to a climatic situation. Thus in the higher areas of Guatemala wheat and sheep are important, although the latter are perhaps more important for their wool than for their meat. The major change in diet of Meso-America, however, is not a result of a gradual diffusion of European products into the older Meso-American system, but of a gradual and differential shift of the entire culture to a new tradition. Where food patterns are found to be different today in Meso-America, the differences basically reflect the fact that the entire cultures are different. While there has been a certain amount of food habit syncretism, the greatest consistent differences evident in the studies of the Institute of Nutrition in Central America are between Spanish Americans and Indians, and between the rural and urban components of the population (23, 24, 25, 55, 56, 57, 58, 64). Rice, wheat bread, tubers, greases, and the greater use of meats are the mark of the Spanish-American culture and urban aggregates. In the rural areas it is the wealthier families that partake of these essentially urban habits; the poorer families tend to eat beans, corn, vegetables, and meat whenever available. A curious nutritional consequence of this differential is that in some communities it is the poorer families who show a nutritionally superior diet; the wealthier have been drawn away from the better-balanced Indian diet by the urban habits of consumption of sweets, wheat bread, and fats. This is not universal, but it has appeared in enough of the INCAP dietary surveys to suggest that it is certainly not unique. The same situation is to be found where people of the Spanish-American heritage live side by side with Indians in Central American communities. The Spanish-Americans' diets turn out at times to be nutritionally inferior to those of their lower-class Indian neighbors. In the urban, Ladino, and wealthy categories we find a general decrease in the amount of corn consumed.

The Andean countries, unlike the Meso-American, have undergone a significant regional change in patterns. The difference becomes evident when we move from Costa Rica, across the border into Panama. Although indigenous patterns have remained dominant in the Andean highland population, the lowland diet has shifted strongly toward a base of European-introduced staples. The most important of these is rice. From Panama, south along the west coast of Peru and the eastern region of the Andes, rice has become a major staple. Although the reasons behind this are complex, the following circumstances may account for it.

The Andean area, like Central Mexico, underwent an enormous population decrease following the conquest. In the first fifty years of Spanish control the population of the Inca Empire dropped from approximately six million to one and one half million, roughly the same proportion as the loss in Central Mexico. While data are far from complete, the research of Rowe (61) suggests that the greatest loss by far was in the coastal rather than the highland areas. The

Chincha Valley was reduced from fifty thousand to two thousand and the Rimac Valley (where Lima is located), from one hundred and fifty thousand to nine thousand. When the population finally began to recuperate, in the eighteenth century, the population increase on the coast was basically Spanish-American, while in the highland there tended to be a renewed population maintaining a basically Indian tradition.

The fantastic loss of population along the coast, plus the Spanish demand for the lowland cereal, rice, probably account in part for the successful dominance of that food. The Spanish consistently introduced their crops and animals all over the Andes, but altitudinal differences precluded the acceptance of some, while the highland populations simply undertook the cultivation of wheat and barley as a necessity for tribute payment and seldom took these foods into their own diet. Thus, while many crops of European origin were being cultivated extensively in the highlands, in 1600 the diet of the Indian could still be described as consisting of quinoa flour, potatoes, and dried llama meat. The highlanders rejected the new crops because they did not need them, but, of more importance, the social structure of the agricultural producing unit was not broken down. The Spanish conquest merely placed a new leader on top and broke up the Incaic redistribution system.

Urbanization in the Andean coastal valleys started before the conquest, as did the strict control of food production. By the eighteenth century rice was a crop of important urban consumption supplied by the coastal area. South of Meso-America, in Panama, rice is the major staple. In rural Panama it is two to four times as important as corn, but in urban Panama rice vastly outweighs the aboriginal grain. In studies of the Peruvian Institute of Nutrition, rice consistently appears as an important staple on the coast. The importance of rice on the jungle side of the Andes answers to another set of historical circumstances. There the European staple was preferred by the Spanish-American settlers to the native corn, and the new communities that grew up in that region were populated by these immigrants.

The Andean situation differs from the Meso-American picture, then, in that there is also a strong regional difference in terms of highlands and lowlands as well as rural-urban differences. While altitude differences are of local importance in Meso-America, there is no vast areal distinction simply because the staples, corn and beans, grow equally well in both areas. Quinoa and potatoes grow neither in the tropical jungle nor on the coastal valleys of Peru, nor does rice survive in the highlands. Where wheat, barley, and other European crops have been successfully taken into the highland diets, there is a strong Spanish-American component in the population as is the case in the eleven-thousand-foot-high Jauja Valley of Central Peru. The Isthmian-Andean area has become further differentiated today than it was at the time of first contact, and this differentiation has taken place along geographic, urban-rural, ethnic, and wealth lines. In all, however, the dominance of European-derived food habit patterns is to be found only as they have been synthesized with aboriginal habits, specifically, as they have been carried by actual population segments with a general European or Spanish-American tradition. Introduced staples have not significantly diffused into the indigenous populations; indigenous staples, on the other hand, have been taken over to a great extent by the Spanish-American population.

Events in the other aboriginal areas have been similarly

complex. The pampa collectors of the far south, following the introduction of the horse, experienced a development parallel to that of our own Plains Indians. Meat became the major item of their diet. The Spaniards, availing themselves of the pasturage of the pampa region, developed a cattle culture that dominated their diet. Jesuit missionary reports of 1750 claimed that the rural farmer ate two kilograms of meat per meal, and that he consumed nothing else except water and *mate*. The rank and file of the army at this period received between three and four kilograms as their daily ration, and nothing more, and to this was added biscuit and dried *pimiento* for the officers.

The present area of northeast Argentina, Uruguay, eastern Paraguay, and southern and central western Brazil is what de Castro regards as a generally well-fed region (18, 19). The food patterns in this area vary, with heavy emphasis on beef in the south, manioc as a staple in the west and interior section, and a wide variety of commercial crop production in much of it. Here are to be found patterns of the variety of European settlers combining with the aboriginal manioc, beans, and corn. In the rural areas, particularly toward the interior, the aboriginal complex dominates, with rice for urban consumption added in irrigated regions.

In this area and in northeastern Brazil the aboriginal population has essentially been extinguished. In some cases refugee groups have pushed back into the interior, but for the most part we know these groups only through early accounts. They were first friends, then enemies, then slaves and labor for the developing plantation systems of eastern Brazil. A few, such as the Cayuá, have until recent years stayed just out of reach of the neo-Brazilians. Among surviving aboriginal groups, the degree of change in food patterns is directly related to the degree to which their hunting and collecting activities have been restricted and the degree to which they have undertaken to trade with Westerners. The Cayuá, as an example, have shifted more than ever onto a diet dependent upon agricultural products, but the staples are still of aboriginal origin. Tribes of the area that we called the interior at the time of contact have been touched less directly, but they have received various indirect influences and have maintained an aboriginal adjustment to the habitat to a greater degree than have any other Indians to the east or west.

Manioc, corn, and beans—the first is the principal staple—have survived over most of the Amazon basin. Although, as James (37) has pointed out, the Amazon flood plain is a strong potential rice-producing area, very little of it is so used. Evidently the movement of Ibero-Americans into the area has been such that an adjustment to aboriginal patterns has been easier than the introduction of new cereal crops. One of the consequences of contact between some of these tribes and the expanding Brazilians has recently been described by Murphy and Steward (50). In former years many of these groups were organized in tribal societies with leaders and, presumably, there was considerable exchange of foodstuffs. The contact with Brazilian economic needs has tended to break down the societies into individual family units, each of which works more or less alone in the process of extracting jungle products for sale. This breakdown reflects a shift in dependence from extended kinship and tribal territorial ties to dependence upon profits and goods derived from trade with the outside and a consequent breakdown of the reciprocal exchange fundamental to the earlier groupings. Although the food insurance of the tribal and kin-based society has thus deteriorated, the basic food patterns of these people are doubtless similar to those of earlier years.

Nutritional studies of semi-horticultural, semi-hunting tribes are few. In one such study, on the Miskito of Nicaragua, Pijoan (53), concludes that although eating is irregular, the diet is generally adequate. The major staple of this group is the banana, but there is both extensive and varied supplementation from numerous wild meat and vegetable sources.

An Overview

The foods of the Europeans have made rather less impression on the New World than have other aspects of their culture. Whereas European languages and political systems, European religions and territorial organizations have eliminated the aboriginal from many parts of the continent, and have markedly altered it elsewhere, almost nowhere have European foods entirely pushed aboriginal foods out of the picture, and in very few places have they taken over as staples in essentially aboriginal populations. If one were to pick the introduced foods that have made the greatest impression on contemporary diets, they would probably be rice, wheat, the plantain, cattle, pigs, and chickens. The last of these is mentioned with some reservation, for although every rural yard has chickens, most are for sale rather than consumption. Of these, and the other foods once available to tribal societies, nothing has successfully replaced the wild meat which was subsequently restricted from the general diet with the pre-Columbian higher cultures of the Isthmian-Andean region. Beef is nutritionally sound, but economically out of the question for many. Although wheat, barley, and other European grains have become of major importance in much of Latin America, it is in areas of European culture tradition that they are staples. They are secondary or unimportant where aboriginal traditions dominate. On the other hand, beans, corn, manioc, and a variety of New World crops have been taken over by many Ibero-American populations in essentially the same form, but not necessarily to the same extent, as used by the Indians.

The segmentation of society that characterizes the Western urban-rural axis has led to differentiation in food patterns not only as between the urban and rural, but also along ethnic lines, wealth and occupational differences, and regional specialization of production. As nutritionists have long been aware, the differential distribution of food due to these factors is just as important in determining nutritional status as is the outright absence of foods due to reasons of environment or taboo. Although transportation of foods can today sustain such metropoli as Mexico City, Buenos Aires, Sao Paulo, and Rio de Janeiro, food taboos, class prestige, and economic ability still reduce the effectiveness of some diets.

While publicists and politicians have from time to time felt the necessity of calling the world's attention to the fact that many of the people of Latin America are malnourished, there has also been some prejudiced reporting on the matter. The International Labor Organization (36), after consulting with a few people, declared almost all aborigines to be in an incredible state of undernourishment. De Castro (19) claims that all but a small portion of the southeast coast of South America is in dreadful condition. These claims cannot be sustained on the basis of the present survey. Where intensive dietary studies have been made, the results have varied. In a study of over one thousand Otomi Indians in 1946 (1), it is reported that they have a well-balanced diet. The work of

INCAP, while demonstrating serious infant malnutrition, has certainly not shown that general diets adversely affect the individual. Although there are specific lacks, these are often regional in nature, and the reasons for their presence or absence are not always clear on the basis of our present knowledge of food habits.

The present survey suggests that while European foods have added greatly to the range of diets in Latin America, the surviving aboriginal diets have sometimes proved to be more satisfactory nutritionally than the mixed diets of new tradition. Because of socioeconomic factors, the new mixed diets are so limited in their distribution that it is virtually impossible to generalize concerning their effect on nutrition. The development of a diet, well adjusted both to the habitat and the necessities of the population, is a delicate process at best; when it is beset by a multitude of accelerating changes, such as Latin America has experienced in recent years, it can hardly stabilize with ease. Unfortunately, our knowledge of this subject is just beginning. The dietary surveys are as yet few and far between; fewer yet have taken into account the social variables that can be significant for understanding differences in food distribution and preference.

Finally, it is clear from these glimpses into a vast and underexplored field that food habits, if anything, have tended to change rather less rapidly than other aspects of culture, and that where they occur, they signal a much vaster change in the entire social structure. The entrance of wheat bread, milk, and more meat in the Meso-American diet today is a part of ladinoization and urbanism, and the motives leading to their acceptance are not, fundamentally, an interest in better nutrition. The dominance of rice in the lowland Andean zone heralds the fact that these populations are no longer basically Indian.

If a change in the pattern of staples means a change in the entire culture of a society, the nutritionist is indeed engaged in a momentous and far-ranging task. It may, in fact, be more difficult than the recent attempt to eliminate the family in Communist China, or the almost successful attempt to eradicate the American Indian in the course of our own westward expansion.

REFERENCES

1. Anderson, R. K.; Calvo, S.; Serrano, G. and Payne, G. L.: A Study of the Nutritional Status and Food Habits of Otomi Indians in the Mezquital Valley of Mexico. *Amer. J. Pub. Health, 36:*833-903, 1946.
2. Aschmann, Homer: A Primitive Food Preparation Technique in Baja California. *Southwestern J. Anthropol., 8:*36-39, 1952.
3. Beals, Ralph L.: *Cheran: A Sierra Tarascan Village.* Smithsonian Institution, Inst. of Soc. Anthropol., Pub. No. 2, 1946.
4. Beals, R. L. and Hatcher, E.: Diet of a Tarascan Village. *America Indigena, 3:*295-304, 1943.
5. Benedict, F. G. and Steggerda, M.: *The Food of the Present-Day Maya Indians of Yucatan.* Carnegie Inst. Wash. Pub. No. 456, 1937, pp. 155-188.
6. Bennett, Wendell C.: The Andean Highlands: An Introduction. *Handbook of South American Indians, 2:*1-60, 1946.
7. Bennett, Wendell C. and Zingg, Robert M.: *The Tarahumara: An Indian Tribe of Northern Mexico.* Chicago: University of Chicago Press, 1935.
8. Blom, Frans: Letters to Editor. *Amer. Anthropol. 58:*185-186, 1956.
9. Carr, L. G.: Survival Foods of the American Aborigines. *J. Amer. Dietetic Assoc., 19:*845-847, 1943.

10. Collazos, Carlos: La Dieta del Indio. *Arch. Venezol. Nutricion,* 5:343-346, 1954.
11. Collazos, Carlos; White, Hilda S.; Reh, Emma; Huenemann, Ruth L. and White, Philip L.: Dietary Surveys in Peru, I: San Nicolas, a Cottan Hacienda on the Pacific Coast. *J. Amer. Dietetic Assoc., 29:*883-889, 1953.
12. Collazos, Carlos; White, Hilda S.; Huenemann, Ruth L.; Reh, Emma; White, Philip L.; Castellanos, Aurora; Benites, Rosa; Bravo, Yolanda; Loo, Angelica; Moscoso, Irma; Caceres, Carmen and Dieseldarff, Aida: Dietary Survey in Peru, III. Chacan and Vicos: Rural Communities in the Peruvian Andes. *J. Amer. Dietetic Assoc., 30:*1222-1230, 1954.
13. Committee on Food Habits, National Research Council: *The Problem of Changing Food Habits.* Washington: National Research Council Bulletin 108, 1943, p. 177.
14. Committee on Food Habits, National Research Council: *Manual for the Study of Food Habits.* Washington: National Research Council Bulletin 111, 1945, p. 142.
15. Cook, S. F.: The Mechanism and Extent of Dietary Adaptation among Certain Groups of California and Nevada Indians. *Ibero-Americana, 18,* 1941.
16. Cook, S. F. and Simpson, Lesley Byrd: The Population of Central Mexico in the Sixteenth Century. *Ibero-Americana, 31,* 1948.
17. Darling, R. C.; Johnson, R. E.; Pitts, G. C.; Consolazio, F. C. and Robinson, P. F.: Effects of Variations in Dietary Protein on the Physical Well-being of Men Doing Manual Work. *Nutrition, 28:*273-281, 1944.
18. de Castro, J.: Areas Alimentaies do Brasil. *Trab. e Pesq. Inst. Nutricao. Univ. Brasil, 1:*19-45, 1948.
19. de Castro, Josué: *The Geography of Hunger.* Boston: Little, Brown, 1952.
20. Departamento de Nutricion del Ministerio de Salud Publica y Asistencia Social (Peru): La Familia Peruana: Suma y Resta de su Nutricion. Biblioteca de la Revista, *Salud y Bienestar Social,* No. 1, Lima, 1954.
21. Dickens, D. and Ford, R. N.: Geophagy (dirt eating) among Mississippi Negro School Children, *Amer. Soc. Rev., 7:*59-65, 1942.
22. Driver, H. E. and Massey, W. C.: Comparative Studies of

North American Indians. *Transactions Amer. Phil. Soc.*, 47:165-456, 1957.

23. Flores, Marina; Caputti, Telma H.; Leyton, Zela; Pineda, Luz Maria et al.: Estudios Dieteticas en Nicaragua, Municipio de San Isidro, Depto. de Matagalpa. *Boletin Sanitario Min. de Salubridad,* July, 1956, pp. 2-21.

24. Flores, Marina; Leyton, Zela and Garcia, Berta: Estudios Dieteticas en Nicaragua, II Barrio de San Luis, Ciudad de Managua. *Boletin Sanitario Min. de Salubridad,* July, 1956, pp. 31-52.

25. Flores, Marina; Meneses, Berta; Flores, Zoila and de Leon, Marta: *Estudio Dietetico de la Hacienda Chocola.* Unpublished manuscript.

26. Foster, George M.: *Empire's Children. The People of Tzintzantzan.* Smithsonian Inst., Inst. of Soc. Anthro., Pub. 6, 1948.

27. Gillin, John: Houses, Food and the Contact of Cultures in a Guatemalan Town. *Acta Americana, 1:*344-359, 1943.

28. Gillin, John: *Moche: A Peruvian Coastal Community.* Smithsonian Inst., Inst. of Soc. Anthro., Pub. No. 3., 1945.

29. Gladwin, Thomas: Climate and Anthropology. *Amer. Anthropol., 49:*601-611, 1947.

30. Gonzales, S. M.: Una Encuesta Alimentaria en 103 Familias de la Parroquia de El Valle (Dist. Fed.). *Arch. Venezol. Nutricion, 7:*167-209, 1956.

31. Gonzales Puccini, A. et al.: Estudios Sanitarios Sociales en un Centro Experimental Rural. Aspectos Generales y en Cuesta Alimentaria en Santa Teresa del Tuy. Primera Communicacion. *Arch. Venezol. Nutricion, 3:*113-177, 1952.

32. Henry, Jules: The Economics of Pilaga Food Distribution. *Amer. Anthropol., 53:*187-219, 1951.

33. Hewes, Gordon W.: The Rubric "Fishing and Fisheries." *Amer. Anthropol., 50:*238-246, 1948.

34. Holmberg, Allan A.: *Nomads of the Long Bow.* Inst. Soc. Anthropol., No. 10, 1950.

35. Huenemann, Ruth L.; Bruch, Hans A. and Scholes, Robert T.: A Dietary Survey in the Sta. Cruz Area of Bolivia. *Amer. J. Trop. Med. and Hyg., 6:*21-31, 1957.

36. International Labor Organization. *Indigenous Peoples.* Geneva, 1953.

37. James, Preston: *Latin America.* New York: Odyssey Press, 1942.
38. Jelliffe, D. B. and Williams, L. L.: A Clinical Nutrition Survey in a Rural Jamaican Village (with especial reference to the children). *J. Trop. Med. Hyg. 57:*27-40, 1954.
39. Klatsky, M.: Studies in the Dietaries of Contemporary Primitive Peoples. *J. Dent. Res., 26:*473, 1947.
40. Kubler, George: The Colonial Quechua. *Handbook of South American Indians, 2:*331-410, 1946.
41. Levi-Strauss, Claude: The Use of Wild Plants in Tropical South America. *Handbook of South American Indians, 6:*465-486, 1950.
42. Lewin, Kurt: Forces Behind Food Habits and Methods of Change. *Bull. National Research Council, 108:*35-65, 1943.
43. Linton, Ralph: *Crops, Soils and Culture in America.* In: *The Maya and Their Neighbors,* Ed. C. L. Hayes et al., New York: D. Appleton-Century Co., 1940, pp. 32-40.
44. Lowie, Robert H.: Property Among the Tropical Forest and Marginal Tribes. *Handbook of South American Indians, 5:*351-367, 1949.
45. Lowie, Robert H.: Social and Political Organization of the Tropical Forest and Marginal Tribes. *Handbook of South American Indians, 5:*313-350, 1949.
46. Mason, J. A.: Report: The Third Round Table Conference in Mexico. *Amer. Anthropol. 46:*118-123, 1944.
47. Mills, Clarence A.: Influence of Environmental Temperatures on Warm-blooded Animals. *Annals N. Y. Acad. Sci., 46:*97-105, 1945.
48. Suarez, A. Mosqueda: La Arepa Criollo. *Arch. Venezol. Nutricion, 5:*407-423, 1954.
49. Munsell, Hazel E.: Food and Nutrition Problems in Puerto Rico. *J. Amer. Dietetic Assoc., 20:*305-307, 1944.
50. Murphy, Robert F. and Steward, Julian H.: Tappers and Trappers: Parallel Process in Acculturation. *Economic Development and Culture Change, 4:*335-355, 1956.
51. Parsons, Elsie Clews: *Peguche, Canton of Otavalo, Province of Imbabura, Ecuador.* Chicago: University of Chicago Press, 1945.
52. Passin, Herbert and Bennett, John W.: Social Process and

Dietary Change. *Bull. National Research Council, 108*:113-123, 1943.

53. Pijoan, Michel: *The Health and Customs of the Miskito Indians of Northern Nicaragua: Interrelationships in a Medical Program.* Mexico: Ediciones del Instituto Indig. Interam, 1946.

54. Planchart, A.: Estudio Nutricional de la Problacion Obrera de Chacao Durante el Ano 1948. *Arch. Venezol. Nutricion, 1*:59-82, 1950.

55. Reh, Emma: *Paraguan Rural Life—Survey of Food Problems.* Washington: Inst. Inter-American Affairs, 1946.

56. Reh, E.; Castellanos, Aurora and de Rueda, Yolanda Bravo: Estudio de la Dieta y de las Condiciones de Vida Existentes entre los Trabajadores de una Plantacion a Zucaheha de Guatemala. *Boletin de Oficina Sanitaria Panamericana, 37*:32-52, 1954.

57. Reh, Emma and Fajardo, Gloria: *Condiciones de Vida y de Alimentacion de Algunos Grupos de Poblacion Urbana y Rural de la Zona Central de Honduras in Estudios Nutricionales en Honduras.* Min. de Sanidad y Beneficencia, Tegucigalpa, Honduras, 1955, pp. 7-48.

58. Reh, Emma and Fernandes, Claudia: Condiciones de Vida y de Alimentacion en Cuatro Grupos de Poblacion de la Zona Central de Costa Rica. *Boletin de Oficina Sanitaria Panamericana, Suplemento No. 2,* 66-89, 1955.

59. Robinson, W. D.; Payne, G. C. and Calvo, J.: A Study of the Nutritional Status of a Population Group in Mexico City. *J. Amer. Dietetic Assoc., 20*:289-297, 1944.

60. Romero, Emilie: *História Económica del Perú.* Buenos Aires: Editorial Sudamericana, 1949.

61. Rowe, John Howeland: Inca Culture at the Time of the Spanish Conquest. *Handbook of South American Indians, 2*:183-330, 1946.

62. Santa Maria, Julio V.: Nutrition in Chile. *J. Amer. Dietetic Assoc., 20*:312-314, 1944.

63. Sauer, Carl O.: *Agricultural Origins and Dispersals.* American Geographical Society, Bowman Memorial Lectures, Series II. New York, 1952.

64. Sogandares, L.; de Galindo, Antonia P. and Mejia, Hilda

P.: Estudios Dieteticas de Grupos Urbanos y Rurals de la Republica de el Salvador. *Boletin de Oficina Sanitaria Panamericana, Suplemento No. 1:*27-37, 1953.

65. Stefansson, V.: Food of Ancient and Modern Stone Age Man. *J. Amer. Dietetic Assoc., 13:*102-119, 1937.

66. Taylor, Douglas: The Meaning of Dietary and Occupational Restrictions Among the Island Carib. *Amer. Anthropol. 52:*343-349, 1950.

67. Thomson, A. M. and Duncan, D. L.: The Diagnosis of Malnutrition in Man. *Nutrition Abstracts and Reviews, 24:*1-18, 1954.

68. Van der Sar, A.: Incidence and Treatment of Kwashiorkor in Curacao. *Doc. Neerland. Indones. Morb. Trop. 3:*25-44, 1951.

69. White, H. S.; Collazos, C. C.; White, P. L.; Huenemann, R. L.; Benites, R.; Castellanos, A.; Bravo, Y.; Moscoso, I. and Dieseldorff, A.: Dietary Surveys in Peru, II. Yurimaguas, A Jungle Town on the Huallaga River. *J. Amer. Dietetic Assoc., 30:*856, 1954.

70. Woodbury, R. M.: *Food Consumption and Dietary Surveys in the Americas.* Montreal: International Lab. Off., 1942, p. 64.

71. Yacoleff, E. and Herrera, F. L.: El Mundo Vegetal de los Antiguos Peruanos. *Revista del Museo Nacional, 3:*243-322, 1934; *4:*31-102, 1935.

FOOD AND FOOD HABITS
IN ALASKA
AND NORTHERN CANADA

Vilhjalmur Stefansson

IN 1906 I resigned as teaching fellow in anthropology at
Harvard University to become field anthropologist of a
polar expedition. I spent the midwinter, 1906-1907, studying
the rich and difficult Eskimo language, and learning whatever I could about the Mackenzie Delta Eskimos. My book
(9) tries to tell the whole story, and so does my report to
the American Museum of Natural History, published in
1914, but in this paper I concentrate on food, housing and
clothing. The winter houses and the clothes I liked from
the start, but the food was at first a problem.

I had somehow acquired in childhood the notion that I
"couldn't eat fish," and we were facing a winter of nothing
but fish, except for some 200-pound bags filled with white
whale oil and seal oil, and also a little polar bear fat. The
tea would give out in the late autumn, there would be no
sugar, salt, flour—in short, nothing but fish to eat and water
to drink. It took a day or so before I could do more than
nibble at and reject fish. I lived on water. Then I began to
nibble and swallow. In a few weeks I was eating square
meals, and in a few more I was enjoying fish, boiled or raw.

I want to describe now a typical midwinter round, from an afternoon to a forenoon of clear skies, little or no wind, a temperature anywhere from 20° to 50° F. below zero, and no sunlight, but so bright a twilight that one could have played football during the three or so hours around noon.

We begin the day's story at about four in the afternoon. We were on a four-meal schedule. We had enjoyed a frozen fish lunch around eleven o'clock and were looking forward to a dinner of boiled fish at half past four. Since about noon I had been sitting on a block of snow, with my back to the wind (if there was any), and jigging for river fish through an eighteen-inch hole in the three-foot-thick ice of the Mackenzie's easternmost channel.

Around four o'clock we began watching each other more closely, for when one fisher stopped, we all stopped. Then we put on our mitts—Eskimos fished with hands bare—scooped up the fish, and poured them into a bag. It was not good form to hurry. With cultivated deliberation I filled my bag, shouldered it, and walked slowly toward the fish platform, high above the reach of the dogs, where were heaped already tons of glass-hard fish. At the fish cache there was some social order: the older people first, irrespective of sex and, first of all, the visitor, myself.

Two persons were never on the platform together, unless for a special reason. Each emptied the fish bag, turned around, and climbed down. Then, unless there was something special to chat about, he or she would walk to the ever-open vertical six-foot door which led into an eight- or ten-yard-long alleyway which was sleeping quarters for the dogs and storage space for non-edible things, although most of these were kept outdoors atop platform caches.

Our house was as nearly airtight as the Eskimos had been

able to make it, with only two openings: the trap in the floor which let in fresh air and through which people entered, and the ventilator in the ceiling for the escape of hot and vitiated air. The trap was some thirty by fifty inches, and was kept wide open day and night all winter. The roof ventilator had about the diameter of our stove pipes—six or eight inches; but its aperture seldom achieved its full size, because the diameter varied according to the tastes of the occupants, and depended, too, upon the abundance of fuel. The ventilator's aperture was the sole control of the welling-up of the fresh cold air, its spread over the floor, and its gradual rise upward into the warmth of the house. If you found the house too hot, you could sit or sprawl on the plank floor in the coolest layer of the newly risen fresh air; for more warmth you could sit on a bed platform or, for still more heat, you might sit higher on a bench or stool. Thus the air of the house was pretty well stratified.

As I mounted the treads beneath the trap door and entered the house, I stripped off my upper garment, the *attigi* (the Siberian word *parka* had as yet never been heard in the Delta). Looking around in the soft glow of the lamps, I saw my twenty-three housemates, the children completely naked, and the adults stripped from the waist up and from the knees down. The heat was around 90° or 100° F. Perspiration was streaming down faces and torsos, and children were busy carrying around flagons of ice water for we had to drink a lot to balance the sweating.

Few things were ever scheduled with these Eskimos who were just emerging from the Stone Age, or at least not scheduled by the clock, though there were clocks in the house and several of the men had watches. What regularity there was followed the daylight. Our fishing, for instance, would cease earlier on the few cloudy days than on the usual clear ones. We seldom got home before the meal was cooked, though we often had to wait for it to cool off because the Mackenzie Eskimos liked their boiled fish luke-warm or cold, and likewise the soup, which was the broth the fish had been boiled in. We took it from flagons, or dippers, that were passed around, like communion cups of wine in the devotional ceremonies of my youth, and, indeed, as typically shown in our medieval religious paintings.

The preparations for dinner, as I watched them on bliz-zardy days when we did not fish, started soon after the eleven o'clock lunch. Two women would go out together, one climbing up on the platform to select fish for the meal, the other standing below it with a whip to keep the dogs at a respectful distance from the food. The fish chosen were those judged fattest, for these were preferred to others where the desired fat had to be supplied from our store of white whale oil.

At home the fish were rolled out gently over the floor planking. They were hard as glass and required the same care against breakage. After an hour or so on the floor, when the fish were soft enough to indent slightly when the women pinched them, the heads and tails were cut off and placed as tidbits in a pot for the children's dinner, which was earlier than ours. The rest of each fish was cut into three- or four-inch segments and the entrails removed and set aside for the dogs. Since the river was convenient to our house, water was fetched and enough poured into each pot to cover the fish segments. The pots came to a boil slowly. At the very first bubbling, they were removed from the fire and set aside to cool.

In the serving of the boiled fish dinner I was reminded of

our corn-on-the-cob dinners on the farm in North Dakota. We used to select the ears, or somebody else did it for us, according to certain standards, especially as to the ripeness or hardness of the kernels. With our fish at Tuktuyaktok there were standard preferences, for example, species of fish, part of the fish, fatness. The women went through a friendly and complicated process in selecting pieces for each diner's taste. In the family they were familiar with the preferences of all of us; with visitors they inquired solicitously. When the piece had been selected, the server would squeeze it so that nothing would later drip from it, for we ate without plates, picnic fashion, and sat on a bed platform covered with fur bedding that must not get damp under any circumstances.

The extreme heat produced by the cooking began to decrease while we had dinner. In two hours or so it would be something like 70° F. at our shoulder level as we sat listening to stories, singing songs, or conversing. At this point somebody would stick a wad of fur into the ventilator to decrease the size of its opening, and thus to slow the cooling of the house. As we had our nine o'clock supper of cold fish leftovers, the warmth remained constant. We then went to bed and slept naked under light robes. The final stage of temperature and ventilation adjustment came around ten o'clock. The ventilator was not further constricted for added warmth, for the Mackenzie people liked the air fresh; but the lamps were trimmed down to a candle-like flame, and some lamps were extinguished. At the level where we lay flat on the bed platforms, I think the usual temperature was around 60° F.

I noted that, sprawled on the floor to cool off, a foot or so lower than the bed platforms, the temperature felt like 50° F. above zero, and that the air rising from the alleyway to flood the plank floor was at outdoor temperatures ranging from 0° F. to 50° below. Why then wasn't the first ten-inch layer of air above the floor colder? I explained this to myself by what I had learned in school about "the principle of diffusion of gases," and also by noting that the air in the house was being stirred up constantly, especially by the quick movements of children, but also by the slower ones of adults.

Active preparations for breakfast usually started by one young woman challenging another to a race in dressing, which was a matter of seconds, surely not over half a minute. The race between the women was, of course, concerned with who would have the honor of selecting the fish for breakfast and who would have the chore of swishing around with a whip to make sure the dogs kept their distance.

After the fish were rolled out on the floor, each of these early-rising women tended her own lamp, bringing its flame from taper-size to the point where it spread along the straight burning-edge of the half-moon-shaped soapstone lamp to perhaps ten inches. The idea was to raise the house temperature to about 70° F. without decreasing the upwelling of fresh air through the trap door in the floor, which would have resulted if the house warmth had been increased by constricting the ventilator.

Except for special reasons, nobody else dressed before breakfast; the self-chosen pair who had brought in the fish were thereby elected to do whatever else was necessary to prepare the meal. When the fish began to soften, the first step was again to cut off heads and tails, these for the children who would have a warm breakfast prepared for them immediately after we fishers had breakfasted and gone out to the river ice. The rest of each fish was skinned sideways.

Then segments were cut in the same lengths as for cooking, but these segments were to be eaten while still frozen about as hard as ice cream.

To some extent at all meals, but more so at the frozen ones, we added straight fat to all but the fattest of our river fish. Mostly we used white whale (beluga) oil that had been fermented through the hot summer in a sealskin bag or poke (a process analogous to our aging of wine in barrels) which produces an amber color in the previously colorless or white oil and produces, too, an odor that is pleasantly vinegary and a taste that is delicious to those who are used to it. With the breakfast fish, which felt under our teeth like an ice cream dessert and tasted delicately creamy, we drank sparingly of ice water, for there had been no perspiring in the night to create thirst.

Before midwinter I had become a Stone Age Eskimo in practice; it took me years to become one in theory. However, by the end of January 1907, I was convinced that I was healthier on the Stone Age regimen than I had ever before been on any diet or in any way of life. I already liked the same things the Eskimos liked about their food, and I had never liked any food better. I looked forward to every meal and could not have wanted any of them otherwise than they were. The smells of the house, which I had disliked at first, I now liked; they were the smells of foods which I now relished. I did not mind them any more than Europeans mind the aroma of coffee or the fragrance of bacon.

During the midwinter I had learned not to dread the absence of the sun, and I had acquired confidence that in any good fishing country I could support myself, and a dog team as well, by fishing. Already in the autumn, when on a trip to the caribou-hunting Eskimos south of the Richardson

Mountains, easternmost outlier of the Brooks Range in Alaska, I had gathered that I could learn to be equally self-supporting on caribou with an equipment of rifle and binoculars, and this was to be confirmed in northern Alaska by spring.

The Last of the Eskimo Stone Age

We have described the Mackenzie Delta Eskimo ways as they were just emerging from their Stone Age. Now we proceed to a description of the ways of a people still fully in their Stone Age.

Our second northern journey, 1908-1912, was commissioned by the American Museum of Natural History of New York. Their Department of Anthropology had discovered on the most recent Canadian government maps a region of the Arctic, to the north of Great Bear Lake, which had been stamped, "uninhabited," and which they thought might not be uninhabited after all. They reasoned that, if it was populated, the inhabitants would almost certainly be Eskimo-speaking, since that language was believed to be mutually understandable among all groups from Greenland to Alaska.

The Museum knew me as an anthropologist who liked the Eskimos and their way of life, and who had already spent a year studying the Mackenzie dialect. Perhaps I could find in the "uninhabited" part of arctic Canada a people who had never before seen a white man. Thus they commissioned me, and, later, my Iowa classmate, zoologist Rudolph M. Anderson, to secure information and specimens. We were called the Stefansson-Anderson Arctic Expedition.

Dr. Anderson and I spent 1908-09 in northern Alaska, east of Barrow, and 1909-10 in northwestern Canada, east of the Mackenzie, he gathering museum specimens and zoological information, I learning more of the language and increasing my skill as a hunter. In late winter Anderson agreed to become liaison officer and remain behind in the Mackenzie district to keep up our contacts with New York, chiefly through the Yankee whaler-traders and the Hudson's Bay Company.

I left Langton Bay on April 21, 1910 with three Eskimo companions. To be as Eskimo-like as we could manage, and for other reasons also, we had only one sledge, six dogs, no food supplies, and only the simplest equipment needed to secure food and to record our impressions: three rifles and ammunition, field glasses for all, a camera, and writing materials for me.

We found no difficulty in feeding men and dogs from game along the way—caribou, seals, and an occasional polar bear. We crossed an uninhabited coastal stretch of three hundred miles, saw our first traces of people on May 9, near Sir John Richardson's Point Wise. The next day we reached an abandoned snowhouse village at Cape Bexley, and on May 13th we had attained success in our main initial objectives: We had reached a people who understood the dialects we spoke and whom we could understand; and they told us that I was the first white man they had ever seen.

I learned, moreover, that they had never seen a match lighted or heard the noise a gun makes. Their hunting gear for caribou was the bow and arrow and lance; for the seal, of course, the harpoon; for fish it was the three-pronged spear and also the copper fish hook; for the grizzly bear and polar bear, the lance; for ptarmigan (but not for fish), a net. Excepting eggs, which were little esteemed, their only food was flesh, their only clothes the skins of animals, including some fish and bird skins.

During a year of living and traveling with the Coronation Gulf people I grew to feel that their most striking difference from other groups of Eskimos was in their relatively slight use of stone weapons and tools, though theirs was on the whole a most orthodox Stone Age culture. In place of stone they used chiefly native copper, which they picked up here and there for eventual hammering and grinding into missile points, knives, and needles. So it occurred to me, as they had no one designation for themselves, to name them the *Copper Eskimos,* a term that has appealed to scholars and seems likely to endure—though a more popular name for them is *Blond Eskimos,* because a few of them, especially in Victoria Island, look as if they might have some European blood.

Among the Copper Eskimos, food was more seasonally determined than among groups further west. From October to May the food in and around Coronation Gulf was more than ninety-five per cent seal and less than five per cent polar bear; during midsummer it was more than ninety-five per cent caribou and less than five per cent grizzly bear, plus moulting geese, and a few oddments, such as marmots. Only in spring, when the people were moving from the sea ice sealing grounds to the caribou hunting ranges inland, did they catch a few fish, by jigging through the ice—in the manner I learned at Tuktuyaktok. During this season, too, a few grouse (ptarmigan) were netted. There was one place, below Bloody Fall on the Coppermine, where a few people spent most of the summer fishing, chiefly depending on spearing and on the use of fish traps.

As determined by custom and taboo rather than by seasonal change of hunting and fishing conditions, the chief difference in food and food habits was the stricter Copper

Eskimo avoidance of vegetable foods. South of Coronation Gulf they not only avoided berries and other vegetables but felt it necessary to apologize and explain about eating vegetables. They admitted to us that, like the grizzly bear, they sometimes ate masu roots (the roots of the knotweed, *Polygonum bistortum*), even though they knew they were "not proper human food" and, besides, were very constipating. But, they emphasized, they did this only in time of dire necessity, just before they started killing and eating their dogs, the step that immediately precedes cannibalism.

Most striking to us was the Copper Eskimo attitude toward the eating of salmonberries or cloudberries, those of *Rubus chamaemorus*. These were numerous south of Coronation Gulf and my Alaska Eskimo companions rejoiced, for they were fond of the *akpek,* as they called this fruit. The Copper Eskimos called it *akpek,* too, but the first thing we heard about it locally was from a woman who told us what a grief it was to her that her daughter was getting to be a big girl and was nevertheless still eating *akpek!*

Eventually it became common knowledge in Coronation Gulf that Mackenzie Eskimos and Alaskans like and use extensively not only the *akpek* but also many other berries and some roots and leaves. Some of the local men started sampling these berries and leaves. The local women were obviously distressed by this male weakness of backbone. However, four years later (1914), when our 1913-1918 expedition revisited the Copper Eskimos, the taboo against the *akpek* was only a memory, even to middle-aged women.

During 1910-1911, hunting with the Copper Eskimos south of Coronation Gulf to the edge of the Great Bear Lake woods, I had the chance to compare not merely vegetable but also meat preferences between them and the Eskimos of

Barrow and Mackenzie; a little later, in the same region, I also had the chance to compare the food tastes and practices of the Bear Lake Athapaskans with those of the Mackenzie Athapaskans.

We found similar preferences concerning fat and lean of caribou and seal, which are the two standard Eskimo meats from Bering Strait to Coronation Gulf. Also, we found the Bear Lake Athapaskans—Dogribs, Slaveys and Yellowknives —similar to, though not identical with, the Mackenzie Loucheux, who are the only Mackenzie Athapaskans with whom I have hunted and lived.

Both Copper and Mackenzie Eskimos are fond of their dogs and of their children, and both discriminate by saving the best food for the children and letting the worst go to the dogs. Both groups consider that in time of plenty one person should get as much of a caribou as two dogs. In times of famine the dogs are first stinted of their meals, then they are eaten, which is, as we have said, the last resort before cannibalism, a practice as much abhorred by them as by us; but they come to it at the last, as we do.

When a Mackenzie or a Copper Eskimo secures a caribou he divides it between family and dogs. The children get the kidneys and the leg marrows nearest the hoof. All Eskimos known to me think the sweetest meat is nearest the bone; they boil the hams and round shoulder bones and the children pick from these the cooked lean that goes so pleasantly with the uncooked fat of the raw lower marrows. Perhaps the whole family and any visitors will share the boiled caribou head. (An Athapaskan would roast the head.)

The Eskimo likes the tongue well enough, and the brains; but what he prefers from the head is the jowl, and after that, the pads of fat behind the eyes. His next preference is brisket, then ribs, then pelvis. From the hams and shoulders he will peel off the outside meat as dog food, but will keep some of the inside meat for his family. The neck of the caribou is considered halfway between human food and dog food.

Dog food, especially if the team is big, would consist first of the lungs, but not the windpipe or the bronchial tubes, for the Eskimo likes cartilage. The liver goes to the dogs and everything else from inside the body cavity except the kidneys. The heart is considered intermediate, not especially bad but not especially good. The dogs get the stomach and the entrails, but not the fat from the entrails. They also get the tenderloin and much of the meat from the backbone; but the Stone Age Eskimo likes to leave some meat on the vertebrae; he enjoys picking them when boiled.

Formerly, the Athapaskan Indians agreed on most of these things. They were even more sure than the Eskimos that the liver was dog food. If today either Athapaskans or Eskimos seem to like caribou liver, it is a sign that they have been influenced by Europeans, who will pay high prices for the makings of liver-and-bacon. Also, if an Eskimo contemplated making dried meat, he might save for that purpose both the wholly lean tenderloin and the outside lean meat of hams.

Eskimos tended to prefer boiled meats and Athapaskans to prefer them roasted. Both roasted and boiled meats were cooked underdone or medium, but only the Eskimos would eat raw meat. Athapaskans were horrified when they saw Europeans eating rare steaks and roasts, but that is the way the Eskimos liked them.

Fat hunger among caribou hunters was common with the Athapaskans; it was rare with the Eskimos, for inlanders bought pokes of seal oil from the coastal people which they

carried with them in case of shortage. The Athapaskans used
to die from fat starvation. This was called by the Hudson's
Bay Company, "rabbit starvation," because it was commonest
among rabbit hunters, though it could occur among Athapaskans in a caribou country at seasons when the game was lean.

After the last scrap of fat is gone from the diet of a
hunting people, headache and diarrhea will start. Fur traders
believed that death from fat starvation would come in from
four to eight weeks; old Hudson's Bay men told me it would
come quicker on lean meat and water than on just water.
When traders heard of rabbit starvation among a group of
Athapaskans, they tried to remedy it, usually by sending
them some bacon or lard.

The heads are the preferred parts of game among northern
moose hunters, both Eskimos and Athapaskans. Then the
tidbit is the nose, with the jowl second.

The four tidbits of northern meat eaters, whether Athapaskan or Eskimo, are all of them high-fat items and at their
best must always be boiled but not overcooked. They are:
beaver tail, caribou jowl, loche liver, and moose nose. These
are, in our farthest north, what the fat tail of their sheep
was to the Old Testament Hebrews and still is to the tropical
Arabs. These delicacies should all be fresh, particularly
loche liver, which starts to get rancid within a few hours
during the warm summer, and within a few days in the
winter, even when the weather is at its coldest.

When seals are eaten, heads are not the favored parts and
the dogs often get them. A seal's tongue, like the caribou's,
is looked on as a food of intermediate quality, but incon-
siderable because it is so small. Seal liver never goes to dogs,
as the caribou's usually does, and is ordinarily eaten raw
whenever it may be had frozen. Flippers never go to dogs if

there is time and fuel to boil them, but raw flippers are dog food. At a meal of boiled seal the flippers are the tidbits, and after them, the first joint of either pair of legs.

It is frequently asked whether Eskimos formerly had any equivalent to champagne at their festive meals. Their attitude toward the preferred fats was something like the European's toward wines and similar also to the attitude of Icelandic and other northwest European fishermen toward fish oil cocktails or morning "eye-openers" of fish oil, especially (at least in Iceland) cocktails of halibut liver oil.

I have been told that when an old-fashioned small-boat fisherman—not the steam-trawler kind—gets up early to go down to his boat on a blustery winter day, he takes a wineglass of halibut oil and feels exhilarated. I have never seen or heard of Eskimos drinking oil, but I have been told of the like effect on them of their preferred fats, only they used them as we do cocktails—not as "eye-openers" in the morning, but at the end of a hard day or at the beginning of a festive meal.

The thing most nearly analogous to our use of alcoholic cocktails, or of the Icelandic halibut cocktail, is the use of summer-fermented seal oil, though I have here been reminded more of our use of a brandy or Benedictine after dinner. The preparation of this liqueur-oil reminds one of our aging of wine or the ripening of our cheeses.

Around Coronation Gulf, preparation for the summer fermentation of oil began late in April or in May. Seals were "cased," meaning that they were skinned through the mouth. All the natural openings were then closed up, the bag was turned inside out as a sock might be, all blubber and fascia were removed, and the bag inflated. The hair was left on the inside of the skin if it was intended for oil fermenting, and removed if it was to be used as a float. Several of such air-distended pokes were ready at the beginning of the season.

Preparations for blubber fermenting were almost as meticulous among the Eskimos as pemmican preparations among the Plains Indians. A freshly killed seal was used, preferably dead only within the half hour, with all tissues still full of the warmth of life. It was skinned immediately, whether cased or not, and then the sheet of blubber removed, as if another skin were being peeled off, leaving the carcass red, speckled in only a few places with fat inadvertently left behind.

There is no appreciable fat inside the body of a seal nor any inside his bones; the marrow looks like blood and coagulates like the white of an egg if boiled. In some instances the blubber was allowed to remain on the carcass, apparently to keep the blubber warm till each piece was ready to be cut off and stuffed into the mouth of the bag, usually in strips two or three inches wide and six inches long. The strips look white and firm, but here and there a little blood colors them. When the blubber was being skinned off the carcass, the Eskimos would seemingly rather have a little red meat come along with the fat than to have bits of fat clinging to the lean meat. Those traces of blubber that did cling to the lean meat were, in some cases, carefully removed because if the meat were later boiled, these pieces were liable to taste mildly rancid, a flavoring that not many Eskimos liked.

The filled bag would usually weigh one hundred fifty or two hundred pounds. Its mouth was lashed tight; it was placed, preferably, on a platform, but alternatively under a heap of stones, in either case for protection from birds and beasts. Though heat was desired, the usual custom was to arrange an awning of hairless, blackish sealskin above the bags on the platform. Striking this dark surface, the sun would create heat, on occasion probably well above 90° F.; thermometers would sometimes register 80° and even 90° in the shade around our camps.

In the autumn, when we opened the bags and poured out the oil into small containers, enough for a meal or two each time, the color was that of nut-brown ale and it had a slightly vinegary flavor and fragrance, to the connoisseur like the bouquet of a suitably aged wine. But our use of this brown oil was more parsimonious than the quaffing of wine, more like our use of a liqueur or a sauce. The Eskimos did not sip, as if this were a Benedictine, but attained the same end of savoring and of minimum use by dipping a finger into a bowl of oil and sucking it off, or dipping and eating morsels of food.

Inland parties of caribou hunters often carried bags of this fermented oil. If they had none, and a feast was coming up, they were not likely to replace it with ordinary, insufficiently ripened seal oil, but would instead use at the end of a meal the raw fresh marrows of caribou.

To cook with grease—to fry food—was unknown to the Eskimos, and probably to the Athapaskans, until introduced by Europeans. This method was at first used only for the preparation of European foods such as doughnuts. Then it began to be used for native foods. In some sections it is now a usual method of cooking for the sorts of food that they have seen us fry, whether essentially a native food or not, for example, goose eggs or caribou brains.

Nor was the direct heat of a fire applied to the extraction of oil from blubber till the Eskimos saw whalers "trying out" whale blubber. Formerly, the special and, to most, disagreeable flavor of fire-rendered oil was unknown to Eskimos. The sort of trying out that results from boiling in water was, of course, not unknown. The boiling of fatty caribou meat produced a certain amount of tallow; and the making of bone tallow was accomplished by hours-long boiling of crushed bones. But seal fat was usually pared off before the lean meat went into the pot. Thus there was a minimum of fat atop any broth drunk at the end of a seal meat meal.

In one case—the making of blood soup—there might be a considerable amount of fat. Cold liquid blood (or chipped ice made by demolishing a lump of frozen blood) was added to the broth derived from a potful of meat and briskly stirred. This would result in a lukewarm mixture about as thick as our ordinary pea soup, for the broth was not brought to a fresh boil. This blood soup was passed around in dippers, or in tin cups if the Eskimos were in the process of getting civilized.

Being human, the Stone Age Eskimos naturally had the world-wide practice of eating decayed, or at least stinking, animal products. Like most of us, they disliked making entire meals of the strong foods, but preferred main dishes fresh, with a little pungent food at the very last, as the British do with their savories, indeed, as many other Europeans do with their strong cheeses. The favorite Mackenzie equivalent of a powerful cheese was a bit of decayed herring. The kind I helped prepare during my first northern autumn was of Bear Lake herring (Leucichthys lucidus), a fish known to my Eskimo hosts as *kaktak*.

After my third northern journey—the Canadian Arctic Expedition of 1913-1918—I spent several years lecturing in, among other places, Australia, Britain, Canada and the

United States. I often mentioned that several of us, not counting Eskimos, had gone several years without ever tasting food that came directly from the vegetable kingdom. One time I was booked to speak at the Mayo Clinic, in Rochester, Minnesota. After an hour's talk the several hundred doctors and nurses questioned me another two hours, whereupon Dr. Will Mayo invited me to come back as guest of the Clinic, saying they wanted to give me a thorough examination to see if there were in my carcass traces of any of the "dreadful things supposed to happen when your diet contains no vegetables." I accepted eagerly, but was unable to begin because of my lecture schedule and my writings which kept me on the road or in New York. One day, a fashionable Park Avenue doctor, an old friend from Harvard, Clarence W. Lieb, suggested that there were good doctors in New York also and, that if I agreed, which I did, he would organize a team of specialists to give me a pretty rigorous examination without charge. He brought together several "Who's Who" doctors; they examined me off and on for weeks, and finally Lieb summarized their findings in an article (5).

Meanwhile a small furor over my case had been stirred up by Dr. Raymond Pearl, head of the department of Biometrics and Vital Statistics at Johns Hopkins. As adviser to Herbert Hoover's Food Administration, he had called me in, interviewed me before a stenographer, and circulated the result among nutritionists, to be met with general skepticism, but a few conversions.

Lieb's article (5) had not been long in print when he received a request from what is now the American Meat Institute of Chicago, for permission to reprint for circulation to doctors and teachers. Lieb consulted me, and I suggested calling in Pearl, who had remained on my side in spite of the negative results he had received from the circulation of the stenographic report. Pearl came up from Baltimore and we arrived at two decisions: We would say no to the re-printing and circulating of Lieb's paper, but we would make a counter-proposal.

If the meat people would pledge enough money, with no strings attached, and turn it over to a mutually satisfactory group of scientists, we would arrange that one of my Arctic colleagues, who had lived with me several years exclusively on meat, would join me in a test. We would enter a selected institution and have our health thoroughly checked on a standard mixed diet as a preliminary to living twelve months under ordinary New York "white collar" conditions exclu-sively on whole fresh meat. There would be all the applicable calorimeter and other tests, and chemical analysis.

After all loopholes had been closed to the satisfaction of both sides, the expense money was pledged, the institutions selected, the technicians arranged for, and the committee of supervising specialists chosen. The Russell Sage Institute of Pathology of the Cornell Medical School was to be in charge under the leadership of the young physiologist, Dr. Eugene DuBois; the place was to be the nutrition ward of Bellevue Hospital. The supervisory committee was to consist of the following men: from the American Meat Institute, Dr. Robert C. Moulton; from the American Museum of Natural History, Dr. Clark Wissler; from Cornell University Medical College, Dr. Walter L. Niles; from Harvard University, Drs. Lawrence J. Henderson, Ernest A. Hooton, and Percy R. Howe; from Johns Hopkins University, Drs. William G. McCallum and Raymond Pearl; from the Russell Sage Institute of Pathology, Drs. Eugene F. DuBois and Graham

Lusk; and from the University of Chicago, Dr. Edwin O. Jordan. Unattached members of this committee would be Dr. Clarence W. Lieb and Vilhjalmur Stefansson.

The long story of the 1928-1929 Cornell-Bellevue tests has been told in various technical and other papers which are listed in my book (8).

In Bellevue Hospital Karsten Andersen and I lived the usual New York clerical or business sort of life. We had good ventilation, frequent baths, and numerous spells in calorimeters. Everybody watched us—not merely to check on what we ate at meals but to see that we ate nothing in between! We never went to a telephone booth without a doctor or nurse to watch us.

I had been in such good health that an improvement in me would have been hard to document. But, fortunately for the test, Andersen showed at the beginning two conditions that worried the doctors: his blood pressure was higher than they liked, and the state of his colon was such that Professor John C. Torrey, Cornell's intestinal flora specialist, said that if this man had come to him as a patient, he would have told him to avoid meat. But, after a few weeks on an all-meat diet, Andersen's pressure was dropping satisfactorily, and Dr. Torrey said his colon was improving faster than he could have expected from the treatment he would have advised.

Dr. Lieb assembled the findings of the other watchers, and on July 6, 1929, published "The Effects on Human Beings of a Twelve Months' Exclusive Meat Diet" (6). In a later article, he wrote:

A physical inventory made of Stefansson in 1922, when he was 43 years old, was as follows: Weight 70.8 kgm. He was 5 feet 11 inches (180.3 cm.) tall. . . . He looked his years but no older. . . . Men in the various specialities have examined Stefansson and the reports have been entirely negative. . . . The following is a clinical and laboratory summary of the [Russell Sage-Cornell exclusive-meat-year] findings:

Caloric intake: Stefansson averaged about 2,650 calories a day; 2,100 calories consisting of fat and 550 of protein. . . . Carbohydrate in the meat varied between 20 and 50 calories a day.

Blood pressure: . . . 105 systolic and 70 diastolic (average) during the entire (12 month) course of his diet . . .

Vitality: In neither subject (Andersen or Stefansson) was there a decrease in physical vigor. Both led sedentary lives throughout the experiment . . .

Heat Tolerance: Andersen affirms that he endured last summer's (1928) heat if anything better than during former years.

Appearance: Both men appeared ruddier at the end of the experiment than at the beginning.

Teeth: In neither case has there been any deterioration of the teeth. . . . There was also a notable absence of pyorrhea in both subjects.

Bowels: . . . In both these men the stools were non-odorous and there was no evidence of gaseous distention or flatus at any time . . .

Pulse, temperature and sleep: There was no variation from the normal and usual.

Metabolism: The basal metabolism of these subjects showed a uniform variation between minus 10 and minus 20 percent by the Aub-Du Bois standards . . .

Weights: Stefansson's original weight was 72.5 Kg. At the end of the first month it was 68 Kg.; at the end of the second month it was 69, and at the end of the year's meat diet it was 69.4 Kg. From April, 1928, to March, 1929, there was no change in weight. Stefansson's concluding weight, after the calorimeter studies had been completed, was 69.7 Kg.

Effect on kidneys: 1. No albumin, casts or block was found at any time during the course of the experiments. 2. (Refers to Andersen only). 3. Urea clearance showed 100% plus . . . 4. Roentgen examination of the kidneys before and at the conclusion of the meat diet did not show any change in size.

Chemical analysis of the blood: The chemical composition of the blood was little affected, except for a slight increase in uric acid and a temporary lipemia. The latter occurred only after unusual amounts of fat were taken . . . [7].

At seventy I began to notice what I took to be signs of age. My right knee, in which I had suffered an injury a decade before, now began to stiffen. The stiffening spread to various joints, and if at night I lay on either side more than three or four hours, I would be awakened by an ache in both hip and shoulder and would need to turn on my other side for relief. With hope to slow the stiffening I took therapy from the physical medicine department of Dartmouth's Hitchcock Clinic.

On my seventy-fifth birthday my colleagues gave me a big dinner and, for the first time in my life, I listened to general talk that I was carrying my years remarkably well. From this I realized that they saw decrepitude advancing upon me; and come to think of it, I saw it too.

This was indeed not my first decrepitude shock, for I had suffered a mild stroke the year before. My speech became thick, the left side of my face sagged, my right hand trembled. On the advice of Dean Rolf C. Syvertzen of our medical faculty, I put myself in the hands of the professor of neurology, Dr. R. W. Hunter, who said a blood clot had stuck, that alcohol was supposed to relax the walls of blood vessels, and that I had better take rather more numerous cocktails and highballs, or at least more regularly than I had been doing; at the same time he thought me overweight and wanted me to shed ten pounds.

Increasing my drinks proved relatively easy, decreasing my

weight more difficult. I would starve off as much as five or six pounds at a time; then I would start feeling out of sorts, sorry for myself, headachy; I would yield to temptation, particularly when dining out, and my poundage would return.

Then came the illness of President Eisenhower in Colorado, and the din of press and radio swelled that our President's misfortune should be a warning to a nation that was bent on destroying its own health by the eating of too much animal fat. This clamor, even while less strident, had long been an irritant to me, for I believe a diet of fat meat the most wholesome of regimens. So I asked my wife's permission to stock up our freezer with fat mutton, my preferred of domestic meats. My health would improve, I promised her, and, among other things, I would then automatically take off the pounds the doctor wanted me to lose. Then I organized for myself a diet which included eggs, bacon, cream, butter, chops and steak—all on the public's clamor list.

In the first week of November 1955, I celebrated my seventy-sixth birthday. It was my third week on the high-fat diet. Both my wife and I were interested in and slightly controversial about the expected changes for which we were watching: the decreasing weight, the lessened need for sleep, the growing energy, the near-euphoria which she found near-obnoxious, especially before breakfast. It must have been this watchfulness for the expected that made me careless about the unexpected.

I was climbing our stairs and I realized that I was climbing with an even tread, flexing both knees. I stopped and, with hand on balustrade, stood on one foot and then the other, trying out both knees and finding neither of them stiff, nor any difference between the two. I could not that day get any joint of mine to ache, feel tender or stiff, nor have I succeeded with any of them since.

But I am beginning in the fourth year to discover evidence of what I have suspected from the start: that I have not discovered a fountain of youth. For one thing, no mental youth seems to be returning in step with the physical. I can hail friends as cheerfully as I ever did, but I cannot always recall their names—in fact, I am having more and more difficulty.

What seems to have happened with my re-adoption of the Stone Age diet is a general improvement in health. The most obviously demonstrable is my loss of corpulence and my inability to reacquire it by such devices as sedentary habits and large meals, so long as no carbohydrates are added to the lean-fat diet. Most agreeable to family and friends is my resulting near-inability to feel gloomy and grouchy; most hopeful to my publisher is the energy that keeps me at my typewriter fourteen hours a day seven days a week as I work on my twenty-fifth book; most distressing to my friends is a state of euphoria that makes me garrulous in speech and writing; most financially disappointing to the morticians is my seeming ability to grow younger, their profits being dependent on the turnover.

This is how I feel—younger at seventy-nine than I was at seventy-five, and in my joints at least ten years younger. Perhaps I sound to others, as I do to myself, a little like the side-show barkers that tout Kickapoo Indian Sagwa. And there is the saying that "pride goeth before a fall." I am necessarily aware that many who hear me now will see my obituary. But even they will have to admit that I might have died sooner if I had refrained from living on the fat of the land. They cannot get me to admit the reverse for I shall not be there to admit anything.

The Transition Diets and the Modern

"We saw this people eat no vegetable substances, though they informed us that the buds of the willow were sometimes eaten." So reported the anthropologist, John Murdoch, in 1883 after two years spent intimately with a thousand resident and transient Eskimos in northern Alaska.

Today an anthropologist returning from a similar two-year study in northern Alaska would report: "We saw this people eat many vegetable substances, though they informed us these were mainly dried and canned."

Murdoch's report would have been correct for the Eskimos of Northern Alaska and northern Canada until recently. How recently—and the how and the why of Europeanization, with what general effect on health and longevity—we now consider.

We begin our sketch of the shift from a flesh to a mixed diet with the coastal Eskimo section of Labrador that lies farther north than the Grenfell mission, which serves Europeans and forest Indians living south and west of the Eskimos.

For Labrador background we use the general published literature; and then we base our sketch of what the Eskimo diet was, and of what it is, upon two main sources: (1) on a correspondence going back several years with the superintendent of the Moravian missions in Labrador, the Reverend F. W. Peacock, of Happy Valley, Labrador, and (2) a seventy-four-page quarto book, *Health Conditions and Disease Incidence among the Eskimos of Labrador*, by Dr. Samuel King

Hutton, of the London headquarters of the mission (1). Superintendent Peacock has been in Labrador since 1935; Dr. Hutton served as medical missionary in Labrador during about seven years of the period, 1902-1913.

The Moravian mission to Labrador was founded in 1771. Almost from the beginning, its policy differed from that of many other missions to the Eskimos (though not from the policy of Greenland missions) in attempting to induce people to continue eating native foods prepared the native way. Moravian books show that they considered the native way of life more conducive to health and longevity than such modification of it as would result from Europeanization.

While moderately successful, this Moravian policy of the Eskimos was not wholly so, especially not in the southern districts where contact was most intimate with Europeans, and with semi-Europeanized forest Indians. Both Hutton and Peacock consider that a number of diseases, among them cancer, did not appear among their Eskimos until some years after the diet became heavily Europeanized.

Dr. Hutton, our main source for this part of our story, is still active. In the autumn of 1957 he lectured in the United States and we talked with him. He told us that since he published his book (1), his information about Labrador health conditions has been extended, but that the conclusions there expressed remain substantially unchanged. He believes Labrador Eskimo health to have been better formerly than it is now.

Like all missions, the Moravian keeps records of births and deaths. For the period when he was there—1902-1913—Hutton says: "Old age sets in at fifty and its signs are strongly marked by the time sixty is reached. In the years beyond sixty the Eskimo is aged . . . only very few reach seventy. Those who live to such old age have spent a life of great activity, feeding on Eskimo foods" (1, p.17). He states, further (pp. 20-22), "Scurvy . . . is rare . . . I have seen but one case. . . ." This, he says, occurred in a household "of a semi-European dietary . . . Seal's flesh, especially when eaten raw, has reputed anti-scorbutic properties."

He considers "the effect on the Eskimo of the European dietary adopted as a habit of life. On the southern part of the Labrador coast there are a number of English-speaking settlers [who] live for the most part on tea, bread, salt fish, and pork, and among them scurvy is common. . . . The Eskimos living among the settlers have to a large extent adopted the settler dietary . . . and not only does scurvy occur among them but their physique is less robust than is that of their northern brethren" (pp. 21-22).

He claims that: "Tuberculosis is apparently one of the diseases that has reached Labrador from other lands . . . though more common among Eskimos who have adopted a European way of life, [tuberculosis] also attacks [those] who live a true Eskimo life" (pp. 28-29). Elsewhere he says that those stand up best against tuberculosis who keep most nearly to the Eskimo way, which included drinking large quantities of water and perspiring freely.

Here and there throughout this book Hutton mentions troubles that are rare or absent in the Eskimo way of life. He gives a brief summary of this and clarifies his views on cancer:

Some diseases common in Europe have not come under my notice during a prolonged and careful survey of the health of the Eskimos. Of these diseases the most striking is cancer. I have not seen or heard of a case of malignant new growth in an Eskimo. In this connection it may be noted that cookery holds a very secondary place in the preparation of food—most of the food is eaten raw and the diet is a flesh one [p. 35].

Presumably the "have not heard of" part of this passage should be dated as of 1924 or 1925, for the book was published in 1925 and would cover information which had by that time reached the London headquarters. By 1937 news of cancer among the Eskimos of Labrador had reached the headquarters. At the suggestion of Dr. Hutton, we secured the information direct from the mission. Superintendent Peacock reports it in a letter he wrote us from Happy Valley, Labrador, November 20, 1957, a letter in which he cites known cases.

Westward from Labrador, beyond Hudson Bay, the bitter wind of Europeanization was not tempered to the shorn Eskimo lamb by churches as deeply concerned as the Moravian with the economic and physiological health of the natives. For a general view of health and welfare from the Bay westward, we quote Jenness who was, from 1916 to his recent retirement, the chief Eskimo specialist of the Canadian government and head of the pertinent section of the National Museum in Ottawa.

. . . partly from a misguided imitation of Europeans, many Eskimos now wear woolen underclothing and even the complete European costume, although their earlier garments of loosely-fitting caribou were far more picturesque and hygienic, and offered greater protection against the intense cold.

Very few Eskimos now hunt intensively during the winter months; instead they trap foxes, which are useless to them for either food or clothing. In order to maintain their families during that season they buy European food from the fur-traders, largely flour, sugar, and tea. Now a diet of straight [fat] seal-meat will keep a hunter or trapper in good health, but a diet that consists mainly of bannock and tea is practically starvation. So, over large parts of the Arctic and sub-Arctic the Eskimos are now worse clad, and more ill-nourished, than in the days of their isolation.

There seem to have been about 2,000 Eskimos living between the Alaska-Canada boundary and Cape Bathurst when Sir John Franklin's expedition explored this coast in 1826. In 1929 there were less than 800, and of that number only about twelve were really native to the district, the remainder being immigrants from Alaska. The earlier inhabitants perished from diseases introduced by Europeans; as late as 1900 an epidemic of measles caused great mortality. In 1902 typhus carried off all the surviving inhabitants of Southampton Island, Hudson Bay. Other parts of Hudson Bay, Baffin island, and the Labrador peninsula suffered great depletions in the eighteenth and nineteenth centuries, and during the last few years European diseases have been ravaging the newly accessible groups between Coronation gulf and the Magnetic Pole.

So from a pre-European population estimated by Mooney at 22,500 the Canadian and Labrador Eskimo have been reduced to 8,000 [in 1929]. [3, pp. 421 ff.]

We are inclined to feel the Mooney estimate quoted by Jenness is too small, but we agree with his own 1929 figures. He gives the total Eskimo population west of Labrador at 7,103. Since that figure was announced—shocking the nation —the government and the main churches of Canada (the Anglican and the Roman) have all been more actively concerned than before with the bodily health and the physical welfare of the Eskimos.

Observers in 1881 found negligible dietary change from that of 1852. Similarly, I found, in 1908, but slight change from 1881. But Dr. Henry W. Greist found, in 1920, that a revolution had taken place. This change had been brought on chiefly through the power of fashion; and the fashion change had been caused by the breakdown of the New

England bone-whaling industry and the consequent disappearance of the Yankee fleet.

When I reached those whaling grounds in 1906, I found what had been true since 1889—that fresh meat was the costliest of foods. For instance, in the winter of 1905-1906 the whalers were able to exchange 98 pounds of flour for a 40-pound saddle of caribou; and the Eskimos were cooking up flour soup (hasty pudding) for the dogs; in their estimation, such cheap food was naturally inferior and thus dog food.

The few traders who took the place of the numerous whalers after 1908 were able to get all the fresh meat they needed for a little tea, tobacco, and ammunition. Flour was now costly, so the Eskimos stopped feeding it to their dogs and started eating more of it themselves. Jenness (4) shows that in 1914, about five years after the New England whalers ceased coming, flour-derived foods, such as doughnuts, had become prestige foods. Everybody who could afford it served carbohydrates at every meal, but nobody could afford much. The few small traders offered little work, and the prices of furs—the only marketable things the Eskimos now had—were dropping. Even so, the Presbyterians felt in northern Alaska, as the Moravians did in northern Labrador, that the health of the natives was suffering as the native foods were being supplanted.

However, the lack of purchasing power kept the intruding foods within bounds, till the end of World War I. Congress soon thereafter inaugurated an oil development policy for northern Alaska. The scientific geologists of the past were now followed by oil prospectors and drillers. Jobs multiplied, wages climbed, and prosperity dawned. The whalers had paid two hundred dollars *per year* to an Eskimo family and had supplied the Eskimos with unlimited flour which they fed mostly to their dogs. The Government was soon paying two dollars *per hour* and the dogs were getting little of the costly foods for which the Eskimos spent their wages. The oil boom was followed by the defense industries boom, wages climbed to four dollars an hour, and family incomes of ten thousand dollars a year ceased being remarkable. The diseases we have listed, which the medical missionaries tell us were mild or absent formerly, were now rampant, among them cancer. We tell for Alaska, chiefly from Presbyterian sources, the story we told for Labrador, chiefly from Moravian sources.

Like the Labrador missionaries, those of Alaska believed that Eskimos never get cancer. Dr. Raymond H. Marsh, who had been at Barrow since 1897, told me so when I first talked with him at the medical mission in 1908. His opinion was still the same when I last saw him there in 1912. I did not know the incumbents between 1912 and 1920, when Dr. and Mrs. Henry W. Greist arrived at Barrow after a year with the Bering Strait Eskimos.

My correspondence with Mrs. Greist in 1957 elicited the information that the first recognition of a Northern Alaska malignancy took place some time in the early 1930's.

Like most or all medical workers who have been among the Eskimos, and have been specially interested in cancer, Mrs. Greist appears eager to secure notice not merely for her doctor husband's and her own observations, but also for those of other field workers. Accordingly, she not only wrote me at length herself on this subject, but has referred me to others whom she thinks competent and of extensive experience. There has been special Canadian interest in women's breast cancer, especially in its alleged absence among Eskimos, and Mrs. Greist sometimes dwells on this, for instance in her letter of February 19, 1957:

> This I know, we never found any women with lumps in their breasts, I never knew, in all my 17 years of nursing in the hospital with Dr. Greist, of a single woman who did not breast-feed her child, and nurse it 2, 3, and up to 4 years . . . I never observed a caked breast or a sore nipple.

Mrs. Greist wrote that the very best nurse she knew of in northern Alaska was Miss Mildred H. Keaton, now of the White Pass and Yukon Hospital at Skagway, Alaska. Miss Keaton wrote me on April 15, 1957:

> Regarding the absence of cancer from the pre-white Eskimos of Arctic Alaska, it has ever been a source of wonder to me that during the fifteen years when I was a field nurse in the Kotzebue and Barrow districts . . . among the more primitive Eskimos, only once did I come in contact with a diagnosed case of cancer.

> We field nurses have wondered why the women did not have breast cancer due to the way they carried their babies on their backs with a strong leather or reindeer skin belt fastened right around their chest . . . the pressure on the mammary glands of the breast must have been severe.

> The late Dr. Ray Edward Smith was hospital physician in Kotzebue for some 16 years . . . [serving] a population of native [Eskimo] people totalling about three thousand coming to Kotzebue Hospital. He once told me he had always been most pleasantly surprised at the absence of cancer of any kind among these people.

To check on her report of what Dr. Smith had said, Miss Keaton suggested getting in touch with his widow, who wrote us on July 19, 1957:

It has long been my wish that Dr. Smith's observations concerning the incidence of cancer . . . be made known. I was with him after 1936, and many times he remarked that he had never encountered cancer among the natives [Eskimos] prior to that time.

During that time I was in Kotzebue, 1936-41, we had only two malignancies, one in 1938, the second I believe in 1940 . . . [Since leaving the hospital] I have personally known of two [Eskimo] women in their thirties who have died from cancer of the cervix. . . . Both had acquired the white man's way of living.

During the time I was there I believe there were on the average one or two cases of non-native cancer per year.

We close this section with some comments on southwestern Alaska by Dr. Joseph Henry Romig who, as a medical missionary, was in his day to subarctic Alaska what Dr. Albert Schweitzer is now to tropical Africa. They were written for an Arctic encyclopedia I compiled for the United States Navy.

Tuberculosis was their most dangerous disease and killed many children before they were two years old; but, as a whole, they resisted tuberculosis quite well. They did not have gastric ulcer, cancer, diabetes, malaria, or typhoid fever, or the common diseases of childhood known so well among the whites. For the most part they were a happy carefree people . . . Accidents and surgical care was the most of the emergency work . . . They did not have any venereal disease except some old syphilis handed down from contacts not their own. [There had been Russians and other Europeans in southwestern Alaska for more than a century, though without much influence on their way of life.]

With the advent of gold discovery, government schools and missions, and the high price of furs, came a new era. They were taught to build [European-style] houses; where wood was scarce, the place was cold as soon as the fire went out in the stove. They were able to buy white men's food and clothing, neither of which fitted their real need. . . . These people have changed from the old way to eating pancakes with syrup and canned goods from the store. The children have poor teeth now, as well as the older ones. They have white men's epidemics, and neither the homes nor the food that once were good for them . . .

The government is now doing much to cover up and ease these changes in the native life. . . . It is with regret that we can see the slow passing of these once hardy people . . .

Controversies

Concerning longevity and corpulence among Eskimos there is some controversy. On one side are the anthropologists and the medical missionaries, and, on the other, the famous "big city" and university scientists, particularly doctors of medicine.

A perhaps extreme spokesman for the "big city" viewpoint on longevity is Dr. Ancel Keys, Director, Laboratory of Physiological Hygiene, University of Minnesota. He wrote on December 30, 1958:

. . . extremely little is known about the health of primitive peoples, including the tiny remnant of primitive Eskimos. It is known, however, that their life expectancy is very short and that a primitive Eskimo over the age of 50 is a great rarity.

For the anthropologist-missionary point of view, we cite Dr. Henry W. Greist:

For untold centuries . . . the Eskimo of the far North had solely a carnivorous diet . . . He was healthy . . . barring

57

accidents, starvation in lean years, and epidemics of unknown character, he lived to a very great age . . .

Among people who have lived with the Eskimos we have found all testimonies and views to be similar to those of Dr. Greist. We summarize a few of them:

On *corpulence* the case is much the same as on longevity— the city doctors believe that Eskimos tend to be fat and the anthropologists and frontier doctors, especially the medical missionaries, believed that Eskimos, particularly the more northerly ones, are inclined to be thin—so long as they remain on their former diets. I never saw or heard of a corpulent Eskimo until 1912, when I first visited Nome, and first saw Eskimos who were living on European foods. They were about as corpulent, on the average, as Europeans.

Murdoch and others have pointed out that the mistake of Europeans, in reporting Eskimos as fat, derives from their puffy clothes, their round Mongol-type faces, and from the usual European idea that anybody who eats a lot of fat food must himself be fat.

Says Dr. Diamond Jenness, speaking of Coronation Gulf around 1916:

> . . . the Copper Eskimos are about middle stature, and sturdy and robust in build. The fur clothing, in which they are habitually enveloped, give them an exaggerated appearance of corpulence whereas in reality they incline to slenderness, the body tapering a little below the broad shoulders . . . no markedly thin person was seen [2].

Dr. Jenness believes that the precivilized Eskimos of northern Canada had, on the average, better health and longer life than their present partially Europeanized descendants.

Diseases and Difficulties which Civilization Allegedly Brings

Briefly, there are two groups of diseases which our discovery of the New World brought to the northern peoples: those which everybody agrees are caused by germs, and those which the medical missionaries believe are caused by nutritional change.

Of the germ diseases most students agree measles has proved the deadliest. Other deadly ones have been smallpox, influenza, venereal diseases and tuberculosis. Measles has killed the largest number in the past; tuberculosis is leading presently.

The nutritional diseases are thought by the medical missionaries to have been introduced by our culture—by our discouraging old foods and encouraging new ones, by our cooking and other methods of food processing and food handling, perhaps to some extent by our clothing, our housing, and by some of our other customs, such as encouraging the tub bath and discouraging the sweat bath. We repeat here a partial list of the allegedly nutritional disturbances which we are supposed to have started or made worse. We have put in italics those on which the medical missionaries are in substantial, and in many cases emphatic, agreement: appendicitis, arthritis, *beriberi, cancer, caries* (dental), constipation, *corpulence,* diabetes, epilepsy, gallstones, gastric ulcer, hypertension, night blindness, *pellagra, ricketts,* rheumatism, *scurvy.*

REFERENCES

1. Hutton, Samuel King: *Health Conditions and Disease Incidence among the Eskimos of Labrador.* Poole, England: Wessex Press, 1925.

2. Jenness, Diamond: *Physical Characteristics of the Copper Eskimos*. p. 38.
3. Jenness, Diamond: *The Indians of Canada*. Ottawa: F. A. Acland, 1932.
4. Jenness, Diamond: *Dawn in Arctic Alaska*. Minneapolis: University of Minnesota Press, 1957.
5. Lieb, Clarence W.: The Effects of an Exclusive Long-Continued Meat Diet, Based on the History, Experiences and Clinical Survey of Vilhjalmur Stefansson, Arctic Explorer. *J. Amer. Med. Assoc.*, 87:25-26, 1926.
6. Lieb, Clarence W.: The Effects on Human Beings of a Twelve Months' Exclusive Meat Diet. *J. Am. Med. Assoc.*, 93:20-22, 1929.
7. Lieb, Clarence W.: A Year's Exclusive Meat Diet and Seven Years Later. *Am. J. Digestive Dis. & Nutrition*, 2:473-475, 1935.
8. Stefansson, Vilhjalmur: *The Fat of the Land*. New York: Macmillan, 1956.
9. Stefansson, Vilhjalmur: *Hunters of the Great North*. New York: Harcourt, Brace, 1922.

FOOD AND SOCIETY IN CHINA AND INDIA

Karl A. Wittfogel, Ph.D.

THE NUTRITION specialist dealing with the food of a given area may be concerned primarily with its biochemical aspect. The social scientist will focus his attention primarily on the institutional setting in which the people of that area produce and consume. Comparing the food problem in China and India from the standpoint of the social scientist, we find basic similarities and significant dissimilarities which to a large extent can be clarified by a comparative institutional analysis.

Appearance does not always express essence. It would be too simple to explain the basic similarities by the fact that both civilizations subsist largely on rice; just as it would be too simple to define the dissimilarities in terms of eating habits: the Chinese eat with chopsticks; the Indians eat with their hands; the Chinese sit on chairs during a meal; the Indians squat. The social historian will hesitate to cite institutional causes for these different habits; he will insist on a more differentiated approach to the phenomenon, "rice."

First, rice was not always China's chief crop. In the days of Confucius, and for centuries thereafter, the Chinese, living essentially in the Yellow River basin, grew mainly millet and wheat. Second, it is not enough to state that rice—and, in arid and semi-arid areas, millet and wheat—requires the manipulation of water for the purpose of irrigation.

Water, it will be remembered, may be manipulated by a farmer-producer laboring alone, or it may require comprehensive operations for the maintenance of irrigation and flood control. Experience shows that small-scale irrigation is compatible with various forms of multicentered agrarian societies, whereas large-scale irrigation and "heavy waterworks" tend to involve the growth of single-centered agrarian societies. In certain parts of ancient Greece irrigation was widely employed; but in the fragmented landscape of Hellas the necessary waterworks remained small. As in Japan, they did not become an essential task of an agro-managerial government. In Greece they did not prevent the growth of aristocratic or democratic multicentered societies, and in Japan they did not prevent the rise of a multicentered feudal order.

Agrarian civilizations in which the government manages large waterworks of the productive and protective types have existed for millennia. Because of the location of their most spectacular occurrences, the classical economists referred to them as "Asiatic" or "Oriental" societies. Stressing function rather than geography, I suggest the term "hydraulic societies." For clarification I should like to add that such societies may be "compact" (hydraulic operations covering virtually the whole agricultural domain), "loose" (hydraulic operations covering only certain key areas), or "marginal" (hydraulic operations absent or insignificant, but the derivative despotic state persisting nevertheless) (32, pp. 173 ff.).

China and India were both hydraulic societies. Like other orders of this type, they developed a "state stronger than society." This state was able to atomize the population by blocking the growth of those independent, politically effective, social forces which in the West were instrumental in creating multicentered industrial societies based on private property. Lacking such forces, the hydraulic civilizations perpetuated themselves for millennia. They also perpetuated the ways of producing and consuming food suggested by their specific institutional and cultural settings.

Irrigation tends to make farming intensive. Watering requires planting in rows. Such an arrangement also permits important operations of intertillage that cannot be used when seeds are scattered. Except for certain modifications necessitated by inundation farming, the methods of intensive cultivation prevail in compact hydraulic societies, and they are widespread in loose hydraulic societies. Their advantages are so obvious that, whenever possible, they are also applied to fields which are not irrigated either because the water supply is too limited or precipitation is sufficient.

China and India, along with other hydraulic societies, shared this trend (31, p. 158). They also shared its agronomical and demographic consequences: a preponderance of small farms and a dense population. Since cultivation was labor-intensive, a peasant family could till only a small plot. It generally could live on less land than it tilled, the produce being sufficient to maintain the cultivators and provide revenue for the officialdom and related groups (32, pp. 302 ff., 313 ff., 318).

In pre-Communist China, the average farm comprised 3.76 acres of land. In the rice-growing areas it comprised 2.79 acres (4, p. 268). In India similar patterns persist until today. More than half of all Indian land holdings are less than 2.5 acres, a third more have from 2.5 to 10 acres (34, p. 37).

Buck, whose researches yielded the 3.76 figure for China, contrasts this with an average of 14.28 acres in Holland (Holland practices a particularly refined type of Western agriculture), 21.59 acres in Germany, 63.18 acres in England and Wales, and 156.85 acres in the United States (4, p. 268). Where the average peasant holding is as small as it is in China and India, the land is too valuable to be used as pasture for big cattle, particularly when their labor power cannot be fully employed. In both countries the rural economy is directed toward the growing of plants rather than the raising of animals.

In China and India the dominant groups were essentially the civil and military representatives of the despotic state and their non-officiating aides: in China, a bureaucratic "gentry"; in India, the priests of the dominant religion (32). Similarities in the basic societal structure account for the similarities in agriculture and demography mentioned above. Significant differences in secondary sociocultural developments account for significant differences in the intensity and objectives of food production.

Comparing present-day India and precommunist China, we learn that, unit per unit, Chinese cultivation was superior in the three main grain crops—rice, wheat, and millet (including sorghum). One acre of rice yielded 10.2 metric quintals [1] in China and 5.0, or half as much, in India (33, p. 552). One acre of wheat yielded 4.4 metric quintals in China, and 2.8, or little more than half as much, in India (33, p. 547). Our figures for millet and sorghum refer to the years 1948 and 1949, a time when the Civil War in China reached its climax. Yet, even then, the per acre yields of

[1] One metric ton of rice equals 10 metric quintals, that is, 49 bushels.

millet and sorghum were about three times higher there than in India (33, p. 565).

Among the causes for this difference, two seem particularly important, the Chinese use of human residues as manure and the replacement—more than 2000 years ago—of the communal land system by a system of private land tenure. The first greatly stimulated plant growth (29, pp. 308 ff.); the second provided a maximum incentive for the peasant cultivator whether he was an owner or a tenant (3, pp. 154 ff.).

The Hindu religion, which also influenced some of India's Moslem conquerors, established concepts of cleanliness that virtually precluded the use of night soil. A modern Indian agronomist faces the practical consequences of this attitude squarely by attributing "the present low yields of Indian crops . . . mainly to the gross neglect to return to the soil in the form of manure what is generally taken out of them in the form of crops" (1; 26, p. 23). Hindu religion also taboos the killing of animals. Particular emphasis is placed on keeping bovines alive. The resulting dietary restrictions go far beyond economic requirements. In China an aversion to dairy products did not lead to the rejection of meat as food. In India milk is valued; but the necessity of feeding the work cattle relatively well, and the many useless cattle in all, leaves little fodder for the milk cows and consequently little milk for the population (23, p. 177).

In China, as might be expected, the amount of farm land devoted to pasture is extremely low: 1.1 per cent (4, p. 173 f.). In India only 4.2 per cent of all arable land produces fodder crops (15, p. 100), and this despite the fact that "India possesses the largest number of cattle as compared to any other country in the world" (23, p. 177)—215 million out of

690 million. In the United States pastures constitute 47 per cent of all farm land.

In prewar China the rural population subsisted on a diet which derived 91.8 per cent of its calories from seed products, 5.2 per cent from vegetables, 2.3 per cent from animal products (mainly pork), 0.5 per cent from sugar, and 0.2 per cent from fruits (18, pp. 411, 414). Among the seed products, by far the most important were the grains which constituted 83.1 per cent of the total diet. Legumes constituted only 6.7 per cent; fruits, 0.2 per cent; all varieties of potatoes, 3.9 per cent; and sweet potatoes alone, 2.6 per cent (18, pp. 411, 413).

How nourishing was this diet? Many attempts have been made to answer this question. But while authorities differ considerably on the amount of calories necessary for an adequate diet in the two countries, they largely agree that, even when the amount is sufficient, the character of the food often leaves much to be desired (18, pp. 406 ff.; 22, p. 166 f.).

Being essentially vegetarian and based mainly on cereals, the traditional Chinese diet is lacking in certain nutritive elements, especially minerals and vitamins; and certain other elements are consumed in a form that makes utilization difficult. The extremely low consumption of such products as milk, eggs, green leafy vegetables, and fruits results in a deficiency in protective foods that is only partially counteracted by the high consumption of grain foods, since the protein derived from vegetables is much less easily digested and has a lower biological value than the animal proteins which constitute only 4 per cent of the diet (18, pp. 414, 419).

A scarcity of building foods has a particularly harmful effect on infant growth. In China "even where there is enough protein intake, its quality is not of a kind suitable for the nutrition of young children" (22, p. 167). The grains that are prominent in the Chinese diet are low in calcium, rice having even less of this mineral than wheat. There is also little calcium in potatoes, especially sweet potatoes; and the soybean is not much better in this respect (18, pp. 419-424). Moreover, the low calcium intake reduces the effectiveness of phosphorus, which is more plentiful in the Chinese diet. Maynard and Swen conclude: "A condition of inadequate calcium and phosphorus nutrition, caused primarily by a deficiency of calcium, is the most important finding suggested by our data" (18, p. 425).

There are some mitigating factors. In the Chinese countryside grain is lightly milled (22, pp. 166, 168, 173); it thus retains protein and vitamins that are removed by more thorough milling. Vegetables are usually cooked quickly, that is, without any great loss of vitamins (28, p. 68). The soybean provides protein and, as already noted, some calcium (18, p. 416 f.).

But there are also aggravating factors. A vegetarian diet of the Chinese type suffers from an excess of roughage. The grains are bulky and difficult to assimilate. The digestive organs are overworked, and the body is therefore more susceptible to intestinal diseases (18, p. 415). Unfortunately, the belief that the Chinese by habituation have become immune to the deficiencies of their diet is not correct. According to a study made in the 1930's by Huang Tse-fang, from 25 to 40 per cent of all excess deaths in China are due to gastrointestinal diseases (16, p. 278 f.).

Average data like these reflect in the main the condition of the middle and lower strata of the Chinese population. Well-to-do persons consume greater quantities of the more easily digested and more nourishing foods, such as meat, fish, and leafy vegetables. At a Chinese banquet rice is served not together with the many dishes, but at the end, as a sign that the meal is over.

Vigor and success are popularly associated with diets that include the more nutritious seed foods and meat. In a Shantung village the appearance of a businessman or a missionary used to evoke the comment: "He is a man who eats wheat flour every day, why should he not have a smooth face!" And a man's good luck may be likened to "meat . . . served with wheat flour rolls." To be called a sweet-potato eater was considered an insult, since "the sweet potato is the food of poor people" (36, p. 34 f.).

How similar—and dissimilar—is the Indian food picture! Since standard production was lower in India than in China, standard consumption was also lower. In prewar times the daily intake was probably several hundred calories less than in China. The greater part of the population subsisted on less than 2,100 calories, the standard minimum.[2] A diet consisting mainly of rice or other cereals and very small quantities of pulse, vegetables, milk, and fats is of course poor in building foods and protein. In India, as in China, the light milling of grain is a mitigating factor; but for reasons indicated above, the intake of protein is even lower than in China. All this results in a serious lack of calcium and vitamins (9, p. 157; 19, pp. 208-209; 15, pp. 100-104).

The scarcity of building foods is held to be largely responsible for the high mortality of infants and mothers (15, p. 104). Lack of vitamin A makes night blindness frequent (19, p. 212); it is also believed to be a cause of permanent blind-

[2] Shen (22, p. 166) states that the diet in precommunist China was "200 calories higher than most of the other Asiatic countries."

ness, which is particularly frequent in South India (15, p. 104 f.).

As in China, economic status is reflected in food habits. Persons of means enjoy a more nutritious vegetarian diet than the general population. They may eat their fill of "cool" foods that supposedly, and desirably, do not excite the passions: wheat flour, rice, honey, white sugar, milk and butter, especially clarified butter, *ghi* (5, p. 166), and also, of course, vegetables, fruit, fish, and eggs. "The most important difference between the diets of the well-to-do and the poor throughout India is the greater amount of milk products included in the former" (15, p. 103). Until today, on the occasion of a feast, men may be seen swallowing two pounds or more of clarified butter at one sitting (5, p. 166). This pattern is by no means new. Dubois, who lived in India from 1792 to 1823, was amazed at the amount of food a Brahmin consumed when circumstances permitted. "One often sees a Brahmin, after making a hearty meal of rice and liquefied butter, eat the whole of a huge jack-fruit, which would be enough to give ten Europeans violent indigestion" (8, p. 272).

In China secular and spiritual functions were exercised by a single group. In India they were traditionally separated. Where Hindu norms prevailed the Brahmins set the pattern for the vegetarian diet, while the freer earlier tradition was upheld by the remnants of the old upper class of warriors and rulers. Until today, the *rajputs* eat meat and drink alcohol. It is believed that this diet makes for militancy and virility (5).

Gandhi recalls that as a boy he was much impressed by the popular argument: "We are a weak people because we do not eat meat. The English are able to rule over us, because they are meat eaters" (10, p. 32). Like his schoolmates, he was fond of quoting a bit of doggerel written by the Gujarati poet, Narmad:

> Behold the mighty Englishman
> He rules the Indian small,
> Because being a meat-eater
> He is five cubits tall [10, p. 33].

Gandhi tried to eat meat for a year, so that he would be "strong and daring" in the fight against the colonial rulers. Then, in disgust, he dropped his dietary weapon. But the meat-eating Englishmen relinquished their precious Asian possession anyhow.

India gained her freedom at about the same time that the Communists seized power on the Chinese mainland. In both countries these great political changes produced great social changes. They also affected the production and consumption of food.

In the Republic of India the tendency to entrust all major economic tasks to the state is strong; but there is also a tendency—which seems to be growing—to encourage individual enterprise, particularly in the sphere of agriculture. Attempts are being made to improve farming, first by a land reform which establishes the peasants as the owners of the soil they till, and second by teaching them agronomical techniques that have proved effective in traditional China and Japan. In experimental "development blocks" comprising about a hundred villages each, the peasants, aided by native and foreign (mainly American) instructors, have doubled, tripled, and quadrupled the yield of wheat (34, p. 101).

These results show the potential of agriculture. They also show that the "race between population and food production," which Radhakamal Mukerjee (20, p. 10) and other Indian economists found so threatening, need not mean a constant deterioration in living conditions. Population growth in India—1.32 per cent per year—may not be high when compared with the rate of increase in other countries —1.5 per cent in the United States, 2 per cent in Canada and Communist China,[3] and 3 per cent in Mexico and Venezuela (34, p. 35)—yet it was excessive when measured against the productivity of Indian farming.

This is still the case, but a grave crisis has recently led to a change in policy, to new experiments and a more optimistic prospect. Today some experts believe that the Indian peasants can augment their yield 100 per cent in one or two decades (34, p. 40) if they employ the methods used in the development blocks: more fertilizer, better seeds, and improved cultivation. If, in addition, they can raise the production of vegetables, eggs, fruits (15, p. 107), and such milk-giving animals as goats,[4] then a radical step will have been taken in the reshaping of India's food situation.

Such a development would also affect the social patterns of eating and drinking that previously were determined by considerations of religion and caste. Apparently meat is being eaten in some urban circles today; but in 1956, Woytinsky (34, p. 8) still witnessed a demonstration against the serving of meat in a Bombay hotel. The slogans of protest were: "The cow is our mother!" "Do not kill our mother!" "Do not eat cow meat!" In the villages the taboo is still very

---

[3] For Communist China see *China News Analysis* (6), March 15, 1957, p. 3; April 18, 1958, p. 2.

[4] The number of bullocks can be reduced and milk cattle increased, if means can be found to extend mechanized farming and to find cheap fuel for agricultural machinery. Husain pleads for the increase of goats, although he is aware of their "bad reputation as a destroyer of all vegetation" (14, p. 152).

strong, but the prohibition against members of different castes eating together is increasingly ignored. Again, this is particularly the case in the cities. But in the countryside, too, persons of higher caste may be seen sitting "with their social [caste] inferiors, drinking tea in public tea-shops" (5).

The recent Chinese development is a double one. In the Republic of China (on Taiwan) much of the country's tradition is being preserved. In mainland China, the Communists are deliberately, and often violently, eradicating the old ways of doing things.

In Taiwan change has been gradual and peaceful. A land reform, similar to the one completed in postwar Japan (25), notably improved rural conditions. The peasants "are making more profit" and are therefore willing "to spend more for fertilizer and improved seeds." They are "buying better water buffaloes," and "they frequently have more pork, fish, or fowl to go with the rice" (12, pp. 89 ff.). Impressed by what he saw, Chester Bowles concluded that the land reform in Taiwan "could well serve as a model for every free nation in Asia" (2, p. 180).

In mainland China changes in the production and consumption of food have taken a very different turn. In less than ten years the food producers have experienced a violence-ridden land distribution, the loss of their land through the collectivization, and, most recently, the merging of clusters of collectives along with local industries and communications into "militarized" communes [5] (27, pp. 134 ff.; 35, p. 141; 11, pp. 96 ff.; 30, p. 8 f.; 24, pp. 268 ff.).

[5] The decisive resolution of the Central Committee of the Chinese Communist Party on the Establishment of People's Communes in Rural Areas designates "the 'militarization' of organization, the placing of activities on a 'combatant' basis, and the collectivization of daily living" as key features of the communes. For an astute evaluation of this development see Hudson (13).

This transformation involves features that are part of a general technical and scientific revolution and that need not be discussed here, since, with certain modifications, they are also present in Taiwan, Japan, and India. However, a number of features are specific. Some pertain to the production, some to the distribution, and some to the consumption of food.

Commandeered labor, which will soon include the majority of all able-bodied females, is employed in the construction of extensive hydraulic installations and other public works that serve agriculture. Centralized farming also facilitates the spread of new agronomical techniques. Both innovations heighten productivity, but they are paralleled by others that hamper it: bureaucratic blundering [6] and, above all, the laborers' negative attitude toward their work.[7] Obviously, it is difficult to operate a highly intensive type of farming with quasi-military methods and without private-property-based incentives offered by the traditional system of Chinese agriculture.

The advancing collectivization enables the state more effectively to organize the distribution of food in accordance with the purposes of its power economy. The country's sub-

[6] The Communist bureaucracy tried to introduce a two-wheeled, double-shared plow. However, the heavy implement was poorly adapted to Chinese conditions and the farmers' resistance compelled the government to build smaller types (*Jen-min Jih-pao*, February 21 and 22, 1958; 6, March 28, 1958, pp. 4 ff.).

[7] An article on labor conditions in a Hupeh collective admitted that "the existing efficiency rate is not high." In some cases it was only half the quota (Hankow, *Hupeh Jih-pao*, April 16, 1958). Critics like to stress the "shortage" of labor, but behind the quantitative deficiency there often lies a qualitative deficiency ("Solution of Labor Shortage Problem," Foochow, *Fukien Jih-pao*, February 23, 1958). For an instance of the neglect of crops, see "' Field Platoon' Plays an Important Role" (*Jen-min Jih-pao*, August 15, 1958). On October 19, 1958, an official broadcast (Peking, Chinese Home Service) stated that "investigations everywhere have shown a lack of attention to the autumn harvest work."

sistence economy may be controlled by rationing. This was the method introduced at the beginning of the collectivization in the winter 1953-1954, or by the "free-meal" system. This is also the method now being employed by the communes. In both cases, the government is able to export such items as meat and rice because it can keep consumption down at home. Early in 1957, even supporters of the regime were warning that "the bellies of the peasants are empty," because "the peasants have not been allowed enough food grains in the wake of the agricultural coopertivization." [8] For years the people have been getting little meat, especially pork,[9] but they are being forced to produce—and to eat—more sweet potatoes than they like. The present plan to have sweet potatoes satisfy 20 to 30 per cent of Red China's dietary needs is perhaps the most gigantic modern effort to worsen a nation's nutrition in peacetime.[10]

To be sure, not everyone in the country suffers from a food shortage. In May 1957, when the "hundred flowers" were encouraged to speak out, a courageous critic ascribed the strain in the supply of commodities to the government's method of controlling grain and other goods. He pointed to

[8] Shanghai, *Ch'ing-nien Pao*, March 15, 1957.

[9] *Ta Kung Pao*, May 22, 1955; cf. *China News Analysis* (6) March 2, 1956, p. 8; *Jen-min Jih-pao*, May 31, 1957.

[10] *Ta Kung Pao*, April 27, 1958. Starting with a hypothetical situation in which the farmers consume a moderate quantity of sweet potatoes (a quantity that from the standpoint of nutrition and available means is justifiable), the article suggests a much higher production and intake of potatoes. Analyzing the recommended changes, we find that they would result in something like a 10 per cent increase in bulk and a 20 per cent loss in calories. For a discussion of the Communist potato policy see Peiping, *Ta Kung Pao*, May 14 and 19, 1958; *Jen-min Jih-pao*, June 2 and 12, 1958. Cf. *China News Analysis* (6), August 8, 1958. In the fall of 1958 reports from Hunan revealed that in some communes "most of the food was made of sweet potatoes," and "quite a number of mess halls served nothing but sweet potatoes, meal after meal, to the commune members' great dissatisfaction" (*Jen-min Jih-pao*, November 9, 1958).

the fact that the common people find pork "unavailable." He asked, "Where has all the pork gone to?" Countering the Communist argument that the general shortage was due to the rising standard of living, he asserted that "a higher standard of living" is now enjoyed by "the Party members and the cadres." [11]

This statement aggressively underlines the key issues. On the Chinese mainland there appear new ways of handling food that involve new ways of handling men: a new pattern of agricultural production—(bureaucratically directed labor brigades instead of individuals or family teams), a new pattern of distribution (state planning instead of farmstead budgeting); and a new pattern of consumption (public canteens instead of the family tables).

What does this development mean and where will it lead? These questions are more easily asked than answered. Even persons familiar with Huxley's and Orwell's grim utopias will find it hard to grasp fully the conditions of food and society that emerge today in Communist China.

REFERENCES

1. Acharya, C. N.: Utilization of Village Wastes. In: *Developing Village India: Studies in Village Problems*. Bombay, Calcutta, Madras: Longmans, 1951, pp. 136-139.
2. Bowles, Chester: *Ambassador's Report*. New York: Harper, 1954.
3. Buck, John Lossing: *Chinese Farm Economy*. Chicago: University of Chicago Press, 1930.
4. Buck, John Lossing: *Land Utilization in China*. Chicago: University of Chicago Press, 1937.
5. Carstairs, G. Morris: *The Twice-Born. A Study of a Community of High-Caste Hindus*. London: Hogarth Press, 1957.
6. *China News Analysis:* Weekly Newsletters, Hong Kong.

[11] *Jen-min Jih-pao*, May 31, 1957.

7. *Developing Village India: Studies in Village Problems*
Bombay, Calcutta, Madras: Longmans, 1951.
8. Dubois, J. A.: *Hindu Manners, Customs and Ceremonies.*
Trans. and ed. by Henry K. Beauchamp. Oxford: Clarendon
Press, 1943.
9. "Food Facts." In: *Developing Village India: Studies in Village Problems*. Bombay, Calcutta, Madras: Longmans, 1951,
pp. 155-167.
10. Gandhi, M. K.: *Gandhi's Autobiography. The Story of My
Experiments with Truth.* Washington, D.C.: Public Affairs
Press, 1948.
11. Gluckstein, Ygael: *Mao's China. Economic and Political
Survey.* London: Allen and Unwin, 1957.
12. Han Lih-wu: *Taiwan Today.* Taipei, Taiwan: Hwa Kuo
Publishing Co., 1956.
13. Hudson, G. F.: New Phase of Mao's Revolution. *Problems
of Communism, 7:8-14.*
14. Husain, Afzal: The Nutrition Problem of the Villager. In:
Developing Village India: Studies in Village Problems. Bombay, Calcutta, Madras: Longmans, 1951, pp. 147-153.
15. Kharegat, Pheroze and Aykroyd, W. A.: Problems of Agriculture and Nutrition. In: *Developing Village India: Studies
in Village Problems*. Bombay, Calcutta, Madras: Longmans,
1951, pp. 99-108.
16. Lamson, Herbert Day: *Social Pathology in China.* Shanghai:
Commercial Press, 1935.
17. *Land-to-the-Tiller.* Taipei, Formosa: Information Office,
Joint Commission on Rural Reconstruction for Mutual Security Mission to China, 1955.
18. Maynard, Leonard A. and Swen, Wen-yuh: Nutrition. In:
Buck, John Lossing, *Land Utilization in China.* Chicago:
University of Chicago Press, 1937, pp. 400-436.
19. Megaw, John: Medicine and Public Health. In: Blunt,
Edward (ed.), *Social Service in India.* London: His Majesty's
Stationery Office, 1951, pp. 181-245.
20. Mukerjee, Radhakamal: The Food Supply. *Oxford Pamphlets on Indian Affairs* (No. 8). London: Oxford University
Press, 1946.
21. *Report of the Royal Commission on Agriculture in India.*
Presented to Parliament by Command of His Majesty, June,
1928. Abridged report.

22. Shen, T. H.: *Agricultural Resources of China*. Ithaca: Cornell University Press, 1951.
23. Singh, Sardar Datar: Improving Village Cattle. In: *Developing Village India: Studies in Village Problems*. Bombay, Calcutta, Madras: Longmans, 1951, pp. 177-179.
24. Tang, Peter S. H.: *Communist China Today: Domestic and Foreign Policies*. New York: Frederick A. Praeger, 1957.
25. Tobata, Seiichi: *An Introduction to Agriculture of Japan*. Tokyo: Agriculture, Forestry, and Fisheries Productivity Conference, 1958, pp. 49 ff.
26. Vijayaraghavacharya, T.: The Land and Its Problems. *Oxford Pamphlets on Indian Affairs* (No. 9). London: Oxford University Press, 1945.
27. Walker, Richard L.: *China under Communism. The First Five Years*. New Haven: Yale University Press, 1955.
28. Winfield, Gerald F.: *China. The Land and the People*. New York: William Sloane Associates, 1948.
29. Wittfogel, Karl A.: *Wirtschaft und Gesellschaft Chinas, Erster Teil, Produktions- und Zirkulationsprozess*. Leipzig: C. L. Hirschfeld, 1931.
30. Wittfogel, Karl A.: *Mao Tse-tung. Liberator or Destroyer of the Chinese Peasants?* New York: Free Trade Union Committee, American Federation of Labor, 1955.
31. Wittfogel, Karl A.: Hydraulic Civilizations. In: Thomas, William L., Jr. (ed.), *Man's Role in Changing the Face of the Earth*. Chicago: University of Chicago Press, 1956.
32. Wittfogel, Karl A.: *Oriental Despotism*. New Haven: Yale University Press, 1957.
33. Woytinsky, W. S. and E. S.: *World Population and Production: Trends and Outlook*. New York: Twentieth Century Fund, 1953.
34. Woytinsky, W. S.: *India: The Awakening Giant*. New York: Harper, 1957.
35. Wu, Yuan-li: *An Economic Survey of Communist China*. New York: Bookman Associates, 1956.
36. Yang, Martin C.: *A Chinese Village. Taitou Shantung Province*. New York: Columbia University Press, 1945.

NUTRITION FROM CLASSICAL ANTIQUITY TO THE BAROQUE

Owsei Temkin, M.D.

NUTRITION AND medical ideas on nutrition cannot be independent of the style of living. Eating and drinking are part of the civilization in which the physician has to think and act, and this civilization is encompassed within the borders of the known world (22). Certain foods are prescribed; the cooking and the quantity can be given in detail. But the physician cannot offer that which does not exist or is not available. What is the good of theorizing about all possible foods, when most of them are out of reach? The very fact that the medical literature of the period with which we are concerned tends to cover a large variety of foods, indicates the status of the doctor as the attendant of people not in constant want. This literature does not always tell us what those people ate whose diet was strictly limited by necessity.

We all have impressions of the dietary style of some of the periods we are covering. In the Homeric epic poetry, feasting means heavy eating. Penelope's suitors waste Odysseus' estate by their sumptuous meals consisting mainly of roast beef, mutton, goat meat, and pork. If this had been the daily food of the average Greek of the time, Homer would hardly have dwelled on it at length. The staple diet of the average Greek was *maza,* a dried dough made of barley. In early times, bread, particularly wheaten bread, was not common. Of vegetables there existed mainly beans, lentils and peas, onions, leek, and cabbage; cucumbers, olives, and figs were consumed in considerable quantities. There was milk from cows and goats, and cheeses, and, of course, there were grapes and wine, the latter usually mixed with water. It is not likely that the average Greek ate much meat; pork probably held the first rank. But there the sea offered its supply of food—pickled, salted, or smoked fish was very popular.

The increased trade of Greece facilitated the import of foods from different parts of the world and, more important perhaps, it lessened the dependence on the local supply. Rome, at the height of its power, had to feed the mass of its population with imported grain. Delay in the arrival of the boats, or interrupted communications on land, could spell famine.

Famine, however, was a more pronounced feature of the medieval inland economy. Famines caused by weather conditions, or because of epidemics and wars and sieges, occurred again and again till far into modern times. Such famines might occasionally affect both poor and rich; but the peasant was more frequently threatened since he could count on little else than the resources of his immediate neighborhood. The condition of the peasants varied considerably with the times and with individual countries. It ranged from a bread-and-water existence to a comfortable life with ample bread, vegetables, fruits, milk, cheese, meats, and ale. But there was an insecurity threatening the dietary necessities and, consequently, the possibility of "conspicuous consumption" in the form of food and drink. Spices, which had to be imported, were in great demand. The desire to obtain what was rare probably helped to mold taste. The contrast between workday and feastday, between poor and rich, expressed itself largely through the gullet (12).

Thus we have pictures of changing nutritional styles. The Greeks of the classical period and the Romans of the early Republic appear to us as moderate in their habits. The very name of Sybarite, singling out the inhabitants of the city of Sybaris with its fertile land, indicates that voluptuous living was not considered common. The proletarian of imperial Rome demands bread and plays; his rich and degenerate fellow citizen titillates his palate with a feather to relieve his stomach for more food. This picture gives way to Breughel's vomiting peasant who has gorged himself at a feast: In the baroque period of the seventeenth and early eighteenth centuries, we find in juxtaposition starvation and scurvy, and high living and gout. In between, from the Middle Ages on, is the religious ascetic whose privation is self-imposed. In the Renaissance there appears at his side the Erasmus-like humanist, who not only preaches moderation but whose enjoyment of intellectual values frees him from the excessive pleasures of the stomach. Toward the end of this period, changes took place which again were to modify the picture. In England, the Industrial Revolution posed new problems, and the potato, cultivated gradually from the seventeenth century on, offered a new indispensable food. Tea and coffee came into vogue, first in the elegant world, then in a broader stratum.

The dependence of the medical man on the nutritional style of his time is obvious. Not only does it determine the prevalence of certain diseases; it also determines what the physician is supposed to know. The ancient and medieval doctor knew nothing of vitamins. But he knew something about the differences between the various dishes that were served; for instance, the gobio, a fish of the gudgeon kind, was evaluated differently according to its provenience (9, vol. 6, p. 718). To cite a further example, in 1766, Pennier de Longchamp, a French physician, published a dissertation on truffles and mushrooms. His curiosity had been aroused because at a party a young man was observed indulging heavily in truffles. "Since my profession obliges me to know the virtues of all the plants, I was addressed and asked what effects truffles had" (23, p. 403).

But in spite of prevalent styles and fashions, there also existed a form of nutritional wisdom which withstood changes. It is documented in the *Regimen sanitatis Salernitanum* (18), a Latin poem that purports to speak in the name of Salerno to the King of England. This poem certainly existed by the end of the thirteenth century. Its dependence on traditional medicine is obvious, yet its connection with Salerno has rightly been doubted. It gives the impression of a popular dietetic work written by a medical man for the educated reader, i.e., whoever knew Latin, in a tone devoid of scholastic ponderosity. It stands between antiquity and modern times. Starting with this poem, we shall then look backward and forward. "If you lack doctors," we read, "these three will be doctors for you: a cheerful mind, rest, and a moderate diet" (18, p. 159). The idea of moderate eating is repeatedly emphasized: "A large supper imposes the greatest punishment on the stomach" (18, p. 160), and one should not eat before the previous meal has been digested, for which appetite is a sure sign. There are also, at the very beginning, summary rules for what should or should not be eaten:

> Peaches, apples, pears, milk, cheese, and salted meat,
> Deer, hare, goat, and veal,
> These engender black bile and are enemies of the sick.
> Fresh eggs, red wines, fat broth,
> Together with fine pure flour, strengthen nature.
> Wheat, milk, young cheese,
> Testicles, pork, brain, marrow,
> Sweet wine, food pleasant to the taste,
> Soft-boiled eggs, ripe figs, and fresh grapes,
> Nourish as well as make fat [18, p. 160].

In reading these lines the older among us may be reminded of the days when the doctor was not allowed to leave without having discussed the diet of his patient. My parents' faith in the physician did not necessarily go as far as to order the prescription he left, but I was sure to get chicken broth or cream of wheat if he so advised. The lines also indicate the audience who might benefit by them. When I said that the poem was for the educated reader, I should have added that it was also for the well-to-do reader. The dietary wine list alone bears that out: Wines should be clear, aged, subtle, mature; sweet white wines are considered particularly nourishing. Nevertheless, there are also things for those of modest means: "Cheese and bread are good food for those in good health—if a man is not healthy do not add the cheese to the bread" (18, p. 164).

Before leaving Salerno, I would like to quote two lines which seem to sum up the implications of the practical side of medical nutrition:

> *Quale, quid, et quando, quantum, quoties, ubi dando,*
> *Ista notare cibo debet medicus diaetando* [18, p. 168].

The quality and the kind of food, the when, and how much, and how often, and where to be given—these are the things the doctor has to point out in the diet. There is only one question left out, viz., *quare?* why? It is the why of the regulations that concerns the doctor and leads to a science of nutrition.

A medical science of nutrition presupposes that man's food should be regulated to keep him free from disease and cure him of sickness. We are aware of the fact that Greek medicine held this belief, but we must now probe its strength and possible roots. Immediately we are confronted with the phenomenon that for many Greek physicians since the Hippocratic era, scientific medicine was identical with dietetic medicine (25). The concept of diet was broader than it is today (7). It comprised not only food and drink, but also work, sleep, climate of the home, emotions, and sexual life, i.e., what the medieval doctors came to call the six *res non-naturales,* the six "non-naturals" (30). Since food and drink occupied the main position in the regimen, we shall use the term "diet" in this restricted sense.

To the author of the Hippocratic work *On Ancient Medicine,* medicine emerged from the observation that sick people could not stand the same food as the healthy. To him, this was an elaboration of a much wider thesis: that the diet of civilized man owed its origin to the hardships to which primitive people were subject, people who, like animals, lived on the raw products of the land.

As it is, sheer necessity has caused men to search for and discover medicine, because the same diet did not benefit, just as it does not benefit today, sick and well alike. To go further back still; I hold that the regimen and nutriment which men in health now use would not have been discovered at all, if men were satisfied with the same food and drink as satisfy an ox or a horse or any creature except man, for example, the things that grow out of the earth—fruits, wood and grass [13].

Apart from its wide sweep, this treatise is remarkable for basing nutrition on observation. This too was taken up by later authors. Galen applauded Diocles of Carystus, who, in the following century, warned against too great a faith in one's ability to give the cause of every effect: it was not always possible to say why foods were nourishing, or diuretic, or acted as a cathartic (9, vol. 6, p. 455 f.). As a contrasting example of causal nutrition, I quote this passage from the Hippocratic *Regimen in Health:*

In summer the barley-cake [the *maza*] is to be soft, the drink diluted and copious, and the meats in all cases boiled. For one must use these, in the summer, that the body may become cold and soft. For the season is hot and dry, and makes bodies burning and parched. Accordingly these conditions must be counteracted by the way of living [15, pp. 45-47].

If medicine did not originate directly from nutritional observations, there is yet little doubt that dietetic medicine, rather than surgery or pharmacology, gave the main impetus to speculative reasoning (7; 25). Why then did nutrition attain this great significance in classical antiquity, probably in the fifth century B.C.? There may have been a variety of reasons; together they amount to the belief on the part of the physician that he could form the body of man, just as the contemporary sophist believed that he could form his mind. Surgery dealt with injuries and external disorders. The use of drugs had been established by tradition. But in prescribing food and drink, the physician had the example of the gymnast, the trainer, who built up his protégé to the necessary strength. The preoccupation with the athlete which the Hippocratic doctor shared with the gymnast is indicated in the third Aphorism, which begins: "In athletes, a perfect condition that is at its highest pitch is treacherous. Such conditions cannot remain the same, or be at rest . . ." (15, p. 99).

Nutrition was not only important in the treatment of disease; it guided the life of the healthy as well. It is but another side of the same picture if Greek physicians found the nature of disease in dietetic errors. According to Aristotle, Hippocrates explained diseases in the following way:

> Either because of the quantity of things taken, or through their diversity, or because the things taken happen to be strong and difficult of digestion, residues are thereby produced, and when the things that have been taken are too many, the heat that produces digestion is overpowered by the multitude of foods and does not effect digestion. And because digestion is hindered residues are formed. And when the things that have been taken are of many kinds, they quarrel with one another in the belly, and because of the quarrel there is a change into residues. When however they are very coarse and hard to digest, there occurs hindrance of digestion because they are hard to assimilate, and so a change to residues takes place. From the residues rise gases, which having arisen bring on diseases [14, pp. 35-37].

The rest of the passage, which is taken from Jones's translation of the so-called *Anonymus Londinensis,* need not concern us here, nor need we enter upon the hotly debated question as to whether this really was the opinion of the great Hippocrates. What Jones's translation rightly calls "digestion," if rendered literally, means cooking, and this cooking process, we read, is sustained by the heat of the body. Digestion as cooking was generally believed to be a

Hippocratic idea; it was shared by Aristotle and Galen; it remained the favored theory throughout the Middle Ages and the Renaissance. Together with it went the view of food and air as fuel for the innate heat. But the right kind of food was needed, too much food, or wrong food, can suppress the fire. I take the following quotation from Galen:

> Just as the proper nutriment for fire increases it, in the same manner nutriment that is proper and natural for bodies warm by nature, will always strengthen them and increase their inborn heat. And this is the property of all food. Sometimes, however, too much food weakens the innate heat, after the manner of wet wood. For this too is nutriment for the fire, but if heaped on the fire it is too much and therefore conceals the flame and threatens extinction [9, vol. 15, p. 265f.].

The inborn heat digests food and is, in turn, maintained by food. Food is needed to replace the losses of the body, especially those incurred by insensible transpiration.

> The quantity of food must be proportionate to the quantity of transpiration. If nothing in us flowed away, we would not have come to need food, since the original mass of [body] substance would have been preserved for ever. However, the animal bodies are dissipated by the transpiration that takes place through the pores invisible to the sense. Therefore we need food. For nutrition is the restitution of what has been emptied [9, vol. 15, p. 240].

Here Galen gives us a fundamental definition of nutrition. Food, including air, is needed because the body is constantly discharging material in the process of transpiration: waste products which leave it through the invisible channels of the skin.[1] Here is the idea of nutrition as replacement in a

---

[1] The Greek word is *diapnoë* which may mean respiration as well as transpiration including not only gases but sweat as well.

process of perpetual combustion. Put this way, Greek physiology does not have the static appearance with which it is sometimes credited. There is a constant coming and going of food, drink, and air to feed the body heat and its regulator, the vital pneuma, and to make up for the waste.

But, we are reminded, these ideas lack quantitative reasoning and are thereby sharply at variance with the modern approach. Strictly speaking, this is not even true as far as Galen is concerned. Nutrition to him is that which replaces the material losses of the body without changing it. Herein lies the basic difference between nutriment and drug. What is assimilated and thus helps the body to grow or to maintain its status is nutriment. That which changes the temperament of the body is drug or poison (9, vol. 6, p. 468). Just as Galen has a quantitative scheme for the potency of drugs, so for food too he has a quantitative scheme. If a person's temperament deviates to one side, being too warm by three (imaginary) units, the food must deviate to the same degree in the opposite direction, i.e., it must be three units too cold (9, vol. 6, p. 469). Then, and then only, will it have a purely nutritional effect without increasing the abnormal deviation.

Admittedly, these units *(arithmoi)* of which Galen speaks are purely imaginary and cannot be measured. But 400 years before Galen, it had occurred to Erasistratus to measure emanations from the body.

If one were to take a creature, such as a bird or something of the sort, and were to place it in a pot for some time without giving it any food, and then were to weigh it with the excrement that visibly has been passed, he will find that there has been a great loss of weight, plainly because, perceptible only to the reason, a copious emanation has taken place [14, p. 127].

If in this quotation we replace the bird with the scientist experimenting on himself, we have the experimental design of Santorio Santorio depicted in his *Ars de statica medicina* of 1614. Erasistratus speaks of "invisible emanation" while Santorio attributes the loss in weight to "insensible perspiration."

> If eight Pounds of Meat and Drink are taken in one Day, the Quantity that usually goes off by Insensible Perspiration in that Time, is five Pounds [20, p. 47].

Such losses must, of course, be replaced if man is to survive. The measurement of insensible perspiration is, therefore, a means of regulating the nutritional requirements, a regulation where the physical properties of food are decisive. "The most Liquid Parts of our Food are likewise the most heavy, and the Solid lighter: Bread and Flesh are light, Wine and Broaths heavy. A Glass of Wine is almost three Times as heavy as a Piece of Bread of the same Bulk" (20, p. 58). Heavy and light here refer to the specific weight. Moreover, regulation is safer than reliance on the instinctive demands of the healthy body—an opinion referred to the authority of Celsus (20, p. 188).

The obvious errors of Santorio—his attributing to perspiration what is largely a matter of respiration—must not prevent us from seeing the significance of his vision. Nutrition is viewed as an isolated problem which can be solved on an exact basis of measurement. Santorio preceded Harvey who more felicitously solved the problem of the motion of the heart and blood as a circumscribed problem of cardiovascular physiology (24). We shall see that a similar step was made on the biochemical side.

Santorio's ideas have been compared with the system of

bookkeeping then in vogue among Italian men of business (1). It is quite possible that this exerted an influence on him, just as the influence of his contemporary, Galileo cannot be doubted. However, the existence of a similar thought, some nineteen hundred years before in Alexandria, should make us hesitate to take the analogy between bookkeeping and metabolic balance as proof of influence.

In Santorio's scheme of physiology, food whose particles could easily pass through the ducts of the body and be "perspired" was less nourishing than food of gross particles. Borelli, one of the greatest of the baroque biophysicists, declared that digestion was a grinding of the food into minute particles which, circulating with the blood, could be used for new building material (3). Erasistratus too had defined digestion as a grinding process (4)—an interesting example of the consequences to which similar basic presuppositions will lead across the centuries and differences of so-called intellectual climate.

I am comparing ancient ideas with those of the sixteenth and seventeenth century, well aware of the perils of such a summary procedure. The Middle Ages are a period that cannot be dismissed with a reference to the School of Salerno. Especially now, when we turn to the chemical aspects, we cannot overlook entirely the role of alchemy, ancient and medieval. One example may suffice.

There is a chain of ancient philosophers and physicians, beginning with Empedocles, who declared digestion to be a process of putrefaction (29). The fragmentary nature of the material outside the Galenic tradition does not allow us to determine what exactly was meant by this definition. It may have been the obvious change from fresh food to feces. It may also have implied a closer comparison with the decay of vegetal matter such as stated by an author of the eighteenth century:

> Vegetable Putrefaction resembles very much Animal Digestion. Vegetable Putrefaction is produced by throwing green succulent Vegetables in a Heap in open warm Air, and pressing them together, by which all Vegetables acquire, First, A Heat equal to that of a Human Body. Secondly, A putrid stercoraceous Taste and Odour, in Taste resembling putrid Flesh, and in Smell Human Foeces [2, p. 10].

But then we also have the symbolic language of the alchemist. By late antiquity, alchemical processes were compared with the growth of the embryo and the nourishment of the body. Putrefaction in late alchemistic parlance means revival, the transformation of a substance through its death (26). On the other hand, the Arab physician and alchemist, Rhazes, not only thinks of the plague as leading to putrefaction of the blood, but compares this putrefaction to hot, fermenting must (19, p. 174). The ideas of putrefaction and fermentation were never quite apart. Van Helmont speaks of digestion as a kind of putrefaction, and he thinks of it in terms of fermentation (27, p. 157). What seems new is the emphasis, rather than the details, which, as the comparison of the mechanists of the third century B.C. with those of the baroque showed, can be found a long way back.

Paracelsus claims that all food contains nourishment and poison. This may not seem too far removed from Galen's opinion that most foods also act as drugs. But then Paracelsus says that each creature "has within his body the agent that eliminates this poison from what the body takes up. This is called the alchemist because it uses the art of alchemy" (28). If the alchemist fails, disease will result. It is easy to see how such concepts are in line with a chemical interpretation of normal and pathological metabolism. The Galenic idea of the inborn heat, as Pagel has shown, meets opposition even before Paracelsus. Reuchlin, the humanist, argues that if heat were responsible for gastric digestion, heat outside the body should effect this even better (19, p. 293). With van Helmont, the heat of the body is but an adjunct of life, not a primary fundament (27, p. 160; 21). The demotion of body heat from a vital principle to a vital concomitant of life is one of the premises of Lavoisier's work. To claim, as Lavoisier did, that warmth is communicated to the body through the blood as a result of chemical combustion in the lungs, depends on the possibility of viewing it as a separate process.

Van Helmont distinguished six successive forms of digestion, beginning in the stomach and ending in the tissues where assimilation was completed. As Michael Foster has shown, van Helmont was a careful observer (8, p. 127 ff.). More recently, Multhauf (17) and Pagel (19, pp. 563-568) have debated van Helmont's relationship to older, even Galenic ideas of fermentation, and the use he made of his knowledge of acids. Pagel (19, pp. 524-536) has brought forward arguments to the effect that van Helmont discovered the presence of hydrochloric acid in the stomach. There is agreement that van Helmont was a vitalist and that his chemistry cannot be altogether separated from his cosmic speculations. But his successors, the iatrochemists, from the middle of the seventeenth century, dissociated themselves from his philosophy. They stood close to Descartes and Boyle, being mechanists on the molecular level (6).

With these iatrochemists there began a development on the chemical side that culminated in Lavoisier's discovery of respiration as an oxidative process. Carbon dioxide was discovered by van Helmont. The remainder of the period is divided into two phases. The first is characterized by the names of Boyle, Hooke, and Mayow. Dr. Guerlac's investigations are changing our opinions as to the meaning of some of these and later contributions (11). I shall limit myself to a mere reminder of what seems fairly well established about the second phase, which begins with Stahl's phlogiston theory (16, p. 37 ff.). This theory claims that in combustion, something, viz., the phlogiston, leaves the burning substance. Without challenging this wrong assumption, the chemists of the eighteenth century arrived at a better knowledge of the gases needed for, or involved in combustion. Carbon dioxide, van Helmont's "gas sylvestre," is studied by Joseph Black as "fixed air" (11). He finds that it is contained in the exhalations of animals. A few years later, Henry Cavendish studied "inflammable air," i.e., hydrogen, and Daniel Rutherford discovered "residual air," i.e., nitrogen, in which neither flame nor animal can exist. With the discovery of oxygen by Priestly and Scheele in the early 1770's, and Crawford's measurements of heat production in man, it needed only Lavoisier's "brilliant mind to mold these miscellaneous achievements into a harmonious entity" (16, p. 51).

It is not my intention to describe in detail the work of Lavoisier and Laplace.[2] I am concerned with the road leading to their discoveries. Here then the question may be permissible as to why the work of these two—a chemist and a mathematician—marks an epoch in the history of nutrition. One of the answers is that their work made possible a calcu-

---

[2] Suffice it to say that, by means of an ice calorimeter, they measured the heat produced by an animal and the heat produced by the combustion of carbon, and they compared these figures with the respective amounts of oxygen consumed and carbon dioxide produced.

lation of food requirements in terms of calories and thus an exact science of nutrition.

Now it seems to me that the predecessors of Lavoisier and Laplace can be divided into two groups: the chemists, whom we just discussed, and whose solid work formed a basis for advance in the right direction; and those who made it possible to approach nutrition rationally. This leads us back to the iatrochemists and iatrophysicists.

Van Helmont's separation of digestion from the inborn heat led to the same consequences as Santorio's study of metabolism. Both were steps in the dissolution of what we call "life" into a number of physiological functions. Such a dissolution leads to an embarrassing question: How do all these functions or processes combine to make an individual? This integration could be attributed to the soul; or one could—then as now—look at these processes with the eyes of the engineer, intent on the maintenance of a machine rather than on understanding. Thus in 1730, John Quincy, in an English edition of Santorio's work, spoke ironically of van Helmont. However, he also said:

> In the whole then, so far as a Person can consider a humane Body as a Machine, and by the known Laws of Motion demonstrate the Powers and Operations of its several Parts, so far may be with certainty known how to manage it, in order to produce any Change therein; that is, if he has proper Instruments, and upon the same Principles understands their Efficacy and Manner of Application [20, p. 38].

In the early eighteenth century both physics and chemistry suggested their methods to anybody wishing to base his diet on scientific principles. On the chemical side, John Arbuthnot offered his popular *Essay Concerning the Nature of*

Aliments, from which I cite the following example concern-ing the meat of fish, which he thought to be more watery than that of terrestrial animals. "From which Qualities," he writes, "a Diet of Fish is more rich and alkalescent than that of Flesh, and therefore very improper for such as practise Mortification. The Inhabitants of Sea-Port Towns are gen-erally prolifick" (2, p. 82).

Arbuthnot wrote his book with the express intent of show-ing that nutrition too had a scientific basis (2). Whether he, John Quincy, and others succeeded in convincing the world of this truth is hard to tell. That all nutritional theories before Lavoisier contained shortcomings is no counterargu-ment. People, including physicians, may believe what a later generation deems wrong. Surely the qualities of the ancients are not more convincing to us than Santorio's scales and the acids and alkalis of Arbuthnot. Yet ancient medicine put its trust in nutrition. Nevertheless, I am inclined to say that medicine at the end of the baroque period was no longer dietetic medicine. True, the old tradition was still strong; physicians told their patients what to eat and drink, and they preached temperance to those afflicted with gout. Moreover, palpable progress was made in the use of oranges, lemons, and limes for scurvy. But it must be remembered that when we think of Paracelsus and the iatrochemists, we think of new drugs and the apothecary's shop. When we think of Sydenham, we think of the concept that diseases are entities prevalent at certain times rather than consequences of dietary mistakes. When we think of Ramazzini, we think of diseases as caused by one's occupation rather than by food. In short, the role of food is not denied, but neither does it stand in the foreground of attention. Why this change in comparison with antiquity?

Dietetic medicine was based on the idea that causation of health and disease was in man's power. If diseases, short of epidemics, were caused by dietary mistakes, then knowledge and character determined health and disease. Such a medical system was also based on the view that the physician could build and rebuild the human body, and, with the body, perhaps even the mind.

In 1747 Gaubius (10) wistfully and with regret of past glory, quoted these words of Galen:

Let those who refuse to admit the efficacy of food in making men better or more dissolute, more unrestrained or more reserved, bolder or more timid, more barbarous or more civilized, or more given to disputes and fighting, let them on thinking better of it inquire in order to learn from me what they should eat or drink. For they will profit mightily with regard to moral philosophy, and furthermore they will enhance the virtues of the logical soul, becoming more intelligent, more studious, more prudent, and acquiring a better memory. In fact, I shall instruct them not only as to nourishment, as to what to drink, and concerning the winds, but also concerning the temperaments of the surrounding air, and I shall teach them also what regions they should seek out, or flee [9, vol. 4, p. 807 f.; 5].

At the time of Lavoisier, such faith in dietetic medicine was gone. But was the century without any faith in nutrition? In answer, I quote John Quincy's statement: "I am not at all unaware how severe some will be hereupon, in requiring how often they must weigh themselves, and whether they ought to eat and drink by the Ounce . . ." (20, p. vi). What a modern ring this has! Significantly enough, this remark expresses the sentiments of people at large rather than those of the doctor. If I interpret it rightly, it means the anticipation of a science of nutrition in which authority has switched to measurements and figures. But around 1750 this was no more than a foreboding. In the meantime, people enjoyed a nutritional *laissez-faire* in which neither the imperious doctor nor cold facts tyrannized them.

REFERENCES

1. Achelis, Johann Daniel: Die Ernährungsphysiologie des 17. Jahrhunderts. *Sitzungsberichte Heidelberger Akad. Wissenschaften, 3:*9, 1938.
2. Arbuthnot, John: *An Essay Concerning the Nature of Aliments.* London: Tonson, 1732.
3. Borelli, Alphonsus: *De Motu Animalium.* Rome: Angelus Barbo, 1681, p. 394.
4. Celsus, Aurelius Cornelius: *De Medicina.* Florence: Nicolaus Laurentius, 1478.
5. Daremberg, Charles Victor: *Oeuvres Anatomiques Physiologiques et Médicales de Galien,* vol. 1. Paris: Baillière, 1854-1856, pp. 47-91.
6. Diepgen, Paul: *Geschichte der Medizin,* vol. 1. Berlin: De Gruyter, 1949, p. 295.
7. Edelstein, Ludwig: Antike Diätik. *Antike, 7:*255-270, 1931.
8. Foster, M.: *Lectures on the History of Physiology.* Cambridge: Cambridge University Press, 1901.
9. Galen: *Opera Omnia,* Ed. C. G. Kühn. Leipzig: Cnobloch, 1821-1833.
10. Gaubius, H. D.: De Regimine Mentis. In: *Opuscula Selecta Neerlandicorum de Arte Medica,* vol. 77. Amsterdam: F. van Rossen, 1932, pp. 158-160.
11. Guerlac, Henry: Joseph Black and Fixed Air. *Isis, 48:*124-151; 433-456, 1957.
12. Hintze, K.: *Geographie und Geschichte der Ernährung.* Leipzig: Thieme, 1934.
13. Jones, W. H. S.: *Philosophy and Medicine in Ancient Greece.* Baltimore: Johns Hopkins Press, 1946, p. 67.
14. Jones, W. H. S., *The Medical Writings of Anonymus Londinensis.* Cambridge: Cambridge University Press, 1947.
15. Jones, W. H. S.; Trans.: *Hippocrates,* vol. 4. London: W. Heinemann, 1923-1931.

16. Lusk, Graham: *Nutrition*. New York: Hoeber, 1933.
17. Multhauf, Robert P.: J. B. Van Helmont's Reformation of the Galenic Doctrine of Digestion. *Bull. Hist. Med., 29:* 154-163, 1955.
18. Packard, Francis R., Ed.: *The School of Salernum*. New York: Hoeber, 1920.
19. Pagel, Walter: *Paracelsus*. New York: Karger, 1958.
19a. Pagel, Walter: J. B. Van Helmont's Reformation of the Galenic Doctrine of Digestion—and Paracelsus. *Bull. Hist. Med., 29:*563-568, 1955.
19b. Pagel, Walter: Van Helmont's Ideas of Gastric Digestion and the Gastric Acid. *Bull. Hist. Med., 30:*524-536, 1956.
20. Quincy, John, Trans.: *Medicina Statica: Being the Aphorisms of Sanctorius* (2nd ed.). London, 1720.
21. Rothschuh, K. E.: *Geschichte der Physiologie*. Berlin: Springer, 1953, p. 47.
22. Sigerist, Henry E.: *Civilization and Disease*. Ithaca, N. Y.: Cornell University Press, 1943, p. 14.
23. Sigerist, Henry E.: American Truffles: A Thanksgiving Fantasia. *Bull. Hist. Med., 16:*402-409, 1944.
24. Sigerist, Henry E.: *The Great Doctors*. New York: Norton, 1933, pp. 143, 154f.
25. Temkin, Owsei: Greek Medicine as Science and Kraft. *Isis, 44:*213-226, 1953.
26. Testi, Gino: *Dizionario di Alchimia e di Chimia Antiquaria*. Rome: Casa Editrice Mediterranea, 1950, p. 148f.
27. van Helmont, Ioann Baptista: *Ortus Medicinae*. Amsterdam: Elzevir, 1652.
28. von Hohenheim, Bombastus: *Volumen Medicinae Paramirum*. Trans. F. Leidecker. Baltimore: Johns Hopkins Press, 1949, p. 29.
29. Wellman, Max: *Die Fragmente der sikelischen Ärzte*. Berlin: Weidmann, 1901, p. 34.
30. Withington, E. T.: *Medical History*. London: Scientific Press, 1894, p. 389.

FROM LAVOISIER TO BEAUMONT AND HOPKINS

E. W. McHenry, Ph.D.

IN COMPARISON with some areas of knowledge, the science of nutrition is youthful. It has been said repeatedly that our branch of science began with the work of Lavoisier in the period 1780-1794, but it should be recalled that before 1780 there were some observations in the field which were both scientific and a contribution to modern knowledge. Also, most of the deficiency diseases were known to occur with considerable prevalence long before 1780. However, most modern concepts in nutrition were unknown before that time.

Between the time of Lavoisier and of Hopkins a great many significant contributions to nutrition were made. The great masters of the period were handicapped by the lack of radioactive isotopes and electrophoretic techniques; and they did not even know about DNA and RNA. Nonetheless, knowledge was gained swiftly. However, some of our younger colleagues are better acquainted with the handicaps than with the progress. It is possible that more knowledge of the work of 50 years ago or more might make some modern studies unnecessary.

Since it would be impossible here to review thoroughly

the period 1780-1910, we have chosen to discuss the growth of knowledge in three important areas: (1) energy production and its measurement; (2) carbohydrate metabolism and the endocrine control of metabolism; and (3) the role and the value of proteins.

Energy Production and Its Measurement

It has been said that there was no knowledge of the relation of oxidation to the production of animal heat and energy prior to the work of Lavoisier. There may have been no knowledge, but there were concordant assumptions. In his *Treatise on Chemistry,* published in Paris in 1660, Le Fèvre referred to a universal gaseous element which was involved in the respiration of animals. In 1668 Mayow (in London) stated that there existed in the atmosphere a constituent which supported both combustion and animal life. These hypotheses were in line with Lavoisier's conclusions. He was the first to use a balance and a thermometer in the study of life phenomena. This was to be expected since Lavoisier, like another Frenchman a century later who founded bacteriology, was a chemist. The training and experience are evident in the often quoted sentence from his writing, *"La vie est une fonction chimique."* Lavoisier demonstrated that animal heat is produced by oxidation, a process in which the oxygen of inspired air is utilized. It was he who gave oxygen its name. In collaboration with the physicist, Laplace, Lavoisier studied heat production in small animals and in man. It is a great blessing that Madame Lavoisier was interested both in her husband's work and in art. Thanks to her there are two water-color sketches of scenes in the laboratory showing how the experiments on man were carried out. Only a brief account of the observations on humans was preserved; it was given by Lavoisier in 1790 in a letter to Black in Edinburgh. Lavoisier's principal results, which were recorded in the letter, are that energy production varies inversely with the external temperature and is increased by exercise and during the digestion of food. These fundamental observations are still valid.

Not all Lavoisier's conclusions were as valid. He believed that inhaled oxygen caused the decomposition of a fluid brought to the lungs, that hydrogen and carbon were liberated by the decomposition and were then oxidized. It should be noted that a full account of Lavoisier's studies was made impossible by the use of a decapitating machine advocated but not invented by a French surgeon.

Within a few years of Lavoisier's death it was pointed out that, if oxidation occurred in the lungs, the greatest production of heat would be in those organs. Of course, such was not the case. The next assumption was that oxygen was dissolved in the blood and that the blood was the site of oxidation. This hypothesis was supported by the discovery of Magnus in 1837 that blood contained large quantities of oxygen and carbon dioxide.

In his investigations on animals and on man Lavoisier had been concerned with respiratory exchange. He had calculated that 81 per cent of the oxygen consumed was used to form carbon dioxide and that the balance of the oxygen combined with hydrogen to form water. At the time there was no information regarding carbohydrates, fats, and proteins. For years after Lavoisier's fundamental observations there were conflicts about the relation of oxidation to the production of energy and about other processes by which energy for body heat and for activity could be generated. Near 1820 the Paris Academy offered a prize for the best essay on animal heat. There were two competitors for the prize, Dulong and Despretz. The prize was awarded to Despretz. The results reported by both were roughly similar and did not advance knowledge of energy production. Both workers decided that oxidation accounted for only part of the total energy production. An older theory that friction of moving blood caused production of some heat was still used by Despretz.

Formulation of the law of the conservation of energy by Mayer in 1845 and by Helmholtz in 1847 presently had a definite effect on the explanation of biologic energy production.

The first closed system for respiration measurements was devised by Regnault and Reiset in 1849. Their studies made possible the determinations of respiratory quotients. They demonstrated that the respiratory quotients of animals varied from 0.62 to 1.04 and that the value depended on the kind of food eaten by the animal.

By 1849 there had accumulated a considerable amount of information on carbohydrates, fats, and proteins. Liebig was actively at work. By developing methods of organic analysis he made many significant contributions. It was unfortunate that Liebig propounded theories of vital processes which were later proven to be erroneous. He had a strong influence on his contemporaries and on his students. He was convinced that fats and carbohydrates were oxidized to provide body heat, whereas proteins were utilized to provide muscular energy. Liebig taught that the production of body heat was separate from the production of energy for muscle activity. In this concept fat was the main source of body heat. It is worth noting that there was great controversy from 1840 on as to the role of carbohydrates and fats. One aspect of the controversy was the production of fat from carbo-hydrate. Liebig was convinced that fat could be produced from carbohydrates *in vivo* and that carbohydrates and fats were interchangeable in the food supply. Hence fats were not essential in the food intake. It is interesting to note that German scientists used this dogma in advising their govern-ment in World War I that the populace did not need food fat. The Nazi government seemed to have the same idea. A modern notion is that some food fats are harmful.

In 1857 Edward Smith reported the results of a large number of human metabolic measurements. He utilized a finding by Liebig that urinary nitrogen varied with protein breakdown. Smith reported that work increased the output of carbon dioxide but not of urinary nitrogen. This contra-diction of Liebig's premise regarding sources of energy was overshadowed by Liebig's prestige. In a later study of human subjects on a treadmill, Smith corroborated his primary con-clusions. From experiments on dogs Bischoff and Voit in 1860 reported that urinary nitrogen parallelled nitrogen in-take but, eager to uphold Liebig, they stated that internal work, caused by increased protein intake, was responsible for the increased excretion of nitrogen. Smith's conclusions were substantiated by a mountain-climbing experiment in Switzer-land carried out by Fick and Wislicenus in 1866. The source of muscular energy was settled by the work of Edward Frankland who was the first to measure the energy values of foods and of food constituents. Frankland demonstrated in 1866 that oxidation of muscle substance could not provide the energy expended in muscular activity.

The first calorimeter capable of containing a human sub-ject was devised by Pettenkofer, the first person to be named professor of hygiene (1853) in any university. With Voit,

Pettenkofer measured the respiratory quotients which were associated with the oxidation of carbohydrate, of fat, and of protein. Rubner, who was a student of Voit's, perfected methods used in calorimetry and showed that basal metabolism is proportional to body area. Rubner reported that carbohydrate and fat were interchangeable on the basis of calorie equivalents; he also discovered specific dynamic action, and he was responsible for the standard calorie values of carbohydrate, fat, and protein.

Methods for the measurement of energy production were introduced in the United States by Atwater who had studied under Voit. In Pennsylvania, Armsby built a calorimeter to measure energy production in cattle. Studies on humans were extended by Benedict and later by Carpenter in the Carnegie Nutrition Laboratory in Boston, by Graham Lusk at Cornell University Medical College, and by Du Bois at the Russell Sage Institute.

From the many studies came values for energy expenditure which are still bases for predicting the calorie needs of humans. It is well to point out that the energy expenditures of many people have declined in recent years. Although estimates of calorie needs have been revised in recent years, our current recommendations of calorie intakes may be too great for modern conditions, at least in the overprivileged countries.

Carbohydrate Metabolism and Endocrine Control of Metabolism

When Thomas Sydenham described diabetes he did not note that the urine of diabetics was likely to have a sweet taste, although this had been reported many years previously. The first European report on the sweetness of diabetic urine was made by Thomas Willis in the middle of the seventeenth century. Cruickshanks isolated sugar from urine, reporting the work in 1797. Urinary sugar was identified as glucose by Chevreul in 1815. One of Liebig's students, Schmidt, demonstrated the presence of glucose in blood in 1844. The outstanding discovery of the presence of glycogen in the liver was made by Claude Bernard in 1856, and he was the first person, also, to discover the digestive action of pancreatic juice. The production of glycogen from various sugars was studied by Carl Voit. Bernard had observed that sucrose, injected into the blood, is not utilized but is excreted. He found in 1873 that intestinal juice contains the sucrose-splitting enzyme—invertase—which had been discovered in yeast two years earlier by Hoppe-Seyler.

Claude Bernard produced urinary excretion of sugar by puncturing a groups of cells in the medulla near the floor of the fourth ventricle. This gave rise to the impression that diabetes was essentially of nervous origin. But in 1855 Bernard used the term "internal secretions" and referred to secretions contributed by glands, not through ducts, but directly into the blood stream. Four years later he described the spleen, thyroid, adrenals, and lymphatic ganglia as organs of internal secretion. In 1856 Brown-Sequard removed adrenal glands from animals and found that life could not be maintained without the adrenals. Shiff extirpated the thyroids from 60 dogs in 1859 and studied the effects of such surgery. However, there was a hiatus of about 20 years before there was further progress in studies on internal secretions.

In 1877 Lancereaux associated the development of diabetes with lesions of the pancreas. In 1889, Lepine ascribed diabetes to the suppression of an internal secretion, and a few years later Laguesse demonstrated that the internal secretion related to carbohydrate metabolism was produced by the islets of Langerhans. Several years later, the same conclusion was reached by Opie.

A major step forward was contributed by von Mering and Minkowski, and, later, by Minkowski working alone. This step was the experimental production of diabetes in dogs by removal of the pancreas. Another important contribution was made by Minkowski from observations on depancreatized dogs. This contribution concerned the dextrose to nitrogen (D:N) ratio. This observation led to a great deal of work in a number of laboratories on the production of sugar from amino acids.

The name "insulin" was applied to the internal secretion of the pancreas in 1909 by de Mayer. The preparation of active extracts of the pancreas and recent work on the chemistry of insulin, as well as modern studies on carbohydrate metabolism, are beyond the scope of this review. However, in considering advances in nutrition up to the work of Hopkins, it is well to point out that he related hormones to proteins. For example, he stated that adrenalin must be formed from a dietary precursor. He remarked in 1906 that hormones were derived from the products of protein digestion and that this offered a promising field for research.

Proteins and Their Nutritive Value

The word "albumen" was used originally for the white of egg. In a dictionary published in 1777, Macquer applied the word "albuminous" to animal substances that coagulate on heating and, also, to animal substances generally. He noted that blood, lymph, and seminal fluid are scarcely anything but pure gelatinous matter. A quotation from Macquer's writing is of interest: "Hence we ought to conclude that the gelatinous matter of animals is the true animal substance. It constitutes almost entirely the bodies of animals, it is that which nourishes, repairs and reproduces them." This view was broadened by Thomas Thomson in 1843 when he observed that "animals are principally formed from the glutenous or albuminous principles of vegetables." Observations on the protein content of various seeds had been made as early as 1806 by Vauquelin and Fourcroy. In 1800 several constituents of animal tissues were recognized as separate substances; these included milk casein, blood fibrin, egg white, gelatin, and blood serum coagulum.

The distillation of ammonia from proteins as an analytical tool was first used by Berthollet in 1811. In 1820 Braconnot described the acid hydrolysis of gelatin and the isolation of a crystalline substance from the hydrolysate. This isolated substance had a sweet taste and was named "sugar of gelatin" by Braconnot. Later, the substance was identified by other investigators as the amino acid, glycine. A second amino acid, leucine, was isolated and named by Braconnot. Liebig isolated and named tyrosine from casein in 1846.

In 1839 the Netherlands' chemist, Mulder, advanced an explanation of differences between proteins. Today the explanation appears ridiculous, but it was widely accepted at the time, even by Liebig. The three proteins studied by Mulder were albumin, fibrin, and casein, all containing sulphur. Mulder dissolved these proteins in dilute potassium hydroxide; when the solutions were heated, potassium disulphide was formed. The residual solutions, after the addition of acetic acid, yielded gelatinous precipitates and the precipitates from all three proteins were apparently identical, having even the same elementary composition. Mulder assumed that these gelatinous substances were identical and that they were examples of a common radical which was present in all proteins. Berzelius suggested that this radical be called "protein," the primary substance. Mulder believed that natural proteins were compounds of the protein radical plus differing proportions of sulphur and phosphorus. The analyses of a series of proteins on this basis were reported by Mulder and were confirmed by the work of a student in Liebig's laboratory and by Dumas. By 1849 evidence had been obtained which dispelled Mulder's concept. These erroneous interpretations of protein structure were unfortunate, but, before being critical, we might recall some of the mistakes made in recent years by at least some of us.

The earliest reported observation on the different nutritive values of protein was reported in 1854 by Lawes and Gilbert, who initiated the famous agriculture research program at Rothamsted. They demonstrated a definite difference between the proteins of cereal seeds and of legumes.

Progress on the purification and isolation of proteins was made by various workers between 1850 and 1900. By the end of the century 16 amino acids had been isolated, the last on this list being tryptophan, isolated by Hopkins and Cole.

In 1890 Thomas Osborne began, at first with Russell Chittenden, his highly important work on proteins. Osborne showed that plants contained a wide variety of proteins. In 1909 Osborne and Mendel began the feeding experiments on animals which led to modern knowledge regarding the biologic values of different proteins, and which paved the way for modern studies on protein metabolism. In the course of their work Osborne and Mendel made several discoveries which were off the main track. In their feeding experiments they noted that the progress of the experiments could be altered if rats had access to feces and ate them. This observation led to the use of screens in animal cages. Their feeding experiments were made possible by the use of protein-free milk which, unknown to Osborne and Mendel at the start, supplied nutrient elements and vitamins then unrecognized. From the feeding experiments, however, came classification of proteins as complete or incomplete, depending on the complement of amino acids. The approximate biologic values of a number of proteins were determined by Osborne and Mendel in a very comprehensive program of feeding experiments. Later there developed knowledge regarding the essential amino acids.

Summary

In 1770 there were hypotheses regarding the source of body heat but no certain knowledge. Even the main components of foods were unknown. During the period of 140 years a tremendous number of discoveries were made, many of which have stood the test of later work. Many erroneous explanations were advanced, even by the leaders in scientific work. As early as the time of Hippocrates there existed a belief in the occurrence of some specific universal nutrient substance present in various foods. This belief existed in several forms until near the end of the nineteenth century. William Beaumont, even when interpreting his famous studies on digestion, was convinced of the existence and fundamental importance of the single nutrient. At the time of Beaumont's studies, William Prout stated that all organized bodies are composed of three great staminal principles—saccharina, oleosa, albuminosa. All of these could be found in milk, which was the perfect food. Prout's theory of nutrition was stated by him as follows: "A diet to be complete must contain more or less all of the three staminal principles." For years Liebig taught that carbohydrates and fats served in respiration but that the really important food constituent was protein. Protein was the basis of life. Only those foods were useful which could be converted into blood. Muscle protein was the source of energy for activity. These false notions were not dispelled for years. However, they were dispelled by the end of the nineteenth century. Consider the definition of food advanced by Atwater in 1895: "Food may be defined as material which, when taken into the body, serves to either form tissue or yield energy, or both. This definition includes all the ordinary food materials, since they both build tissue and yield energy. It includes sugar and starch because they yield energy and form fatty tissue."

Many of us will remember Graham Lusk. In his book, *The Science of Nutrition*, published in 1917, he listed the foodstuffs as the following: proteins, carbohydrates, fats, salts, and water. The vitamins were unknown to Lusk when he wrote that list.

We close, fittingly, by quoting from Lafayette Mendel's *Nutrition: The Chemistry of Life,* a title which takes us back to Lavoisier's statement, "La vie est une fonction chimique."

> Notwithstanding the great advances which recent years have witnessed in the science of nutrition almost innumerable problems still confront the critical investigator. The fundamental chemistry of the nutritive processes is scarcely known

in a single detail. The energetics of the organism have as yet been sketched in broadest outlines only. Although the significance of the little things in nutrition is becoming better appreciated their function is by no means completely explained. The history of science should warn us against the dangers of dogmatism in the presence of so much that remains unknown or unexplained.

FROM HOPKINS TO THE PRESENT

Elmer V. McCollum, Ph.D.

FREDERICK GOWLAND HOPKINS (1861-1947) was the outstanding biochemist of his generation. In 1889 he isolated the ornamental pigment of yellow butterflies, later found to be pterin, a component of folic acid. In 1901 he isolated tryptophan, and in 1906, with Willcock, he performed with mice the first feeding experiment which proved the indispensability of tryptophan. This was the first demonstration of the indispensability of an amino acid in nutrition. In 1921 he isolated and described glutathione; afterward he made fundamental studies of oxidation-reduction phenomena in animal tissues.

At first a chemist, he studied medicine, but he devoted most of his active years to researches of fundamental importance in metabolism and nutrition, and to teaching. As a teacher he was pre-eminent. His interest in nutrition, from the point of view of inquiry into the necessity of unidentified nutrients, and his experiments with simplified diets, were more imaginative and constructive than those of any other man at the beginning of this century.

Because of his eminence as a scientist, his oft-quoted statement that natural foods contain many substances not recognized as of dietetic significance, but which are as important in animal nutrition as protein, carbohydrates, fats and inorganic compounds, brought these unrecognized elements to the attention of biochemists who made their search a field of promise to chemical investigators.

Previously, only a few men had devoted themselves to asking why a diet of purified foodstuffs failed to sustain health in young animals, and all these men were less imaginative than Hopkins. When they discovered the existence of unsuspected nutrients, they either failed to pursue experimental studies into their nature, or, having tested the effects of supplementing purified diets with phosphorylated versus phosphorus-free proteins, nucleic acid or lecithin, organic iron versus inorganic (all of which proved of no value in improving diets), they went no further.

Early Advances in Protein Nutrition

The step-by-step advances in knowledge of the composition of proteins made it clear by 1900 that their yields of amino acids on hydrolysis were strongly contrasting in certain cases. Moreover, they revealed the fallacy of the long-held belief of Mulder and Liebig that all proteins, from whatever sources, are essentially alike in nutritive value. The studies of E. Fischer and Osborne attracted wide attention, and dietary proteins overshadowed all other aspects of nutrition for more than a decade. The extent to which enzyme hydrolysis of proteins proceeded in the alimentary tract, and the range of molecular size of the end products of protein digestion puzzled physiologists until Conheim's discovery of erepsin and its power to liberate amino acids showed that the synthetic powers of the body made possible regeneration of body proteins from amino acids. Osborne and Mendel's dramatization of the nutritive significance of individual amino acids extended the work of Hopkins over a wide range of purified proteins prepared from various foods. Protein nutrition became amino acid nutrition.

Early Vitamin Discoveries

The epoch-making experiments of Eijkman and of Grijns (1901) did not influence nutrition investigators to any great extent until after the publication of *Die Vitamine* by Funk (1913). The reason for this was that over 600 medical investigators and writers participated in a controversy over the etiology of beriberi, which was silenced finally by the publication, between 1909 and 1912, of the studies of Fraser and Stanton who proved beyond question that the deficiency theory proposed by Grijns was correct. The bibliography of the beriberi controversy was included by Vedder in his Cartwright Prize essay, "Beriberi" (1913). After 1913 the writings of Funk and Vedder focused attention on beriberi. Its acceptance as a dietary deficiency disease was almost universal.

In spite of this publicity, however, and on the basis of a long series of feeding studies in which he employed partially purified food substances, Röhmann remained, until 1916, an opponent of the vitamin theory.

The immunity to scurvy of experimental animals, other than the guinea pig, prevented the excellent experimental studies of Holst and Frölich on experimental scurvy (1907-1912) from immediately attracting the attention they deserved.

In his *Science of Nutrition* (1906) Lusk did not mention Eijkman, Grijns, or any of the dozen investigators who had experimented with diets of purified foodstuffs; nor did he mention beriberi, scurvy, rickets, or pellagra; nor the requirements of the body for calcium or iron. Anemia was discussed only from the standpoint of its effect on energy metabolism. But before 1910 Sherman was studying typical American diets to discover whether they supplied sufficient calcium and iron.

The first rat colony to be established for nutrition studies on a comprehensive scale was started by McCollum late in 1907. There were two principal objectives in his use of this species: (1) to inquire into the causes of failure of experimental animals, principally mice, fed purified diets, reported by a number of investigators from Lunin (1880) to Pekelharing (1905); and (2) to investigate the nature of the deficiencies of individual natural foodstuffs, such as cereal grains, legume seeds, etc. Experiments with purified food mixtures (the ingredients of which in many cases were not as pure as was believed), together with the failure to recognize the nutritional significance of coprophagy, led, fortunately, to the discovery in 1913 of the first fat-soluble vitamin, vitamin A.

This observation was promptly verified by Osborne and Mendel. It was actually the first discovery of a vitamin which attracted the attention of biochemists everywhere. Priority should have been accorded to Holst and Frölichs's demonstration of experimental scurvy in 1907. Actually, however, this great investigation did not bear fruit until 1914. That year, A. F. Hess made the first critical study on infants which verified the observation of the Norwegian scientists and brought forcefully to the attention of the medical profession the importance and the means of protecting babies against scurvy. As a stimulus to the investigation of foods by biochemists, Hess's announcements were of great influence.

The earliest study of the pathology of vitamin A deficiency was made by S. Mori in 1921-1922 in McCollum's laboratory. He treated the entire contents of the bony orbit, the eyes and related structures, in different stages of vitamin A deficiency, as histological specimens, and described the phenomena of keratinization of epithelial structures. He attributed the later changes seen in xerophthalmia to loss of secretory function in the lacrymal, Harderian, and Meibomian glands and to the consequent drying of the conjunctival sac and surface of the eye.

Origin of the Biological Method for Analysis of Foods

The studies of McCollum and his associates (1913-1915) on supplementing single cereal grains or other seeds, including polished and unpolished rice, with chemically characterized substances aroused the interest of biochemists. When used as the sole food of young rats or swine, individual seeds, without exception, failed to support growth or maintain health. When supplemented with a calcium salt, a source of vitamin A, and those amino acids not sufficiently abundant in cereal proteins, a single cereal was greatly improved as a source of nutrients. With the same supplements, polished rice was still incapable of sustaining life in young rats. A water extract of any one of various natural foods was required to make it complete as a food. Thus, in 1916, after comparing the results of scores of experiments with rats and pigeons on which extracts of various substances were tested for the cure of polyneuritis in birds and promotion of growth in rats, McCollum and Kennedy concluded that there were but two unknown nutrients: a fat-soluble and a water-soluble factor. They erroneously believed their water-soluble, growth-promoting substance to be identical with the antiberiberi substance.

The two-vitamin hypothesis rested on experimental studies with rats and pigeons. At that time, the evidence was convincing that for the human species as well as for the monkey and guinea pig, a third factor, the antiscorbutic substance, was indispensable. In its absence scurvy developed. The rat, then as now, widely used in experiments in nutrition, is immune to scurvy because it synthesizes the vitamin.

Pellagra

As the facts recounted above were beginning to influence scientific thought, pellagra had become a serious health problem in the United States, especially in the southern states. Its symptoms and probable etiology had been discussed by medical men for a century and a half without definitely establishing its cause. First to prove that pellagra was a dietary deficiency disease was Voegtlin. In 1914 he reported his observation that the disease progressed in his patients when they were restricted to a daily diet of wheat bread (300 grams), butter (30 grams), cabbage (100 grams), maize meal (50 grams), hominy (75 grams), corn syrup (75 grams), pork (50 grams), potato (150 grams), prunes (30 grams), turnip tops (100 grams), sugar (40 grams), and milk (40 grams). With a similar diet, supplemented with generous amounts of meat, eggs, and milk, they steadily improved. When the patients were kept on the first diet and were given a fat-free alcoholic extract of yeast, rice polishings, liver or thymus gland, improvement was also prompt and comparable to that observed on the diet containing meat, eggs, and milk. These studies were the first which clearly demonstrated that pellagra was a dietary deficiency disease, and suggested that a fourth un-identified nutrient existed.

About the same time Goldberger began his studies of pellagra in relation to institutional dietaries. He too proved that pellagra involved some kind of dietary deficiency. He induced symptoms of pellagra in volunteer human subjects by restricting their diet. He distinguished between those foods which protected against pellagra and those which did not. In 1916, Spencer, a veterinarian, suspected "black tongue" in dogs to be analogous to pellagra in man. He reported prompt cures by giving milk, meat, and eggs to the sick animals. His report remained unnoticed. In 1917 Chittenden and Underhill produced what appeared to be pellagra in dogs by restricting them to a diet of cracker meal, cooked dried peas, and cottonseed oil. In 1926 Goldberger and his associates produced "black tongue" in dogs experimentally and found that both human pellagra and its counterpart in dogs were cured by yeast or a water extract of yeast. There was no longer any doubt that pellagra was a deficiency disease, and that the protective factor was stable to heat. This characteristic distinguished it from the heat-labile, antiberi-beri factor.

Expanding Education

The Report on the Present State of Knowledge Concerning Accessory Food Factors (Vitamines), written by a committee appointed jointly by the British Medical Research Committee and the Lister Institute, was published in 1919. This excellent account of the status of knowledge of foods and of nutritive requirements of adults and infants was signed on behalf of the Committee by Hopkins and Chick.

The accessory factors discussed were the antiberiberi factor, fat-soluble A, and the antiscorbutic factor. Included also were sections on the prevention and cure of rickets, and all available evidence was put forth to prove that pellagra was a dietary deficiency disease. The Report attracted the attention of nutrition investigators the world over and stimulated interest in dietetics as a factor in public health.

A second edition of this Report was published in 1924. It met with enthusiastic reception and has since exerted great influence everywhere on all those concerned with the description of an adequate diet and the policy that will make it acceptable and available. Chick and Hume have recently published a history of the work of this Committee.

Supplementary Relations Among Foods

From about 1912 onward McCollum and his associates studied the supplementary relations between many common foods. This type of study was based on their observations of the natures of the deficiencies of individual cereal grains and other seeds, as mentioned above. The results showed that any combination of seeds of plants such as wheat, maize, oat, millet, pea, bean, etc., when it comprised the sole food of young rats or swine, led to malnutrition, whereas combinations of one or more seeds with milk, or with the leaf of a plant, in certain proportions, supported the animals in good to excellent nutritive states. Diets composed of a considerable variety of foods such as white flour (wheat), corn meal (maize), potato, muscle meats, sugar, beans, and peas, proved inferior to much simpler diets in which milk and/or leaf substance supplied 20 to 25 per cent of the calories.

The experimental feeding of simple combinations of common foods also revealed the superiority of glandular organs of animals to muscle substance, and placed wheat germ in the same category with rice polishings as notably superior to the endosperm as sources of essential nutrients.

A New Era in Menu Planning

A new viewpoint was the result of these studies. It was apparent that the composition of a food or diet as shown by the standard method for chemical analysis was not a sufficient basis for assessing their nutritive values; that certain foods, each inadequate in certain respects, were so constituted as to supplement each other's inadequacies. The new approach to diet planning was presented in January 1917 by McCollum before the Harvey Society. In 1918 the supplementary relations between our natural and refined foods were discussed in greater detail in the Cutter Lectures at Harvard University. These were published in book form, *The Newer Knowledge of Nutrition,* in the same year.

As a result of World War I there was a serious food shortage in Europe in 1917. In April of that year Herbert Hoover organized the United States Food Administration for the purpose of providing relief to the peoples of the warring nations. There was a world shortage of wheat, fats, and sugar, and a prominent feature of the program was to induce Americans to subsist upon other foods so that wheat, fats, and sugar could be provided for European peoples. New problems in meal planning were posed by the situation which was so serious to such large numbers of people in allied countries. Patriotic fervor led to a vigorous response to the slogan, "Food Will Win the War." The people of the United States and Canada were willing to change their dietary habits for the sake of those in war-torn countries. The time was favorable. Housewives responded to suggestions, not only about how to feed their families, but also how to tempt them with menus made up largely of foods substituted for those with which they were familiar.

Their instructors were women trained in dietetics. These women were conversant with the new discoveries. They taught and demonstrated the importance of planning menus so as to combine foods which made good each other's deficiencies. They showed the housewife how to use cornmeal and oatmeal instead of wheat flour and emphasized the greater use of garden vegetables. They urged the addition of more milk and green leafy vegetables to the white bread, muscle meat, potato, and sugar-type of diet so widely eaten by Americans at that time. "Protective" foods were given strong approval by all who instructed people about foods in relation to health. The dietary habits of the United States and Canada were quickly altered for the better.

Furthermore, the message of Hess on the health significance of fresh fruits and vegetables in the diet for protection against scurvy, and for maintenance of the integrity of the vascular system, became common knowledge and was applied universally in dietetics and meal planning.

The extent of the influence of the new teachings is apparent from the fact that between 1919 and 1926 the national production of milk and other dairy products increased one third and that of ice cream, 45 per cent. The acreage of 19 garden crops nearly doubled to meet the increased demand for fresh vegetables. Fresh fruit consumption was also greatly increased. Great influence everywhere on thought and policy concerning diet met with enthusiastic reception.

Bread Improvement

The publicity given to the new observations on the number and nature of the dietary deficiencies of cereal grains and their derivatives, bolted flour and degerminated cornmeal in particular, brought these foods temporarily into disrepute. McCollum defended the prevailing milling processes on the basis of the impracticability of marketing whole-grain flour and meal owing to hazards of spoilage, and because of established dietary habits which created the demand for refined white bread. He emphasized the fallacy of condemning individual foods because of nutrient deficiencies. As has already been stated, he urged planning dietaries so as to combine foods which supplemented each other.

In 1923, speaking before the National Bakers' Association at French Lick, Indiana, McCollum urged bakers to improve the nutritive value of white bread by including skim milk solids in the bread mix. At that period the demand for cream, butter, and ice cream was so great that an enormous quantity of skim milk was produced in milk plants. Since there was no organized marketing system for selling it or getting it back to farms for animal feeding, it was being thrown away in many places. He pointed out that a combination of skim milk and white flour would make up for the deficiencies of the latter to a great extent, and would silence the criticism of white bread. The baking industry followed this advice and much commercial bread soon contained about 6 per cent non-fat milk solids. It was highly acceptable to consumers.

No further important consideration was given to improvement of the nutritive value of bread until after 1940, when it was proposed to enrich bread by the inclusion of thiamin, riboflavin, niacin, and iron. These vitamins were then available from chemical synthesis and at relatively low cost. McCollum proposed enriching bread by including in the bread mix 1 per cent each of defatted wheat or corn germs and some dried brewer's yeast, in addition to non-fat milk solids. At that time about 100 million pounds of germs were milled out of wheat annually, and about 400 million pounds of germs out of corn (maize). These went into animal feeds at animal feed prices.

McCollum pointed out that defatting germs of cereals prevented off-flavor from rancidity, cleared the germs of insect eggs, and made them easy to store and transport without deterioration. Such germs had been shown by many experiments to contain a full complement of the water-soluble vitamins. It was emphasized that by this procedure all water-soluble vitamins of the B complex would be added to bread (already to a considerable extent fortified by the protein and vitamins of skim milk). Such practice would improve bread to a greater extent than the proposed enrichment with three vitamins and iron. Vitamin enrichment was supported by most distinguished authorities on nutrition and became standard practice.

The Etiology of Rickets

In 1918 E. Mellanby reported the earliest convincing observations that rickets was due to dietary deficiency, and suggested tentatively that it might be caused by deficiency of vitamin A. In 1922 McCollum and his associates at Johns Hopkins described experimental evidence that another fat-soluble vitamin, vitamin D, existed and that it exerted a profound influence on bone growth. They also described the responses of the bones of growing rats to various kinds of dietary errors and variations. They showed that deviations from normal structure, specific in nature, occurred to an astonishing degree. They studied bone changes induced by feeding: (1) various levels of protein of widely differing biological values; (2) many modifications of the composition of the inorganic moiety of the diet, especially the amounts and ratios of calcium and phosphorus; (3) a wide variety of dietary fat; and (4) an extensive assortment of diets that caused arrest of growth. The effect of exposure to summer sunshine was studied in great detail.

Inorganic Nutrients

The significance of inorganic elements in animal nutrition was first noted by Fordyce about 1790. He had observed that his canary hens became ill and that some died as the laying season advanced. He conceived the idea that their diet of seeds might not supply sufficient "calcarious substance." He tried an experiment: he kept some hens on the ordinary seed diet, and gave others the same ration supplemented with old mortar. This they ate greedily and remained in excellent condition through the egg-laying season.

In 1915 McCollum and Davis carried out a series of experiments with a diet constant as to organic constituents but with the inorganic portion varied over a wide range as to total intake, ratios between elements, acidity or alkalinity, etc. Their results showed that growth, fertility, and ability to rear young could be disturbed by faulty composition and amount of the inorganic moiety of the diet.

During the nineteenth century several men observed the beneficial effects of providing supplements of bonemeal or limestone to hogs on certain rations, especially when maize was the principal food. Both the size and breaking strength of bones were improved by such additions.

Phosphorus—Interest in mineral nutrients was stimulated by the discovery that a great farm tragedy in the cattle industry in South Africa was caused by deficiency in the herbage on which animals grazed. Soil depletion of phosphorus was the result of selling successive generations of cattle off the land. Bone-chewing was the most striking abnormality of phosphorus-starved cattle. Provision in the diet of the animals of any of several phosphorus-containing salts corrected this perversion of appetite. This marked the earliest instance of the recognition of injury to the health of animals which comes from grazing on depleted soil.

Copper—In 1925 Hart and his associates made the remarkable discovery that animals cannot use iron for blood pigment formation unless their food provides small amounts of copper. Their data proved this metal to be an essential nutrient. This discovery, together with the generally broadened comprehension of the scope of inquiry into the number and nature of still unknown nutrients, led investigators to undertake to prepare diets complete in organic nutrients, known and unknown, but as nearly as possible free from the single inorganic element to be studied. By feeding such rations to young animals, one could determine which of the inorganic elements was of significance in nutrition. If the element under study was essential, deprivation resulted in a definite and characteristic pathology. By such procedures it was found that manganese, magnesium, and zinc are essential nutrients. A skeletal abnormality in chickens and turkeys known as perosis, and characterized by slipped tendon, lameness, and deformity, had long puzzled poultrymen. It was found by Norris and Wilgus to be due to lack of manganese. Partial deprivation of manganese also causes a low rate of hatchability in eggs.

The pathology of magnesium and zinc deficiency have been extensively studied. These have less practical significance since they occur but rarely in man or animals. However, since they both participate importantly in the metabolic scheme, knowledge of their roles and indispensability in the diet is significant to biochemists.

Iodine—Recognition of iodine as an essential nutrient began with the observation of Baumann (1896) that the small amount of this element in the body was concentrated in the thyroid gland. The studies of Marine and associates between 1908 and 1935 were largely responsible for establishing the relation between iodine deficiency and endemic goiter in humans and animals. G. Ennis Smith, in 1917, made a notable contribution by demonstrating that goiter in cattle, swine, horses, and sheep over large areas between Wisconsin and the Pacific coast, could be prevented by giving small amounts of iodine to the animals, especially during pregnancy. The knowledge gained from these and other investigations resulted in widespread efforts to prevent endemic goiter in man and domestic animals by iodine therapy.

Cobalt—In Australia, New Zealand, Scotland, Florida, and other areas, sheep and cattle suffered from a characteristic type of anemia, the cause of which was long obscure. In 1935 both Underwood and Marston discovered independently that the disorder was caused by deficiency of cobalt. This element was later found to be a constituent of vitamin B_{12}. Certain micro-organisms in the rumen of sheep, cattle, and other ruminants synthesize cobalt into vitamin B_{12}.

Fluorine—About 1805 fluorine was first detected in teeth. It is a normal constituent of tooth enamel. Excessive amounts of this element in drinking water or in foods causes discoloration or mottling of the teeth, as first demonstrated by Margaret Cammack Smith in 1931. Dean and his associates noted a much lower incidence of caries among children living in communities where fluorine was present in the drinking water than among children using a water supply essentially lacking this element. Extensive studies on the caries-preventing effect of fluorine have led to the fluoridation of water supplies of many cities in the United States. Without exception, the incidence of caries among children has been substantially reduced by this means.

Molybdenum, Selenium and Vanadium—The field of inquiry into the number and nature of the essential mineral elements in nutrition is not yet complete. There is evidence that both molybdenum and selenium play biological roles; and a need for vanadium by living things is not yet excluded.

Expanding Ideas About Vitamins

The observations of H. H. Mitchell and of Emmett, before 1920, made it clear that the antineuritic (antiberiberi) factor was not the only unidentified water-soluble nutrient in several foods. They noted that even though polyneuritis could be prevented by certain foods or extracts of these foods, the animals would still fail nutritionally. By 1927 experimental proof by Mitchell, Emmett, Hauge and Carrick, Smith and Hendrick, and Salmon et al., demonstrated beyond question that some preparations which cured polyneuritis in rats and birds were not effective in promoting growth nor in preventing nutritive disaster. It was evident that at least one other unidentified, water-soluble nutrient existed, and that this heat-stable substance was involved in normal nutrition and in the prevention of "black tongue" in dogs.

The announcement in 1922 by H. M. Evans and K. Scott, that a specific nutrient, substance X, was involved in the development of rat embryos aroused the interest of both biochemists and pathologists. Rats raised on a certain diet were of low fertility in the first generation and wholly sterile in the second. Small additions of lettuce, wheat germs, or dried alfalfa leaves restored fertility. Evans' description of the anatomic lesions in the placenta and in the fetal circulation opened new vistas in nutrition investigation.

In 1922, observations on polyneuritis, xerophthalmia, rickets, scurvy, and the sterility in rats resulting from a deficiency of Evans' fat-soluble substance X (later renamed vitamin E and alpha-tocopherol), together with the less well-characterized states of malnutrition due to deficiency of amino acids, created wide interest among chemists, physiologists, pathologists, and clinicians.

Some years after its discovery vitamin E was found to be of much wider significance than Evans' experiments on fertility revealed. On rations lacking this vitamin, rabbits developed muscle dystrophy. Its provision resulted in complete recovery of muscle function in this species. Therapeutic trials of alpha-tocopherol with dystrophic children have not been successful. However, recent investigations by György and Gordon show that a red blood cell defect in infants deficient in alpha-tocopherol may be corrected by its administration in early infancy. The effects of tocopherol deficiency have recently been illuminated by Nason who has shown that this substance plays a role in cytochrome activity.

Vitamin K—In 1929 Damm in Denmark, and in 1931 McFarlane and his associates of the Ontario Experiment Station, Canada, made the initial observations which led to the discovery of a fourth fat-soluble vitamin, vitamin K. Later it was shown to be a naphthaquinone derivative. A deficiency of this vitamin causes failure of prothrombin formation and consequently impairs the blood clotting process. This nutrient soon assumed an important place in the prevention of hemorrhage in the newborn and in the control of the hemorrhagic tendency in some diseases of the intestines and liver.

a-Lipoic Acid—In the course of advancing experimentation on bacterial nutrition the terms protogen, lipoic acid, and pyruvate-oxidation factors were introduced to designate substances which were found in yeast extract and which (a) replaced acetate for growth of some lactobacilli, (b) promoted pyruvate oxidation by cell suspensions of Streptococcus faecalis 10 Cl, grown in a semisynthetic medium, and (c) were growth factors for certain other micro-organisms. Interest in these metabolic phenomena centers upon "6-thioctic acid" (+6:8-dimercapto-octanoic acid). a-Lipoic acid functions in oxidative decarboxylation of pyruvate and a-glutaric acid in the form of a lipoic acid and thiamine pyrophosphate coenzyme (1).

Fractionation of the Vitamin B complex

From the account so far given of advances in knowledge of foods and nutrition, it will be noted that by the year 1930 investigators recognized that an adequate diet must provide the essential amino acids, inorganic elements, a source of glucose, at least one unsaturated fatty acid, the fat-soluble vitamins A, D, and E, vitamin C, the water-soluble (B complex) factors, thiamine, riboflavin, and the still unidentified pellagra-preventive substance generally called P-P factor. It had also become apparent that on a diet which provided all the chemically characterized nutrients and no others, young rats or chicks soon ceased to grow, developed skin and nerve lesions, declined rapidly, and died. Obviously, important discoveries remained to be made. The method of experimenting which promised rewarding discoveries had also become well established. It involved the following principles:

With each new discovery of a hitherto unidentified nutrient, investigators proceeded to prepare experimental diets which contained every known nutrient and nothing more, and to test the effectiveness of such diets on small animals, principally young rats and chicks. In every instance they proved inadequate for the maintenance of the health of the animals or for the prevention of steady decline and early death. At this period biochemists had learned to observe more intelligently symptoms of nutritive failure. Medical investigators of nutrition also were better trained in chemical science. The causes of nutritional failure in experimental animals could now be more searchingly observed and studied.

It was also known that, provided certain fats were included, the chemically characterized experimental diets were made complete and capable of supporting normal nutrition by the addition of water extracts of such foods as yeast, wheat germ, boiled egg yolk, etc. Investigators began to apply chemical methods for separating fractions from such water extracts, and to test their efficiency as supplements to chemically characterized diets. When such fractions were fed to experimental animals, discerning investigators noted that while they failed nutritionally, they did not exhibit all the symptoms seen when the unsupplemented diet only was supplied. Fractions prepared by different procedures, as by adsorption on fuller's earth, charcoal, etc., under carefully regulated conditions of acidity or alkalinity, or selectively extracted from crude materials by organic solvents, were of distinct benefit to the test animals. Although no single one prevented nutritive failure, each did prevent the manifestation of a specific symptom. Such procedures led to the discovery of the following list of the hitherto unsuspected, indispensable nutrients of the groups known as the B-complex vitamins.

Biotin—Between 1931 and 1939, principally as a result of experiments carried out by Parsons and her associates, György and associates, Miller, R. J. Williams, and Kögl, working independently, biotin was isolated and identified. Its biological significance as an essential nutrient for animals, for yeasts, and many other micro-organisms, and its role in preventing "egg white injury" in rats was established.

Pyridoxine—Between 1930 and 1938 György and his associates; Chick, Copping and Roscoe; Lepkovsky; Jukes; Keresztesy, Folkers, Harris, and their associates, investigated intensively a syndrome first called "rat pellagra." This was later renamed, "rat acrodynia" by György. Studies on experimentally induced rat acrodynia led to the isolation and characterization of pyridoxine, and ultimately to its synthesis.

Pantothenic acid—Beginning in 1919, R. J. Williams studied the nutrients necessary for the proliferation and fermentation of yeasts. In 1939 he isolated the calcium salt of pantothenic acid. He had previously described many of its chemical properties. In 1937 Snell and his associates pointed out that the yeast growth factor of Williams, regarded as one of the "bios" factors, was necessary for the growth of lactic acid-forming bacteria. Wooley, György, Daft, Sebrell and Engle, working independently, were prominent in developing and advancing knowledge of pantothenic acid.

Deficiency of pantothenic acid in animals causes many kinds of pathological manifestations. It will suffice to mention dermatitis, adrenal hemorrhage, atrophy, necrosis, depigmentation of hair, loss of hair, thymus involution, myelin degeneration, paralysis, peripheral neuritis, and spinal cord and sciatic nerve injury. Williams has pointed out that only lack of a substance fundamental to cellular physiology in general could cause such diverse symptoms. In deficiency of this nutrient every single tissue exhibits pathological changes. Pantothenic acid plays an important role in the metabolic processes of all living organisms.

p-Aminobenzoic acid—In 1940 Nielson, Oleson, and Elvehjem concentrated a fraction from water extracts of natural substances, a substance which prevented graying of hair of piebald rats. In 1941 Martin and Ansbacher discovered that a supplement of para-aminobenzoic acid in the diet which caused loss of hair and graying prevented these abnormalities. Para-aminobenzoic acid was not a new substance to organic chemists, but the discovery of the above-mentioned properties afforded the first evidence that it possessed any biological significance.

Inositol—In 1940 Wooley observed that addition of inositol to an experimental diet which caused loss of hair in mice corrected the abnormality. He suggested that it be called "mouse anti-alopecia factor." A year later Gavin and McHenry discovered that inositol is essential in the diet of the rat and that deficiency of it caused development of fatty livers.

Inositol was discovered to be a constituent of muscle in 1850, but its nutritive significance was overlooked for ninety years. It was long regarded by biochemists as a substance intermediate in carbohydrate metabolism.

Nicotinic acid—The long search for a dietetic factor in the causation and prevention of pellagra, begun by Voegtlin in 1914, and pursued with sustained purpose over more than a decade by Goldberger and his associates, was rewarded in 1937 when Elvehjem, Madden, Strong, and Wooley demonstrated that administration of nicotinic acid cured "black tongue" in dogs. It had long been suspected that canine "black tongue" was the analogue of pellagra in man. In 1938 D. T. and S. G. Smith first demonstrated the curative effect of nicotinic acid in human pellagra patients. Nicotinic acid was renamed *niacin* to prevent in the popular mind an association of this substance with nicotine.

An astonishing fact was that a diet based on wheat and barley did not induce pellagra symptoms, whereas a similarly constituted corn diet (maize) caused the disease in young swine. An intensive study of the cause of this difference in properties of the two diets led to the discovery by Chick and her co-workers (1938) that administration of the amino acid, tryptophane, was just as effective as nicotinic acid in preventing pellagra symptoms in swine. The conversion of this amino acid into nicotinic acid in the horse, calf, swine, and man was demonstrated. By restricting young rats to experimental diets deficient in nicotinic acid and tryptophane, Chick and her associates were able to induce experimental pellagra in the rat. This species does not develop the disease when starved for nicotinic acid while receiving protein containing a liberal amount of tryptophane.

Choline—Choline, as a constituent of the phospholipid lecithin, has been known for a century. That it played a special role in transport of fat in the body was discovered in 1932 by Best. He showed that choline, administered to rats kept on a diet of mixed grains and fat, prevented the accumulation of hepatic fat, which occurred if choline was omitted from the basal diet. Two years earlier Hershey had found that lecithin possessed this property. Best's investigations revealed that the choline contained in lecithin was the factor of importance. In 1935 Best and Huntsman noted a protective effect of protein. In 1937 Beeston and Channon discovered that administration of methionine had a lipotrophic effect comparable with choline. The remarkable phenomenon of the interchangeability of choline and methionine was understandable when du Vigneaud and his associates, in 1939, introduced the concept of transmethylation, or transfer of methyl groups. They fed rats a choline-deficient diet containing deuterium-labeled methionine. Choline containing deuterium-labeled methyl was isolated from the carcasses of the animals. This series of investigations was of outstanding importance in illuminating one aspect of intermediate metabolism.

The Folic Acid Group—One of the most notable series of investigations in the history of nutrition is that which brought about the discovery of a group of organic substances which are of outstanding importance in certain metabolic processes. The group has been variously called vitamin M, folic acid, Lactobacillus casei factor, SRL factor (Streptococcus fecalis R), depending on the source of material and the organism used for test purposes, e.g., chick, monkey, rat, fish, or lactobacillus casei.

This field of inquiry was opened by Lucy Wills, who in 1931 described her observation that administration of yeast extract was effective in relieving a macrocytic anemia occurring in pregnant women in India. She called the factor vitamin M. She and Bilimoria, by feeding a certain diet, produced in monkeys a macrocytic anemia, accompanied by leucopenia, diarrhea, and megaloblastic bone marrow, which also was relieved by yeast extract. Day and others confirmed the observation of Wills, and found yeast and liver concentrate rich in vitamin M.

In 1936 Tchesche employed xanthopterin to cure the anemia induced in growing rats fed a diet of goat's milk. This brought pterins, first isolated by Hopkins from the wings of butterflies (1896), into the list of biologically important substances. Hart and others found that pterins were to some extent effective in increasing the rate of regeneration of erythrocytes in dogs made anemic by bleeding.

In 1937 Jackson and Subba Row identified xanthopterin as a constituent of liver extracts which were effective in treatment of pernicious anemia. Of special importance was the observation of Wright and Welch that incubation of liver with xanthopterin increased its "folic acid" effect.[1]

Folinic acid, or the citrovorum factor, was discovered in 1948 by Sauberlich and Baumann from their finding that Leuconostoc citrovorum failed to grow on a certain synthetic medium, but could do so when an unidentified factor in liver was added. Increasingly, the studies of bacteria cultured on chemically characterized media have been productive of important discoveries. Folinic acid proved to be a derivative of folic acid.

The folic acid group was eventually found to include p-aminobenzoic acid, pteroylglutamic acid, and the leuconostoc citrovorum factor.

Folic acid possesses hematopoietic activity. Its discovery led to successful therapeutic trials in many macrocytic anemias, principally sprue and pernicious anemia. It would be

---

[1] Folic acid is N-pteroyl, 1-glutamic acid.

difficult to overestimate the significance of these observations. They provided a new and valuable therapeutic agent for two serious diseases, and opened the way for studies in chemical pathology and etiology in these and related diseases.

The folic acid group may be concerned as co-factors in reactions involving transfer of a one-carbon unit. They involve the synthesis of methionine, serine, histidine, and possibly other amino acids, as well as the formation of purines and thymine.

Restriction of chicks and monkeys to a diet deficient in folic acid leads to development of anemia characterized by abnormally large red cells. Such a diet does not cause anemia in rats, since these secure folic acid from bacterial synthesis in the cecum and intestine. The inclusion of a bacteriostatic substance prevents its synthesis and permits the characteristic anemia to develop. In humans lack of folic acid causes an anemia resembling pernicious anemia but without the nerve involvement.

Vitamin B_{12}—In pernicious anemia there is a shiny, shrunken tongue, absence of hydrochloric acid in the gastric juice, nerve changes, and a characteristic macrocytic anemia. Whipple first suggested feeding liver to patients with this disease. Extensive therapeutic use of liver-feeding and of administration of liver concentrates, first prepared by Cohn, was made by Minot and Murphy. Castle discovered that feeding beefsteak had no beneficial effect, but that beefsteak previously digested with normal human gastric juice caused remission of pernicious anemia symptoms. He introduced the concept of intrinsic and extrinsic factors into the etiology of the disease. In 1948 E. L. Smith and E. L. Rickes and associates independently isolated red crystals from liver substance, and found them clinically effective in pernicious anemia. The metabolic functions of vitamin B_{12} are numerous. So great was the interest of biochemists and clinicians in its properties and physiological functions that already more than 2000 publications have appeared describing experimental studies with humans and animals. It is a nutrient of fundamental importance for all types of cells.

The Present Concept of an Adequate Diet

Within little more than half a century experimental inquiry has dramatically advanced our knowledge of foods and nutrition. From a general acceptance of the view that protein, potential energy in the form of carbohydrates and fats, and an ill-defined list of inorganic elements, especially those deposited in the bones, would suffice for the complete nutrition of man or animal, we have arrived at the present knowledge that, in addition to water and oxygen, 16 inorganic elements —potassium, sodium, magnesium, chlorine, calcium, phosphorus, sulfur, copper, iron, cobalt, manganese, zinc, iodine, fluorine, molybdenum and selenium—must be supplied. At least ten amino acids are indispensable nutrients. These are tryptophan, lysine, histidine, arginine, phenylalanine, leucine, isoleucine, threonine, methionine, and valine. Seventeen vitamins, fat-soluble A.D.E. and K; water-soluble, ascorbic acid, thiamine, riboflavin, niacin, pantothenic acid, vitamin B_6 group, choline, biotin, inositol, lipoic acid, p-amino-benzoic acid, folacin or folinic acid, and vitamin B_{12} are essential. In addition, the triply unsaturated linoleic acid is an indispensable nutrient. The total number of essential nutrients at present known is 47. But the importance in metabolic processes of glycine, serine, proline, and hydroxyproline and glutamic acid is so great that there is little doubt that these should be included in the diet.

The Rewards of Practical Application of Knowledge of Foods and Nutrition

Although the specific causes of scurvy, beriberi, iron-deficiency anemias, and rickets remained uncertain, therapeutic measures successful in their treatment were discovered before the end of the nineteenth century. Practical animal husbandrymen were from early times aware that certain combinations of farm crops produced better results with domestic animals than did others, but successful feeding was an art, the underlying principles of which were not known. The science of nutrition had its beginning in the earliest feeble efforts to discover what was lacking in mixtures of isolated protein, carbohydrate, fats, and inorganic salts. The earliest pioneers in this field were J. Forster (1873), N. Lunin (1880), and Magendie, who after 1816 tested the effect on animals of diets of sugar and water and olive oil and water. Rapid progress was made after 1912. The identification of the 47 presently recognized nutrients was achieved by the efforts of many experimenters in less than 46 years.

With the discovery of each organic nutrient opportunity was afforded chemists to determine its structure and to synthesize it. Procedures were devised for quantitative study of its presence in natural foods. Pathologists investigated the effects of deficiency of each nutrient, organic and inorganic, and described in detail the alteration of structure of the tissues most affected. Chemists have progressively inquired into the specific nature of the metabolic errors which result from the deficiency or absence of each nutrient. Numerous studies have extended knowledge of the supplementary values of our more important foods. On the results of these the present-day art of menu planning is based.

Applications of the Science of Nutrition to Human Problems

The demonstration by Vorderman that substitution of whole for polished rice could cause disappearance of beriberi from institutional inmates in Java was not generally known until after the publication of Funk's book, *The Vitamines* (1913). Hopkins, Osborne and Mendel, and later Rose, established the importance of individual amino acids in nutrition. The introduction of the biological method for investigating the number and nature of the deficiencies of natural foodstuffs led to the revelation of the significance of the supplementary relations between certain foods. Between 1915 and 1922 Hess's educational efforts to prevent scurvy in infants, and the demonstration of the efficacy of vitamin D in the prevention of rickets, ushered in a new era in improving the nutritional status of infants and children. With each discovery of a new nutrient, the scope of constructive thought about diet planning was broadened. Recommended allowances for the essential nutrients were decided upon by well-informed committees. Meal-planning reached the stage where expanding scientific data were employed. It exerted great influence on the formation of sound eating habits by people of all ages. Infant nutrition was safeguarded as never before.

By 1922 the dietetic errors causing beriberi, scurvy, rickets, and xerophthalmia were fully established. Prevention of endemic goiter and pellagra soon followed. The differentiation of several types of macrocytic anemias and of the specific vitamins useful in their treatment, and the recognition of kwashiorkor as a distinct type of malnutrition, primarily caused by protein deficiency, are the most important among the recent contributions to our knowledge of the relation of the diet to the preservation of health.

The Newer Knowledge Applied to Animal Industry

So long as ignorance of the existence of essential nutrients prevailed, farmers, with few exceptions, were quite unaware of the frequency and extent of the inadequacies of the rations provided for domestic animals, and the consequent stunting of growth, premature death of young, and low productivity. About 1918 it was discovered that depletion of grazing lands over wide areas in South Africa was the cause of severe malnutrition in ruminants, and that the accompanying ravenous appetite for chewing bones, was caused by phosphorus starvation. These observations led to the recognition that such soil depletion occurred in many regions in other countries. The cause was traced to continuous selling of animals off pastures without the application of fertilizers to restore lost mineral elements.

Extensive loss of newborn swine, lambs, calves and colts in the area of Michigan and westward to eastern Washington and Oregon, and in some other regions, was traced to deficiency of iodine in soils. This disaster was remedied coincidently with extensive use of iodine for the prevention of endemic goiter in the human population.

Slipped tendon and low hatchability of eggs resulting in great economic losses, was traced to deficiency of manganese in the feed of chickens and turkeys.

In Australia, Filmer and Underwood traced the progressive wasting, accompanied by severe anemia and loss of appetite in cattle, to deficiency of cobalt in the forage upon which they grazed. Marston related a similar condition of malnutrition in sheep to this cause, and showed that copper as well as cobalt deficiency was involved in undermining the health of the animals. This type of malnutrition was observed to occur in many parts of the world. The discovery that severe losses of domestic animals resulted from deficiency of one or another of the "trace" elements along with the low cost of supplying the missing nutrients made it possible to restore profitable animal production on a large scale.

Nutrition Investigations in Relation to Biochemistry, Pathology and Medicine

Sixty years ago biochemists knew little about the properties and biological significance of any amino acid, or about the physiological functions of the mineral elements and how they function in metabolic processes. During this period the nutritive significance of iodine, copper, manganese, magnesium, zinc, cobalt, selenium, and molybdenum has been brought to light. Within the same years seventeen vitamins were discovered, characterized, and their metabolic roles as constituents of enzyme systems partially clarified. Previous to these discoveries biochemists made little progress in investigating the metabolic schemes whereby each essential nutrient is subjected to the orderly chemical alterations, degradative and synthetic, which are involved in growth, reproduction, secretion, energy expenditure, and responses to stimuli—the sum of the physiological processes essential to life. Nutrition investigations revealed the existence of the 40-odd elements and compounds, inorganic and organic in nature, possessing the unique properties which enable them to bond with each other into complex macromolecules which in turn function in concatenation to form specialized structures such as the epithelial, mesenchymal, blood-forming tissues, vessels, blood and coagulation mechanism, muscle, and nervous tissues. Collectively, all these function in orderly and sequential catalytic activity to sustain a living organism. Chemical experiments alone were inadequate for making these discoveries. They were the results of the gradual evolution of experimental technics by means of which a living organism was subjected to situations where its physiological responses provided answers to questions in terms of chemical reactions.

We now know that bacteria and other simple forms of life which are not capable of performing photosynthetic reactions as do green plants, require the same nutrients as do mammals. Some micro-organisms possess special synthetic powers for forming this or that nutrient, whereas others lack this ability and require the nutrient in the culture medium. These differences are proving useful to biochemists in designing penetrating inquiry into the phenomena of biochemistry.

The new, analytical concepts which developed from the refinement of animal experiments in nutrition also led to the discovery of the behavior of analogues of some of the essential nutrients, i.e., amino acids, vitamins, etc. In many respects these resemble the true nutrients. In the roles of impostors, they bond into the macromolecules of living tissues. Unlike the true nutrients, they are incapable of functioning and so block biochemical processes. Examples of such antagonists are now well known for individual amino acids, lipids, steroids, and hormones, as well as for some of the inorganic nutrients. Thus the rewards of nutrition investigators have extended beyond the original objectives, and have created a new pathology and a new pharmacology based on the use by organic chemists of clues to the synthesis of new drugs for specific purposes. It is doubtful whether any segment of science has yielded results of such far-reaching usefulness to mankind as has the science of nutrition.

DEVELOPMENT OF IMPROVED CROPS

Henry A. Wallace

MAN FIRST began to improve crops some ten thousand years ago when women here and there over the world found they could systematize the gathering of seeds from such grasses as wild wheat and wild barley. Man for 99.9 per cent or more of his life here on earth lived without the benefit of the starchy grains like wheat, oats, barley, rice, and Indian corn. Man is what he eats. Historically, man's body was evolved on the basis of a diet which contains much less starch than the diet of almost any modern man except the Eskimo, the Gaucho, and possibly a few of the more wealthy Anglo-Saxons, Argentinians, and Australians. Simply on the basis of probable history, I would raise the question whether the Oriental, Egyptian, European, Aztec, Mayan, and Incan civilizations did not introduce more starch into the diet than man's long history had prepared his body to handle most healthfully.

Whatever my questions may be with regard to too much starch in the human diet, the incontrovertible fact remains that modern civilization began when women got the idea of improving primitive wheat, oats, rice, barley, and Indian corn. Men furnished the harder labor, but in most ancient civilizations it seems probable that the women were the custodians of the seed. Women set out the rice plants in the rice paddies. The Indian squaws were usually the ones who stored the corn seed till the planting time next year. Generally speaking, the men were hunt-conscious and the women were crop-conscious.

For many thousands of years steps were taken which were far more significant than anything done during the period 1200 to 1700 A.D. The ancient discoverers of efficient, starch-fixing plants were not skilled plant breeders. They knew nothing about producing mutants and even their selection was an accidental kind of thing. In the case of wheat, ancient man did not deliberately cross the 7-chromosome wild einkorn with a 14-chromosome wild grass of the Aegilops family to produce 21-chromosome modern wheat. But in the Middle East, man, or more probably woman, was around to take advantage of nature's obvious gifts. As time went on, it became more and more difficult for the cultivated grain—whether wheat, Indian corn, or rice—to survive in a wild state. Tribes who could produce a large number of calories per hour of man labor, and who could store grain against a time of bad weather, found that they could develop specialized labor, cities with artisans, trade, banking, writing, large buildings, and all the advantages and disadvantages of money as a store of value and facilitator of trade. While we can say without question that the extensive growing of starch crops was the *sine qua non* of man emerging from savagery, no one can assess with certainty the part played by the crops which produce alkaloids such as coffee, tea, tobacco, coca, and certain types of vision-inducing mushrooms and cacti.

For the purpose of this paper I propose to leave aside the alkaloid and alcoholic aspects of crop production and confine my attention largely to the starch crops, particularly wheat and corn. If our objective here on earth is to crowd our planet with the largest possible number of human beings, no matter what may be their longevity, disease resistance, and creative well-being, then we should center our attention on wheat, rice, potatoes, and corn as human food rather than as food for livestock. For my part, I believe our objective is to develop the highest quality of human being rather than the largest number. I believe that we in the United States have done very wisely during the past 20 years in cutting down our per capita consumption of wheat, cereal breakfast food, and potato by about 30 per cent while at the same time increasing our intake of meat, fish, poultry, dairy products, and fruits and vegetables by about 20 per cent. Actually, of course, we were merely doing what comes naturally; we have the increased income to enable us to eat what we like best, and unless starches are dressed up with sugar, butter, eggs, or meat, they are not exciting food.

Let us make certain assumptions about where we shall be in 1975, barring the possibility of war and amazing new inventions. Probably, we shall have about one third more people, and a total consumer income 70 per cent greater than today. If our per capita output continues to rise as it has been, we may expect the average person 16 years hence to have 35 to 40 per cent more to spend than today. Rex F. Daley of the United States Department of Agriculture, on the basis of such assumptions, estimates that the average person in 1975 will be eating 10 to 15 per cent more meat, about 8 per cent more dairy products, and about 18 per cent more poultry than today. The per capita consumption of the starchy foods would be expected to go down another 5 to 10 per cent. It seems as if each 10 per cent rise in a person's income tends, on the average, to cut down the consumption of the starchy foods by 2 per cent while the animal protein consumption in the form of meat goes up from 2 to 4 per cent. Beef consumption will go up by roughly 4 per cent; the more plebeian pork will go up by only 2 per cent. Poultry meat falls halfway between. Eggs, until the recent ill-founded suggestions that they might cause heart trouble, increased at the rate of about 1.5 per cent for each 10 per cent increase in income. Normally, both fluid milk and eggs respond to income increases to the extent of 1 to 1.5 per cent for each 10 per cent.

What this all adds up to in terms of crops is that by 1975, in order to feed our own people, we shall require about 30 per cent more corn and sorghum for livestock feed, about 15 per cent less wheat, about the same amount of potatoes, sugar, rice, and dried beans. The consumption of the non-saturated vegetable fats and oils, partly because of the propaganda conducted on their behalf, may go up to a total increased domestic consumption by 1975 of 30 per cent more than in 1959. Citrus fruit consumption will go up by at least 40 per cent and possibly by 60 or 70 per cent. Other fruits will go up by a total of at least 30 per cent. Tomato consumption should increase at almost the same rate as citrus fruit consumption. Lettuce, spinach, and green bean consumption should go up only slightly faster than population increase or by about 35 per cent.

To complete the picture on the demand side, we should take into account the extent to which we will use our very great surpluses of food, especially wheat and corn, as an agent of national policy under Public Law 480 and its successors to meet the great and growing hunger which has developed and will develop as a part of the population explosion. This explosion, which has had greater significance even than the atomic bomb, has come to the fore during the past ten years as a result of the widespread use of penicillin, DDT for mosquito control, and a great variety of public health measures which have been applied in a large, really effective way only since 1947. As a result, in many crowded areas of the world, populations are now increasing at such a rate so as to double in 25 to 30 years, whereas their former rate of increase led to doubling only every 50 to 100 years. The Near East, especially Egypt, is a striking example.

Probably our greatest challenge is how to use our enormous food surpluses wisely in the hungry parts of the world. People who are short on food, who earn less than $100 a year, who pay high interest rates and high rents, and see no possibility of owning their own land or getting out of debt almost inevitably have a kindly feeling toward the Communist doctrine even though they know nothing about it except the misinformation handed out by Moscow-indoctrinated people who live as they do and speak the same language. Hungry people do not reason; they strike out in response to emotional appeals. The communist technique thrives on confusion and a falling standard of living. However, it does not follow that if we raise the standard of living of backward peoples and give ever more billions of dollars worth of food to the crowded parts of the world, we will gain the friendship and support of the people we help. This is off the main line of my discussion, but I wish to say briefly that, in my opinion, the only long-range plan of safety for both Russia and the United States is to join together through the United Nations in helping the crowded parts of the world plan ways of doubling their agricultural production every

25 or 30 years or, failing in that, controlling their population. In the meantime, I see every likelihood that the United States will continue to export large quantities of farm products in 1975 for the simple reason that the surplus will still be with us. We shall cut our crop acreage and the number of our farms. But in spite of an increase of one third in our population, we shall still have great surpluses to put on foreign markets unless something drastic happens to our weather or to our social structure.

During the past 30 years the output of the average farm worker increased by more than 100 per cent, whereas the output of the average city worker increased by slightly more than 80 per cent. Yields per acre went up at the same time as the number of acres per man increased greatly. Corn and wheat yields increased on an acre basis by about 50 per cent as a result of using new varieties, more fertilizer, and better types of machinery for soil fitting and soil cultivation. In the case of corn, insecticides were used more intelligently for spraying and seed treatment. The use of tractors for both cultivating corn and pulling picking machines began in a big way in about 1930. Today, it takes only four or five minutes of man labor to produce a bushel of corn as compared with half an hour back in the early 1920's. Farmers today spend about four times as much for fertilizer as they did 20 years ago. As a result of the use of far more machinery and fertilizers, as well as improved varieties, farmers in general, during the past 30 years, have increased their output by more than a third while at the same time they have cut down their labor input by about 30 per cent. Today, one family living on the land furnishes the food for eight or nine families in town. One hundred and sixty years ago, it took four or five families living on the land to produce enough for themselves and have enough left over to feed one family in town. In other words, the farm family of 1958 is about 40 times as efficient as the farm family of 1800 in taking care of the food requirements of the town people. Of course, to be fair, we must admit that the farm family of 1800 did a lot of things which today are done in town. Moreover, the farm family of today must spend each year in town the equivalent of the cost of a farm in the old days. The trends of the past 60 years will no doubt continue and we shall have still fewer farmers and more machinery and fertilizer.

Tremendous as is the effect of improved machinery and fertilizers on increased crop yields, my own field of interest has to do with increasing the yield and quality of plants by the use of genetics. In brief, my greatest interest in plants is as a plant-breeder. To me, the most fascinating of all avocations is watching plants change from generation to generation as a result of selection, hybridization, mutation, irradiation, or treatment with such drugs as colchicine. I have a theory that after humanity has dug deeply for several generations into the interior of the atom, after it has conquered outer space, it will finally begin to place major emphasis on life itself. One of the most important projects will be to achieve full and complete understanding of the nature of heredity in our crop plants so that we may produce adequate food of the highest quality.

Scientific plant breeding was launched in 1694 by Camerarius, a German botanist who made his observations in his garden in Tübingen in southwestern Germany, about 80 miles north of the Swiss border. His paper was called "The Sex of Plants," and it was printed in Latin. The first scientific paper proving the precise nature of sex in Indian corn was based on experiments conducted by James Logan, the famous Philadelphia Quaker, in 1727 on the banks of the Delaware River.

The first man to observe and comment extensively on the hybrid vigor resulting from the crossing of New England Flint corn with Virginia Gourdseed was John Loraine of Germantown, Pennsylvania. Out of the process which Loraine described so accurately in 1813 came the dent corn which is grown on nearly 100 per cent of the acreage of the present-day corn belt.

To Charles Darwin goes the credit for developing most effectively, and at the right time, the theme of hybrid vigor in his book *Cross and Self Fertilization in Plants*. This book inspired William James Beal, professor of botany at Michigan State College, to conduct in 1877 the first careful experiments to prove how much the yield could be increased by the method of planting two kinds of corn in alternate rows in the field, pulling out the tassels of one kind, and using the hybridized seed of the detasseled rows for seed the following year. Later on, in the early 1900's, East and Jones, just north of New Haven, and Shull at Cold Spring Harbor on Long Island regularized the method which Loraine, Darwin, and Beal had grasped in a general way. I myself crossed corn by the detasseling method as a high-school boy in the summers of 1904 and 1905; I was much interested in Shull's ideas when they were first published and later corresponded with East and Jones at New Haven. In 1919 I started inbreeding and crossbreeding with great enthusiasm and in 1926 I founded the first commercial company devoted exclusively to the production of hybrid seed corn. Today this company spends as much money on hybrid corn research as the United States Department of Agriculture or any of the State Experiment Stations. We know the process of finding better corn is an endless one. For many years we have specialized in corn with stronger roots, stiffer stalks, higher yield, and ease of picking. Some kinds of corn pick hard with many husks left on. Other kinds will leave 10 bushels per acre behind in the field.

Hybrid corn today yields on the average at least 30 per cent more than the old-fashioned corn. Today, on 75 million acres, American farmers can grow at least 600 million more bushels annually than they used to grow on 110 million acres.

Growing the greatest amount of corn with the least use of labor and soil is important because it is through corn more than any other crop that the American people can have access to adequate supplies of animal protein. More than 85 per cent of the enormous corn crop is consumed by animals. Less than 2 per cent is consumed as sweet corn or in the form of alcoholic liquors. Less and less corn is consumed as corn bread or in the form of corn meal, mush, or grits. Considerable quantities of corn are converted into starch, corn syrup, glucose, and corn oil. The candy industry of the United States is probably more dependent on corn sugar than cane sugar.

To illustrate the complexities of improving a crop, let us consider the question of protein in corn. Some people have thought that corn should be bred for high protein so that animals fed corn would require less of such high protein feeds as soy bean meal, fish meal, and tankage. The first work along this line began at the Illinois Experiment Station in

1896. After 50 years of continuous selection, they increased the protein from 11 per cent to 19 per cent. By selecting for low protein they reduced the percentage after 50 years to 5 per cent. Does the high-protein corn have any greater feeding value than ordinary hybrid corn? No one knows the complete answer. It is known that in the endosperm of corn the protein is largely in the form of zein, which is an incomplete protein lacking in tryptophane and lysine, both of which are essential to animal nutrition. Personally, I doubt if it is worth the effort to increase by selection the amount of tryptophane and lysine in the endosperm of corn.

At the Purdue Experiment Station they found that hogs did better on low-protein corn, that they ate less of the high-protein corn, and did not gain as fast. High-protein corn is harder and not so easy to chew. If high-protein corn were produced in quantity and sold to the feed trade and the percentage of soybean meal, fish meal, etc., were reduced in the mixture, the resulting feed would probably not be as good as if there were less dependence on corn.

The genius of the corn plant is to produce cheap starch for animals. It may be worthwhile to breed for larger germs because of the corn oil, but when it comes to protein I would suggest we transfer our attention to the soybean plant. Nevertheless, at the University of Illinois they have transferred high-protein characteristics to hybrid corn and it is unquestionably possible to put a high-yielding, high-protein corn on the market. But there is no evidence that such corn would contain adequate quantities of tryptophane and lysine or that it would be as easy to chew as ordinary hybrid corn. To my mind there are other things in corn far more worth breeding for than high protein.

Whenever feeding experiments and economic relationships indicate it is a good thing to have high-protein or high-fat corn, it is easily possible to produce high-protein and high-fat hybrid strains.

One of the interesting methods of developing inbred strains of corn is to pick out the occasional mutants which are haploids, containing only half the normal number of chromosomes. Such haploids can be induced to revert to diploids, but when they do they are homozygous, pure-breeding at all loci. One of the leading corn companies is shifting over rapidly to the use of inbreds derived from haploids. So far as I know, none of the corn companies has yet commercially used inbred hybrids which have been caused to mutate by irradiation. Sooner or later this method will undoubtedly be used.

The method of using colchicine for making corn tetraploids has been tried but nothing has come of it commercially. This method has been used with fruits and flowers, but, thus far, has not proved feasible with corn.

The method of infiltrating corn with other species has not proved feasible, as it has with spring wheat. Efforts have been made to cross corn with sorghum, but without much success. We have planted cytoplasmically male-sterile sorghum in the midst of a corn field without getting any seed. Of course, corn was undoubtedly infiltrated with teosinte or possibly tripsacum thousands of years ago. It was that infiltration which made corn the useful plant it is today.

In this connection it might be well to review briefly a little of the history of the corn plant. By the method of pollen analysis of cores of ancient alluvial deposits underneath ancient lake beds, Dr. Sears of Yale, Dr. Clisby of

Oberlin, and Dr. Barghoorn of Harvard found that 69 meters beneath the Bellas Artes Building in Mexico City there was corn pollen which was 60,000 years old.

Dr. Paul Mangelsdorf of Harvard, by careful radioactive carbon analysis, found cobs of corn 5600 years old which were only half an inch long and carried not more than a hundred kernels which were of a popcorn type, with each individual kernel enclosed by a husk. This was apparently close to the wild type which produced the pollen which fell on the surface of the Mexico City lake 60,000 years ago. Somewhere in Mexico two or three thousand years ago this very small-eared corn must have become infiltrated by teosinte. While teosinte has only about 8 or 9 kernels to the ear, the result of the cross must have been a great shot in the arm. Out of this natural cross the Indians of Mexico selected myriads of types of corn before the white man ever came.

The Indians of the southeastern United States had a large-stalked late corn which produced an ear with 18 to 30 rows of very soft-textured kernels. The Indians used the stalks of this corn in somewhat the same way as the Orientals use bamboo, for building purposes. In New England the Indians used a weak-stalked, very early corn with 8 or 10 rows of very hard kernels. The Indians never consciously crossed the two to get larger yields so far as we know, but during the late eighteenth century the white man in eastern Pennsylvania, New Jersey, and perhaps in Maryland made deliberate crosses simply by interplanting the two sorts. It is out of these crosses transplanted to the corn belt during the early nineteenth century that practically all the inbreds going into modern hybrid corn originate.

The white man's contribution has been combination, selection, and recombination of what the Indian gave him. In all the long history of corn, the most exciting period was that time, perhaps 3000 years ago, when teosinte first introgressed into corn and a vast number of variations in the F1, F2, F3, and succeeding generations began to appear. Whoever it was who did the selection in those days must have been a natural-born plant breeder.

Since the Andean corn does not enter into the ancestry of our modern corn, I will not speculate as to what grass must have introgressed into the type of corn which apparently grew wild not only on the borders of the old Mexican lake, but in the Andean plateau as well. Whatever the origins may have been, we know that the Indians passed on to us enough variability so that we can go in many directions. My fear has been that we might lose some of the ancient types because of the replacing power of hybrid corn. Fortunately, the Rockefeller Foundation has been most helpful in establishing banks of corn germ plasm. By storing at low temperature and growing once every 10 or 15 years, we have found that it is possible to keep ancient stocks going so that we have them in case of some rare disease or other new challenge.

Mention should be made in passing of the contribution made by hybrid corn to the productive power of Europe by the Food and Agriculture Organization. Typically, hybrid corn has increased yields in Europe and North Africa by an average of about 40 per cent. Excellent co-operation with the different government agencies and local experiment stations has made it possible for hybrid corn to contribute to the annual wealth-producing power of Europe fully $100,000,000, representing a total far greater than all the other contributions of the Food and Agriculture Organization put together.

Russia and Rumania came to the United States for hybrid

corn seed two years ago, and Harrison Salisbury, the *New York Times* Russian expert, ventured to say with regard to penetrating the iron curtain effectively, "I think diplomacy with seeds and machinery is more effective than diplomacy with radio waves and parachuted slogans." Krushchev, who is a great protagonist of hybrid corn, probably does not know that Lysenko, the Marxist Lamarckian, fought Vavilov in public meeting over the question of hybrid corn in 1939. Vavilov's exile which followed shortly thereafter probably cost Russia's annual farm productive power more than $100,000,000. Russia and Rumania are taking really effective action on the hybrid corn front only since 1959. At the same time, strangely enough, Lysenko scored a political triumph over his fellow-Russian geneticists at the International Genetics Congress held at Montreal in August, 1958. This would suggest that Russia's Achilles heel may continue to be her backwardness in agriculture.

One method of improvement in corn which has been even more effectively used with oats is the method of backcrossing. For example, a particular inbred strain of corn may be unusually good for yield but susceptible to late blight of the leaves by a disease known as helminthesporium. We know that certain inbreds developed in the east and southeast of the United States are markedly resistant to helminthosporium.

Therefore, we cross the two sorts and the next year inbreed by placing the pollen of each plant on the silk of the same plant. Then we plant these resulting ears on the basis of an ear to the row and artificially infect the whole field with helminthesporium. The rows which are as good as the resistant parent, we crossback to the high-yielding sort. Then we inbreed again and continue to cycle the generations until we have completely transferred the resistance to disease of the one sort to the high-yielding kind. In corn we usually only do two or three top crosses before testing out for yield the segregates which seem to have disease resistance. With adequate numbers and yield-testing, we can usually get what we want in six or seven years, especially if we use two generations a year by going to Florida for a winter crop. Since so much depends on the need for getting recombinations, the numbers of plants needed may run into many thousands in the F2 and subsequent generations, especially if it is necessary to break linkages in order to bring about the transfer of the desired characteristic from one strain to another.

On the basis of my study of the history of corn and my work with the plant for more than half a century, I would say that the first thing to do in plant improvement is to begin with the best foundation stock. Usually this is more a matter of function than form. Having discovered after several years of careful observation the best foundation stocks, it remains to discover the best strains within those stocks for the particular area which you are serving. This partly involves obervation and insight and partly yield-testing. In the case of corn, you then start inbreeding. If you already have some good inbreds, you may use a standard single-cross male to pick out on an "ear-row" crossing basis the best particular ears to inbreed, verifying your yield position by crossing each generation of inbreds on an "ear-row" basis against a standard male. The success of this approach depends on two things: how good your standard male is, and how long you are willing to be tied to it.

It is all a question of sifting out the best genes for your purpose by continually verifying your position as you go along. It is tricky business because in practice about half the variabilities in yield are environmental and the environment varies each year. This is where the judgment and observation and insight of the plant breeder come in. There is no substitute for continually going through the fields during the late summer, looking and thinking, and looking again until you are so tired that you dream of what you saw and wake up with it the next morning! Not until your affections are completely centered can you watch the generations as they go by with the understanding and insight which catches what the IBM machine will never find.

In scientific terms we may say that modern corn improvement is based on controlled heterosis or, in other words, the discovery of those inbred lines which may be crossed to produce the best yield on stalks which can be machine-picked most easily with the least grain left behind in the field. One possible drawback to this method is that hybrid corn of somewhat restricted heredity is more and more replacing old-fashioned corn. In some areas the replacement is now 100 per cent. What about the discarded germ plasm? Some has been lost forever and some is being maintained in corn gene banks. But we must always remember that no present type of apparent superiority is likely to have all the kinds of resistance to future disease. The capacity to vary which is reduced by inbreeding may be important for the future. Because of disease, or change in climate, or nutritional requirements, no one can say certainly just what combinations of genes we need for the future.

Of course, we can always fall back on irradiation to produce variation. But this may involve the use of many millions of plants to find just what we want. I am inclined to think that many apparently abnormal mutations can have some one characteristic of great value and that we should not expect to produce by irradiation, at one sudden, complete jump, just what we want. It may be a slow process, involving back-crossing and selection based on large numbers.

Domesticated wheat has probably been around longer than domesticated corn, and its story is more interesting because it is more closely connected with our own particular ances-tors, and because the ancestors of wheat had 7 and 14 chromosomes, whereas it would seem that corn and the an-cestors of corn, for many thousands of years at least, had 10 chromosomes. The wild prototypes of the species going into wheat are more extant than in the case of corn. Wheat apparently was cultivated in the Middle East at least 7000 years ago. The most ancient of all the wheats is probably einkorn which has seven chromosomes and is harvested with the hull on. In ancient times, according to Mangelsdorf, the hull was disposed of by parching. There is some evidence that the parching method was used in Iraq 7,000 years ago. Curiously enough, the man who lost in his battle for hybrid corn in Russia in 1939—Vavilov—was also the man who did more than anyone else to puzzle out the ancient history of wheat. He especially studied the 14-chromosome wheats which were the first to come free from the hull. The most noted of these wheats is durum, which first made its appear-ance in the Near East and southeastern Europe about 100 B.C. Just when or how the 14-chromosome wheats were com-bined with the 7-chromosome wheats to make modern 21-chromosome wheat, no one knows, but it must have hap-pened at about the same time that men settled down in the villages of the Middle East to weave, to make pottery, and to domesticate animals. In a sense, European civilization was born on that day when some sharp-eyed person recognized the naked kernel of that first 21-chromosome wheat and was able to increase it so that wheat in volume could be produced from the hull. It was when man first became dependent for his life on crops that he watched the seasons with utmost care, became an astronomer, developed religious systems governing the sun, moon, planets, and crops, and, finally, emerged into the realm of philosophy. The wheat which could be winnowed free from the hull made it possible for farmers to produce the surpluses out of which cities and trade were born.

According to Mangelsdorf, the 21-chromosome wheat has never been found growing wild. His theory is that the 14-chromosome wheats accidentally crossed with a 7-chromosome grass of the aegilops family.

During the past 66 years, the art of improving the hereditary qualities of wheat has become ever more complicated. Take for example the hard spring wheat of the Dakotas, Montana, and Canada—the wheat with the most gluten and the best baking quality. All of it traces back to a single head of a sort which had come to Canada about 70 years ago from Poland via Scotland. The variety was called Red Fife and the mutant variety of Red Fife was crossed with an early, heat-resisting sort from India called hard red Calcutta. After the cross was made, painstakingly by hand, came the long-drawn-out problem of finding in the second generation which of the kernels had produced the most vigorous plants and the most vitreous kernels. According to Mangelsdorf, it took 15 years after the original crossing in 1892 to develop only 23 pounds of seed. But in the next 11 years, this 23 pounds of seed had multiplied into 300 million bushels of Marquis wheat put on the markets of the world, the first really superior bread wheat with high-yielding qualities adapted to the climate of western Canada, Montana, and the Dakotas. The world owes a great debt of gratitude to the Saunders family and especially to Charles Saunders for originating a variety which to this day is found to some extent in the blood lines not only of nearly all of our spring wheat, but of many of our winter wheats as well.

For 20 years Marquis completely dominated the spring wheat area of the great Northwest. Then new types of leaf and especially stem rust came in and the good qualities of Marquis had to be combined with something which had stem-rust resistance. In 1916, while Marquis was still at the height of its triumph, a South Dakota farm-boy by the name of Edgar McFadden, working at the South Dakota Experiment Station at Brookings, crossed 14-chromosome Yaroslav emmer with the 21-chromosome Marquis wheat in order to get the quality of stem-rust resistance. For several years after the cross there was great sterility and a high percentage of shrivelled grains. Nevertheless, the cross was kept going year after year and the plumpest grains were selected out. McFadden went into farming by himself, but he never stopped working with his cross, and in 1923 he found a promising selection called Hope. The milling quality was poor, but for the first time a hard spring wheat had resistance to stem rust. Today nearly all the hard spring wheat has in it not only the blood of Marquis but also of Yaroslav emmer. The percentage of emmer blood is probably less than ten, but by backcrossing, the undesirable Emmer characteristics were thrown away and the all-important disease-resistant character was kept. Although Hope was a spring wheat, some of its unique properties were transferred into some of the hard winter wheats of the southern Great Plains.

To get greater leaf-rust resistance, the 14-chromosome durum wheat was also incorporated into some of the hard spring wheats with great success. Still more recently, I learn from L. B. Reitz, head of the United States Department of Agriculture wheat work, that in order to get more effective resistance to leaf rust they have transferred by crossing a whole block of genes from aegilops umbellulata, a wild grass, to common wheat. Durum wheat crosses more readily than common wheat with emmer and has been improved for disease resistance by such crossing. More than 20 years ago both the Russians and our own Department of Agriculture began crossing a relative of the common, grassy weed known as quack grass with wheat. Many of these crosses were perennial, and for some years the Russians made great boasts about their perennial wheat. While I very much doubt that perennial wheat will ever be so very practical, Reitz claims that 1000 pedigree lines involving the agropyron wheat cross are being maintained. The ultimate value of this cross may come via disease resistance in an annual wheat rather than in the perennial characteristic of some of these 1000 lines. More recently, the Department is looking to wheats from Kenya in Equatorial Africa for resistance to some of the worst strains of rust.

When the United States was first settled in the seventeenth century, most of the small grains were brought from northwestern Europe. When these sorts, evolved under rather cool, moist summers and rather mild winters, were taken to the violent climate of the Great Plains, the hot, dry days of late June and early July caused great havoc. The German-Russian Mennonites from the Volga who came to central Kansas in 1873 brought with them a wheat which had had long experience with drought and heat. For some strange reason this Mennonite wheat from Russia was called, "Turkey."

At first the Turkey wheat spread slowly, but by 1929 200 million bushels of it were being grown in the United States—mostly in the Great Plains. Then disease began to hit the Turkey wheat and it was realized that yield and milling quality, as well as disease resistance, could be improved by hybridization and selection. Today all the winter wheat of the Great Plains has in it traces of Turkey wheat, or allied wheats imported more recently from Russia, but an analysis of the pedigree of the more recent varieties indicates that all of them have a most complex ancestry. Several of the most widely grown sorts have Marquis as one grandparent, while Turkey in the background furnishes several of the great-grandparents. At least one sort has durum wheat for a great-grandparent combined with Turkey and Marquis. One sort has in it a hard white wheat from Australia, combined with a strong infusion of Turkey and Marquis. Another sort has in it a soft red wheat from Indiana combined with Turkey, Marquis, and durum. No doubt 20 years from now strong shots of Kenya strain will begin to appear.

I shall not attempt to discuss the ancestry of the soft winter wheats grown in the eastern United States, Idaho, and Washington. For the most part their ancestry is quite different because the greater summer rainfall and the milder winter climate have resulted in the foundation stock coming more from western Europe, the Mediterranean, and Australia. The soft wheats are used for fine cake flour and crackers. Everywhere there is the same problem of adaptation to changing diseases and insects, changing fertilizer, and the need for a shorter straw which will stand up better under adverse climatic conditions. The need for wheat breeding to continue at its present rate will never cease, simply because the environment and pests never stand still. Increased radioactivity in the air will probably result in greater variability in many of the micro-organisms which attack wheat and other plants.

A brief survey of oat varieties in Iowa (which is the leading oat state) demonstrates in principle how similar is the oat history to that of wheat. Like wheat, there are species with 7, 14, and 21 chromosomes. Like wheat, the cultivated oats have 21 chromosomes. Like wheat, the first varieties of oats to come to the Middle West were from western Europe. Naturally, they did not like the sudden burst of hot, dry, weather which so often comes in late June. The first effort to avoid the hot, dry weather was directed to finding early sorts among the American varieties which had originated in western Europe. Next, in the early part of this century, attention was directed to oats from Kherson, in southern Russia, where the summers are usually hot and dry. For 20 years Iowa oat varieties were largely of Kherson origin. Then rust and smut diseases became increasingly serious and resistance was temporarily obtained by crossing the Kherson selections with a variety from Uruguay called Victoria. In three years' time, the Victoria-derived varieties almost completely replaced the sorts which were of Russian origin. From 1943 to 1947, the Victoria-Kherson crosses dominated the Iowa oat picture. Then Helminthosporium or blight struck down these new sorts, and from 1948 to the present the Iowa oat picture has been dominated by oats which are a cross of Russian oats with an Australian oat which, in turn, was a cross of an Algerian oat with a famed Swedish variety known as Golden Rain.

Dr. Franklin A. Coffman, head of the oat-breeding work of the Department of Agriculture, writes me that new races of rust are now beginning to attack these new Iowa varieties and that the breeders are now turning to minor species, e.g., a European sort known as Avena Strigosa, and also to a Kherson type that has been selected under African conditions for many years. Just as in wheat, oat diseases change rapidly and, therefore, a continual search must be made for resistant foreign varieties or wild species—an ever-shifting and never-ending battle.

Your head swims as you contemplate the millions of hours spent crossing, multiplying, observing, selecting, and recording, year after year, the small changes in any program of plant improvement. It is exciting to make violent species crosses, but it is slow to backcross and grow thousands of plants in an effort to find just one good segregate which is both new and useful. Usually the segregate is merely useful to cross again and again in a continuing program of crossing, selection, backcrossing, and reselection. Usually it takes 15 years and hundreds of thousands of plants to attain a goal which has been clearly defined. Patience, land, money, and a genuine love for the organism to be improved are all required.

Looking to the future, I place foremost emphasis on the "germ plasm bank" or storehouse. Worldwide surveys like Vavilov's are vital to our knowledge of where we can continue to obtain the different varieties of the various species. In this connection, I would call special attention to the work of Anderson, Mangelsdorf, and Brown with corn. Working with a remarkably variable species extending over many latitudes and altitudes, they have puzzled out the travels of the corn genes and, knowing their material, have worked out with the Rockefeller Foundation the establishment of "corn germ plasm banks" in a number of localities.

The second point is to learn to rearrange the genes for specific purposes. Here many techniques come in. One of the most interesting, which I have not mentioned before, was started on its way shortly after World War I by Dr. H. V. Harlan of our Department, working with barley. Dr. Harlan assembled 28 varieties of barley from various parts of Asia, Africa, the Soviet Union, the Mediterranean, and Scotland. Three hundred and seventy-eight crosses were made and the mixture was carried to the eighth generation. Then, 2,921 selections were made on the basis of the new mixing. A lot of labor was required in making the 378 crosses, but after that, for eight generations, nature did the work of selecting. Many of the 28 original varieties were totally non-adapted, and for five generations the yield of the composite was 20 per cent less than the best commercial variety. It took from 10 to 20 generations before the composite mixture was definitely better than the commercial sorts produced by traditional plant-breeding methods. Out of this composite, three different nations and thirteen different states have isolated promising varieties. This type of breeding might almost be said to be based on the psalmist's theme: "The stone which the builders rejected is become the head of the corner."

In the eighth generation, there were many mutants. Some were dwarf; some were very stiff-strawed. Some were obviously undesirable, and it seems a miracle that such poor competitors could maintain themselves in a composite mixture. Some of the "screwball" sorts had heads which were short and almost round. Professor Jack Harlan of the Oklahoma A. and M. University, in discussing the work started by his father, stated two years ago:

> The composite cross bulk population method is so inexpensive that it could be used extensively to survey world collections which are, in fact, often too large and cumbersome to explore thoroughly in any other way. In the course of a survey of this sort, varieties may be found which induce a high frequency of variants or produce exceptionally valuable progenies in certain matings.

Again and again, Harlan makes the point which many plant breeders have made, that varieties, when used for breeding purposes, must be judged not on the way they themselves perform, but on the way their descendents perform perhaps several generations hence. The right new characteristics for the crop of the future must invariably be combined with other characteristics. This takes a long time.

Harlan issues an interesting warning to users of the composite method based on melons:

> Some years ago, the melon industry was very seriously threatened by attacks of mildew. . . . Explorers were sent out. A world collection was assembled. The melon breeders screened the collection, found sources of mildew resistance, and discarded the susceptible types. After a period of breeding to introduce resistance into the types that produced, shipped and marketed well and which received good public acceptance, the problem was in fact rather satisfactorily solved. No sooner had the bulk of the susceptible material been thrown away than attacks of virus began to threaten the industry. Much of the

material had to be assembled a second time and the entire procedure repeated to solve this problem. . . . Still a third collection will no doubt be necessary to solve the next problem that comes up.

In the meantime, the sorts which are temporarily superior tend to spread over the entire world and the primitive gene pools to which we have been driven again and again, for a renewal of our strength, tend to disappear. Perhaps we can recreate some of them by irradiation, but certainly not a majority of them. *Practical* plant breeders have to be ruthless in their discarding. But *fundamental* plant breeders must remember the possible value, not only of the stones which the builders *rejected,* but also of the stones in the out-of-the-way places of the world where the artificial and passing standards of civilization may cause the loss of much that is precious.

All life is precious. Man, as he creates his own environment, must continually reassess the changing ways in which life of all kinds including diseases react to him. Just as the various types of rusts, mildews, and virus seem to change to meet our new types of plants, so, also, they seem to change to meet the changing environment created by man. There is no permanent answer; as Heraclitis stated so long ago, everything is in process of change. The doctor of medicine and the plant breeder both must respect and revere all forms of life and recognize that the virus, bacteria, and fungi which threaten both plants and man will be forever changing, and probably more rapidly in the future than in the past. As a result, all of us must strive more and more to understand what the life processes are really like.

I regret I have paid so little attention to nutrition. I have consciously avoided any discussion of the truly remarkable improvements in varieties of sugar beets and sugar cane.

Both refined sugar and refined starch, unless properly supplemented, can lead to various kinds of trouble. Protein containing the right amino acids is undoubtedly very important in the diet. Nevertheless, I very much doubt the feasibility of breeding either the sugar or starch plants for a high percentage of high-quality proteins. However, I certainly would urge a far more extensive use of unrefined starches and sugars. A considerable percentage of high-quality animal protein in the diet is vital at all ages; also vital, are such fruits as tomatoes and oranges and those vegetables that have a dark green or orange color. These protective foods, with which we are all familiar, will inevitably play an ever-increasing part in the diet of those who have enough money.

It is the function of the scientific dietician to define the goals from the standpoint of health. Synthetic vitamins undoubtedly will and should play an increasing role, especially in the diet of the aged. Fertilizers by enriching the soil also enrich the crops both in protein and minerals. Eventually a sewage-wasting and soil-destroying civilization will have to pay a very great penalty. In the meantime, the plant breeders, machinery manufacturers, and fertilizer manufacturers, working through the intelligent, hard-working farmers of the western world, will produce a great surplus of food for the next 30 years at a time when most of the rest of the world is going hungry.

Eventually mankind will become surpremely interested in quality rather than quantity. Man will realize that plants are what they eat, that animals are what they eat, and that man is what he eats—that the soil is the mother of us all and that she also must be fed with quality food. Today our knowledge of this broad related field is too fragmentary to permit more than superficial speculation. As long as any of us live, we must rely in large measure on crops bred, fertilized, and cared for in the traditional way with a certain amount of protection against poisons. There is little scientific proof that plants grown on animal and green manures are superior in food value to crops grown with chemical fertilizer. Nevertheless, I feel that it is a supreme privilege for all of us who can afford it to grow vegetables produced chiefly on soil richly fertilized with barnyard manure or a compost pile.

PRINCIPLES AND PROBLEMS OF INCREASING FOOD CROPS AND ANIMALS IN LOW-PRODUCTION AREAS

J. George Harrar, Ph.D.

ALTHOUGH SOCIETY continually faces grave problems, those related to human nutrition are among the most pressing. These often lead to a variety of social disturbances which, in turn, are detrimental to human progress. It is frequently difficult to realize the extent to which dietary deficiencies exist in essentially all the "underdeveloped" areas of the world. The contrast is so great between them and the Western nations that one must see the situation at first-hand to become truly aware of its implications.

Essentially all interested groups agree that progress toward peace and the well-being of mankind is, in general, dependent upon the availability of sufficient quantities of appropriate foodstuffs to provide an adequate diet for the world's population. As a consequence, many efforts have been made to introduce into the diets of rural and urban populations in food-deficient areas increased quantities of critical

171

foodstuffs. Usually the first effort is directed toward the diets of infants and young children with the introduction of milk and meat or their products, plant proteins, and vitamins, in order to supplement or enrich diets which are excessively high in carbohydrates. In combination, these efforts have been useful and effective and their continuance and intensification should result in still greater benefits to the peoples concerned.

It is generally recognized that it would be uneconomic to attempt to resolve the dietary problems of the world solely through the contribution of protein and other foods from the surplus-producing countries of the world. The only permanent solution is the development of ways and means by which the people concerned can be helped to increase and diversify their own agricultural product, and, when necessary, modify local food habits toward a more balanced diet. This is neither a simple nor a quick process, but it is fundamental to the human and economic development of the nations concerned.

In response to an official invitation, The Rockefeller Foundation in 1941 agreed to collaborate with the Government of Mexico in an effort to increase the quantity and quality of the basic food crops available to the Mexican people. This program got under way early in 1943 and has continued until the present time. It was a new venture for The Rockefeller Foundation, and the field staff in agriculture, which has been created in response, has had to learn a great deal in order to be able to function effectively. The first requirements were to learn the local language and to become completely familiar with agricultural and economic situations. A study then had to be made of government and private organizations dealing with agriculture and the capacity and potential of agricultural institutions and available manpower resources. There then had to be agreement as to the most important areas of investigation, priorities with respect to crops to be improved, initiation of projects, and arrangements for program support on a co-operative basis.

During the past fourteen years, the program in Mexico has produced a number of definitive results. Among these has been the increase in average yields of corn and wheat to the point at which the country is self-sustaining with respect to these two basic foods. This development has made it possible to expand into projects on the improvement of potatoes, vegetables, forage crops, poultry, and livestock. At the same time, opportunities have been afforded for the training of increased numbers of young nationals in the several specialized fields within the agricultural sciences. These young men, who are now occupying important government and institutional positions, are fully aware of local dietary problems and are deliberately and effectively moving toward their solution.

As a result of the demonstration in Mexico, other countries have requested similar co-operative programs, and three additional operating centers have been established in Colombia, Chile, and India, respectively. These have been used for the training of young scientists from still other countries who, upon their return to their own institutions, have been encouraged and supported in efforts to initiate programs for the improvement of the quantity and quality of local food crops.

As a result of the experience in Mexico and subsequently in a number of other countries, it has been learned that at least a considerable number of the underdeveloped countries could, within a reasonable period of time, begin to satisfy their basic food requirements if given an opportunity to do so. This opportunity involves not only financial assistance such as loans or improvement of transportation systems, power plants, communications, water impoundments, etc., but, equally important, the development of sound agricultural programs which can be expected to play a major role in making these and other developments economically feasible. Perhaps too often there has been a tendency to attempt "crash programs" or "break-throughs" which in some mysterious way might, with great rapidity, convert the economy of an underdeveloped nation to the level of the highly developed countries of the West. Efforts of this sort almost inevitably fail. The altruistic motives which lead to attempts toward extremely rapid progress are understandable, but the rational examination of local situations inevitably reveals the need for the application of substantial doses of time in order that change will come about through understanding and local enterprise rather than as a result of heavy applications of cash and kind from external sources.

Often it is necessary to proceed indirectly toward an established goal. For example, those countries which are identified as cereal-eating, e.g., corn, rice, and wheat, often find themselves in situations in which there is an inadequate supply of these food grains to satisfy the normal demand. Under such circumstances, attempts to rapidly diversify local diets and perhaps introduce exotic foods are viewed with doubt and distrust. If, however, the local problem is recognized and understood, and sound effort is made to resolve it, the response is unhesitating, and the confidence thus engendered can be utilized effectively in the development of projects and programs which, although not dramatically different from accepted practice, are oriented toward improvements in production systems and food habits.

The traditional belief that dietary patterns of many rural peoples cannot be changed because of cultural convictions has been shown on numerous occasions to be a false premise. Farmers in general tend to cling to those materials and habits which have proved most successful in the past, and do not drop them lightly, at the suggestion of people whom they neither know nor understand. They depend on the results which they have obtained over a period of years through local systems of farming and are unwilling to risk crop failure and even famine by abandoning tradition in favor of methods and materials which to them are untried. On the other hand, once they have been shown that there are simpler and better ways to accomplish their own purposes, they are eager imitators and the community leaders quickly become ripe for innovations. Their neighbors readily follow these leaders, and with skill a chain reaction can be initiated which will gradually extend throughout individual communities and ultimately the country concerned.

As is true everywhere, the older people are the least amenable to rapid change. They will modify their habits and practices only if they have ample opportunity to recognize and understand the benefits of so doing. On the other hand, the younger members of the community are instinctively curious and willing to take chances and to learn, and as they do, they become the greatest single force for progress within the community. In many instances their influence on their elders is the most important leverage which can be employed.

Once confidence has been won and useful results demonstrated, the rapidity with which technical co-operation programs are accepted and extended is frequently startling. At this stage, the program is in danger unless long-range plans have been laid to assure that there will be supply in answer to the rapidly growing demand for information, seed stocks, fertilizers, and the other materials essential to production. As these requirements are satisfied, opportunities become available for introduction of further improved methods and materials, the use of more efficient mechanical devices where these are economically feasible, and a gradual diversification of family patterns. One of the most important benefits is the at least partial emancipation of women and children from heavy work in the field, with resultant improvements in family life and educational opportunities.

The entire process of entry into and establishment in a foreign country requires tact and patience, and, from the outset, the association of the foreign specialist with local individuals who will one day undertake total responsibility. Training can best begin at whatever level is encountered locally, whether this be elementary, vocational, or relatively advanced. In each instance there must be "learning through doing" and a gradual increase in self-confidence on the part of the individual trainees. As more and more persons become qualified for specialized responsibilities, there will be among them individuals who can be trained to the succeedingly higher levels, until ultimately each of the various educational stages is being properly developed with increasing output of qualified individuals for local tasks. Then leaders can be selected in order to give imagination and stability to the program and to stimulate and train younger groups who will one day have to accept important responsibilities.

Programs such as those described here can be in themselves of significance in the improvement of the level of nutrition of the populations concerned. Ideally, however, they should be built into the local structure and economy and be co-ordinated with related efforts directed toward economic and social improvement. This results in synergistic effects and more rapid progress toward the goal of an adequate diet for an increasing proportion of the world's population.

EFFECT OF PROCESSING ON THE NUTRITIVE VALUE OF FOODS

David B. Hand, Ph.D.

Introduction

THERE IS a widespread belief that processed foods are less nutritious than fresh foods and that this is due to the destruction or removal of vitamins during processing. The basis for this belief is the knowledge of the deleterious effects of processing in some instances. The prevalence of beriberi in the Orient is a well-known example of a nutritional deficiency due to food processing, in this case, the milling of rice. There are a number of other examples of processed foods in which the nutritional value has been diminished. The high incidence of dental caries in civilized societies is widely held to be associated with the use of sugar and refined foods.

Food processing serves a dual function. The first is to prepare foods in a form suitable or convenient for cooking. In this sense food processing includes such operations as cleaning, peeling, trimming, and even partial cooking. Recent extensions of food processing have included the blending and cooking of ready-to-eat dishes that require only a final warming before serving. In its primary function food processing has taken over the operations preparatory to cooking and even part of the cooking as well.

The second function of food processing is to prepare foods with adequate keeping quality so that they can be stored and distributed in areas far removed from the farms where they originate. In carrying out these two main functions the food processor submits foods to treatments that are very different from ordinary kitchen practices. The question before us is: to what extent does food processing cause a diminution in the nutritive value of food that goes beyond the unavoidable losses resulting from cooking?

It is impractical to treat the question that is before us exhaustively, i.e., to consider the effect of every kind of process on every essential nutrient. There are 17 vitamins, 16 mineral elements, and 10 essential amino acids. Each of these 43 essential nutrients is present in numerous foods that are subjected to a large variety of processes, including canning, freezing, drying, fermenting, smoking, salting, curing, pasteurizing, concentrating, milling, baking, lyophilizing, tenderizing, and many others. In processing foods, 500 or more chemical additives are used with the possibility in some instances of interreactions with the nutrients.

Since it is impractical to examine all the effects of processing on all the essential nutrients, the question will be simplified to include only the effects of processing on the availability of an adequate diet. We will limit our consideration to nutrients that are sometimes in short supply and to those processed foods that contribute significant amounts of the critical nutrients. From the practical standpoint we would like to know if the trend toward increased use of processed foods requires us to make any changes in the foods we select for our diet.

For people in this country who eat a varied diet, there are only 6 vitamins that are apt to be in short supply. The recommended daily allowances for these vitamins have been published by the Food and Nutrition Board of the National Research Council (6). In order to be sure of obtaining an adequate supply of these critical vitamins, it is necessary to plan the diet carefully. However, the remainder of the 17 known vitamins are so widely distributed that they will automatically be included in a varied and well-balanced diet that is adequate with respect to the six critical vitamins.

The critical vitamins are vitamin A, ascorbic acid, vitamin D, thiamin, riboflavin, and niacin. Of these, ascorbic acid, thiamin, and vitamin A are the most susceptible to damage in processing. It remains to be seen if this damage is nutritionally significant. The simplest approach to the question is to take each critical vitamin in turn and determine what foods serve as important sources for each and what processes are used in the manufacture of these foods.

There are no significant quantities of ascorbic acid (vitamin C) in three of the major classes of foods (12). The vitamin is almost entirely supplied by certain fruits and vegetables. Good fruit sources of vitamin C are citrus fruits and strawberries. Among the vegetables, cabbages, potatoes, sweet potatoes, and tomatoes are important sources. Fruits and vegetables are subjected to a wide variety of processing, including canning, freezing, fermentation, and dehydration. No food can be preserved without some sacrifice in vitamin content. Losses must be evaluated in comparison with losses that occur during the handling, shipping, and cooking of fresh foods.

Vitamin C

Processing of fruits and vegetables causes a greater loss of vitamin C than of any other vitamin. Vitamin C is lost by oxidation and by leaching during washing, blanching, water-cooling, brine flotation, and other processes preparatory to freezing. Blanching is a preliminary step in canning and dehydration as well as in freezing. Nearly all blanching is carried out in hot water rather than in steam.

Many fruits and vegetables contain an ascorbic acid oxidase that rapidly inactivates vitamin C during the warming-up stage of the blanching process. At the blanching temperature, the enzyme is inactivated. Losses of vitamin C during storage may result from inadequate blanching, contamination of the food with copper, and from participation of ascorbic acid in the browning reaction in the presence of free amino groups.

Losses of vitamin C in properly processed fruits and vegetables are not large enough to create nutritional problems. The over-all average retention of vitamin C in citrus juice is 97 per cent (1). In tomato juice, also a good source of vitamin C, the vitamin is less stable and average figures of 67 per cent retention have been reported (2). Typical values for the retention of vitamin C during blanching of vegetables are as follows: peas, 71 per cent; green beans, 64 per cent; asparagus, 89 per cent; kale, 56 per cent; beets, 63 per cent; potatoes, 62 per cent; cabbage, 48 per cent; and carrots, 55 per cent (13). In spite of these losses, frozen vegetables are as rich in vitamin C as fresh foods. This is due to the fact that the ascorbic acid oxidase is inactivated by blanching, resulting in less loss of vitamin C during the cooking of frozen vegetables than during the cooking of fresh vegetables (11).

Vitamin C is stable in the storage of frozen fruits and vegetables for six months, provided the temperature does not rise above 0°F. (11). During the process of canning, the ascorbic acid is not seriously affected by the sterilization operation. An exception to this general statement is the observed loss of 20 and 26 per cent during the sterilization of green beans (13). Vitamin C is very stable in canned foods during storage under commercial conditions. More than 90 per cent of the ascorbic acid is retained in canned peas, orange juice, and tomatoes stored for one year (2). Roughly 50 per cent of the original ascorbic acid in cabbage is retained after the fermentation and canning of sauerkraut (8).

The older literature states that vitamin C suffers almost complete destruction in most dehydrated products (4). This is still true for sun-dried fruits, but modern methods of dehydration have made possible substantial preservation of vitamin C as a result of preliminary blanching and rapid drying (10). Sulfuring aids in the retention of vitamin C but causes the almost complete loss of thiamin. A considerable number of foods have been dehydrated under commercial conditions that retain significant quantities of vitamins (2), e.g., tomato flakes, sweet potatoes, pea soup, milk, eggs, carrots, and cabbages. Unsulfited, dehydrated cabbage contains 218 mg. ascorbic acid per 100 gm. of dry sample. The use of dehydrated foods is not extensive enough so that they make a major contribution to the supply of any essential nutrients. They are, however, important in military rations.

Vitamin A

Fruits and vegetables supply three quarters of the vitamin A activity in the diet. This is principally in the form of the precursor, beta carotin. Yellow vegetables like sweet potatoes and carrots, red vegetables like tomatoes and red peppers, and dark green vegetables like peas, snap beans, broccoli, asparagus, and spinach are rich sources of vitamin A. Yellow fruits like citrus and apricots have high vitamin A contents. Vitamin A also occurs in milk fat and hence in such foods as whole milk, cream, and cheese.

Vitamin A is sensitive to oxidation by lipases and peroxidases. It is similar to vitamin C in that its stability in storage depends on adequate blanching. Vitamin A is not water-soluble and hence is not removed during water blanching.

Losses of carotene in canning are comparable to losses of vitamin C. For example, average reported retentions of carotene for tomato juice are 67 per cent, for clingstone peaches, 77 per cent. There is no measurable loss of carotene from canned peas, orange juice, and tomatoes stored for one year in commercial warehouses (2).

There is some disagreement in the literature concerning the losses of carotene during blanching and freezing. In their review, Tressler and Evers (11) summarize by stating that very little loss occurs during the preparation for and the freezing of most vegetables. Losses may occur during the frozen storage of asparagus and lima beans. Asparagus may lose as much as 40 per cent of its carotene in six months and lima beans a similar amount in eleven months.

Carotene is destroyed by sun-drying, but modern methods of dehydration preserve the vitamin A activity. Losses ranging from 0 to 34 per cent have been observed in the dehydration of carrots (2). Spray-dried eggs retained 91 per cent of their original vitamin A. However, this may be relatively unstable on storage at 70°F. where half the content is lost in three months.

Thiamin

Thiamin, along with the other B vitamins, riboflavin and niacin, is very widely distributed in foods. It occurs in vegetables, dairy products, meats, poultry, fish, eggs, and cereals. Thiamin is sensitive to destruction by heat and thus undergoes greater losses during processing than do the other B vitamins, riboflavin and niacin. All these vitamins are soluble in water and are equally vulnerable to losses by leaching during washing, blanching, etc.

Because of the wide distribution of thiamin, the processes to which it is exposed are very diverse. A satisfactory picture of the extent to which it is retained in processed foods can be obtained from examples of processes involving high temperatures. Baking bread causes a 5 to 9 per cent loss of thiamin. There is an additional loss of 12 to 24 per cent on toasting (3). Thiamin is pretty well maintained during the sterilization process of canning, as shown by the following typical figures for retention: asparagus, 66 per cent; corn, 47 per cent; green beans, 73 per cent; lima beans, 71 per cent; peas, 67 per cent; tomatoes, 89 per cent; and tomato juice, 74 per cent. Over 80 per cent of the thiamin in canned peas, orange juice, and tomatoes was retained during 12 months' storage in commercial warehouses (2).

Losses of thiamin from frozen vegetables are less than for canned vegetables because blanching is a milder heat treatment than sterilization. A loss of 25 per cent of thiamin during the blanching before freezing has been reported. No further loss during freezing and storage has been observed (5).

Losses of thiamin on dehydration of vegetables ranging from 22 to 56 per cent have been reported. Dehydrated pork may retain 63 per cent and dehydrated beef, 76 per cent of its thiamin. The thiamin in dehydrated pork is stable for 130 days at 38°F., but is largely destroyed in the same time at 80°F. Thiamin is fully retained in the spray-drying of eggs but is not stable on storage above 70°F. for periods of over three months (2).

The loss of thiamin which occurs during dehydration of vegetables and fruits if they are treated with sulfur dioxide has already been mentioned. Due to the low consumption of dehydrated foods, this destruction is of very little nutritional significance.

Very significant losses in thiamin (and also of riboflavin and niacin) occur during the milling of wheat and rice. These losses are not as nutritionally significant in the United States as in countries where the consumption of cereals is much greater. However, in the United States, the enrichment of flour and rice has largely corrected the losses in the nutritive value due to milling.

Protein

To get a complete picture of the effect of food processing on the nutritive value of foods, consideration must be given to still another essential nutrient, namely protein. It is well known that the biological value of proteins can be destroyed by high temperatures. As a matter of fact, some food processes do lower the biological value. The "puffing" of cereals, by treating them with steam at high pressures and then suddenly releasing the pressure, results in considerable destruction of protein. Whether food processing causes a nutritionally significant loss of protein will depend on whether foods that are important sources of protein suffer serious losses in the biological value of their proteins. There is also the question of whether protein is ever a limiting nutrient in the American diet. Protein-deficient diets have not been observed in this country.

The most important source of protein is the group of foods comprising meat, poultry, fish, and eggs. This group of foods provides one third of the dietary protein. Alternate sources of plant proteins are dried beans, peas, and nuts.

Dairy products are a close second to the meat group providing one fourth, and cereals, in third place, supply one fifth of the available protein.

In general, moderate heat treatments, such as those involved in home cooking and in most commercial processing operations, do not significantly alter the nutritive value of the protein (9). There is no indication that frozen foods have undergone any change in the nutritive value of their protein.

There is a wide variety of foods that are subjected to sufficient heat to become brown in color and to develop a desirable flavor. This change is called the browning reaction and it involves, among other reactions, a condensation of protein and reducing sugars. A few examples of products whose attractive qualities depend on the browning reaction are broiled meat, certain breakfast cereals, French-fried potatoes, maple syrup, beer, whiskey, sherry, coffee, and cocoa. These products would all be entirely unacceptable without their characteristic color and flavor. In the case of the meat, the protein destruction is limited to the surface and is a small percentage of the total protein. The breakfast cereals with damaged protein are generally eaten with milk which, due to its high lysine content, substantially offsets the damage done to the cereal during processing. The remaining foods that have been browned by heat treatment are not important sources of protein.

Polyunsaturated Fatty Acids

In recent years there has been considerable discussion of still another group of nutrients that are altered by processing. These are the highly unsaturated fatty acids, linoleic, linolenic, and arachidonic acids, sometimes referred to as "essential fatty acids." The indication that a balance between unsaturated and saturated fats is a factor in the prevention of atherosclerosis has thrown the spotlight on an important food process, namely, hydrogenation.

Evidence suggests that there is a desirable ratio of relatively saturated to relatively unsaturated fats in the diet (7). The opposing effects of saturated fatty acids and the polyunsaturated fatty acids on blood cholesterol levels have been demonstrated clinically. All polyunsaturated fats do not show this effect, e.g., tung oil which is highly unsaturated but with conjugated double bonds. The polyunsaturated fatty acids of fish oils do lower blood cholesterol levels although they fail to show other biological effects on which the definition of "essential fatty acids" is based.

Partial hydrogenation of fats may cause a preferential destruction of essential fatty acids. As a result of partial hydrogenation a number of isomers are formed that can be metabolized normally to produce calories but which are inactive in lowering blood cholesterol or in functioning as essential fatty acids. This applies to the cis-trans and trans-trans isomers of linoleic acid as well as to fatty acids with conjugated double bonds.

It is true that processing results in the destruction of polyunsaturated fatty acids in vegetable fats. Until more facts are available, it will be impossible to say whether the practice of hydrogenation is detrimental from the nutritional standpoint. Further research will be needed to establish the desirable ratios of saturated and polyunsaturated fats in the diet.

Improvements in the Nutritive Value of Foods due to Processing

A considerable number of processed foods are fortified with added vitamins. Bread, flour, corn meal, macaroni, and white rice are enriched by the addition of thiamin, ribo-

David B. Hand

flavin, niacin, and iron. They also may contain calcium and vitamin D as optional ingredients. The enrichment of these products has been endorsed by the Food and Nutrition Board of the National Research Council on the grounds that substantial segments of the population require additional supplies of these nutrients. There is also a certain logic in restoring to these foods the vitamins that are removed by milling.

The addition of vitamin D to milk, and iodine to salt are also approved practices. Children have the most critical need for vitamin D, and milk is a logical carrier for this vitamin since it is the most widely used food among children. Iodine deficiency is widespread and salt is the most widely consumed food to which iodine can be added and in which it is stable.

Vitamins are also added to many other foods, not because of a public need but to enhance sales. Addition of vitamins in many of these cases cannot be considered as a nutritional benefit. It would be unfortunate if the addition of vitamins to foods should be extended widely and indiscriminately.

The shift toward the use of processed foods has provided the consumer with a much greater variety of foods independent of season and independent of the distance from the farm to the market. The availability of canned and frozen foods throughout the year insures a steady supply of ascorbic acid and vitamin A which were not so readily obtainable before the development of these processing methods.

REFERENCES

1. Clifcorn, L. E.: Factors Influencing the Vitamin Content of Canned Foods. In: *Advances in Food Research,* vol. 1. New York: Academic Press, 1948, pp. 39-104.
2. Clifcorn, L. E. and Peterson, G. T.: Effect of Canning and

Dehydration on the Nutritive Value of Foods. In: *Handbook of Food and Agriculture,* Ed. F. C. Blanck. New York: Reinhold, 1955, pp. 365-388.

3. Hoffman, C.; Schweitzer, T. R.; and Dalby, G.: The Loss of Thiamin in Bread Baking and Toasting. *Cereal Chem., 17:*737, 1940.

4. Kohman, E. F.: The Preservation of the Nutritive Value of Foods in Processing. *J. Amer. Med. Assoc., 120:*831-838, 1942.

5. Moyer, J. C. and Tressler, D. K.: The Thiamin Content of Fresh and Frozen Vegetables. *Food Research, 8:*58-61, 1943.

6. National Research Council: *Recommended Dietary Allowances.* Washington, D.C.: National Academy of Sciences, Publication No. 589, 1958.

7. National Research Council: *The Role of Dietary Fat in Human Health.* Washington, D.C.: National Academy of Sciences, Publication No. 575, 1958.

8. Pederson, C. S.; Whitcombe, J.; and Robinson, W. B.: The Ascorbic Acid Content of Sauerkraut. *J. Food Tech., 10:* 365-367, 1956.

9. Rice, E. E. and Beuk, J. F.: Effects of Heat on the Nutritive Value of Protein. In: *Advances in Food Research,* vol. 4, New York: Academic Press, 1953, pp. 233-279.

10. Tressler, D. K.: Nutritive Value of Dried and Dehydrated Fruits and Vegetables. *N. Y. State Agric. Exper. Sta. Tech. Bull., 262:*1-44, 1942.

11. Tressler, D. K. and Evers, C. F.: *The Freezing Preservation of Foods.* Westport, Conn.: Avi Publishing Co., 1957.

12. United States Department of Agriculture: Essentials of an Adequate Diet. *Agric. Information Bull., 160,* 1956.

13. Wagner, J. R.; Strong, F. M.; and Elvehjem, C. A.: Nutritive Value of Canned Foods—Effects of Commercial Canning Operation on the Ascorbic Acid, Thiamin, and Niacin Contents of Vegetables. *Ind. Eng. Chem., 39:*985-990, 1947.

THE MEAT INDUSTRY

Herbert E. Robinson, Ph.D.

ALL THE edible meat produced in the United States is consumed every year. There is essentially no carry-over of this product from day to day. The bulk of our beef, veal, lamb, and pork carcasses produced are marketed within four or five days and all move into consumer channels in less than two weeks. The amount of meat which is kept in freezer storage in the United States is negligible. This is not quite so true in the enormous broiler industry where more frozen product is offered for sale. The carry-over here, however, is largely for turkeys which are produced seasonally.

From the standpoint of the meat processor, it is purely a practical matter that leaner meat animals are the most desirable. Apart from any nutritional considerations, it is very difficult to dispose of excess animal fat except at a severe loss, as compared to live animal costs. The day of the fat hog is nearly finished. Each year sees 10 or 15 per cent more of an increase in production of the meat-type animal. It is possible that the next five years will see considerable inroads in the practice of feeding beef cattle to excessive fatness. A second governing factor is the housewife's clearly expressed desire for leaner meat.

This preference for leanness is an obvious commercial expression of practical calorie consciousness by the American public as a whole. It does seem certain that the American homemaker throughout a cross-section of the population is striving to hold down her weight and that of her family, frequently without much co-operation by the latter. Another readily apparent measure of the trend away from calories is the tremendous lowering of the per capita consumption of foods such as flour and potatoes, which are primarily carbohydrate in nature. Eight-to-nine-week-old broilers marketed at about 2.5 pounds, dressed weight, have led the increased consumption of foods which are primarily protein in nature. There is essentially no waste, other than bones, in poultry consumption. The actual waste of fat in much of the meat consumed is sometimes not fully considered in calculations of the average calorie consumption of the individual American, if there is such a thing as an average.

There is no current impression among advertising and commercial people in the food fat field that any of the publicity given to fats as related to atherosclerosis has affected the sale of shortenings, frying or table fats. There was some concern within the industry that premature discussions of unsaturated versus saturated fats as causative factors in vascular corrosion might lead to premature manufacturing changes and misconceptions of fat usage. The dairy industry was quite upset over discussions of the relationship of butter to high cholesterol values. Hydrogenators of cottonseed, soybean, and peanut oils were likewise somewhat concerned over possible changes in manufacturing procedures. It would, of course, be possible to produce culinary and table fats without hydrogenation. At one time, the major baking and frying fat of the southern United States was a compound type of shortening made up of liquid vegetable oils and solid animal fats. This product could be produced and perform satisfactorily in the light of current knowledge, if such were indicated to be in the best interests of human nutrition. It would be extremely difficult to get the same performance for commercial baking purposes, particularly as regards emulsification, creamability, and for cake manufacture from products which are not hydrogenated as at present.

Irradiation and Nutrition

Extensive physiological and nutritional studies which we have conducted on rats and dogs showed no toxic effects of severe irradiation and no unusual nutrient damage as compared to other modes of processing. No significant protein damage was observed.

One of the more recent nutrition ventures for the meat processing industry was the introduction, about ten years ago, of extremely lean, finely ground or comminuted meats for babies. Sales of these products now run into millions of pounds annually, and acceptance by the pediatrician and the housewife has been very good. A considerable number of clinical studies have been made using these products for premature infants and at all stages up to a few years of age. Results, from a nutritional standpoint, appear to justify the use of such products, although it is difficult to prove the point because nearly all infants today receive fortified milk products, specially prepared fruits, vegetables, fortified cereals, as well as meats. Inevitably the question arises whether or not the infant's rapid growth in physical size combined with apparent robust health is a good measure of the eventual health status of the adult. Many of us who have grown up in the tradition of rapidly accelerated growth curves without plateaus for animals are inclined to favor similar progress for the human young. This appears to be a moot question, but one which may deserve considerably more study over human generations than it has been possible to carry out up to this date.

So much has been said in the past year about the ready-to-heat-and-eat or convenience foods that but little further discussion seems in order here. There is no doubt that a rapid change in home cooking procedures is taking place in this country. The American homemaker is reaching for meal preparation times of 45 minutes or less and the food industry is gearing more and more to the production of partially cooked full meals or all the elements thereof, which need only be heated in a hot oven for 35 to 40 minutes to yield appetizing and nourishing food. Nutritional studies in this field are by no means complete, but it is quite evident that the bulk processor, in order to produce the appetite appeal essential to the growth of a convenience food business, must use only the highest-quality raw materials. These, in turn, must be carefully handled to preserve freshness. The partially cooked product must not be overcooked and processing schedules which protect flavor and color also protect the nutrients. Rapid freezing further protects these products and over-all contribution of nutrients to the table is greater than for similar products which are prepared at home from raw ingredients.

The meat industry is nutrition-conscious and is striving to follow the teachings of research for the betterment of the products of that industry.

THE DEVELOPMENT
OF DAIRY PRODUCTS

Leonard A. Maynard, Ph.D.

THE DOMESTICATION of milk-producing animals and the use of milk for food constitute some of the most important nutritional landmarks in the food habits of primitive man. Exactly when dairying began, and how cheese and butter were first made, nobody knows. These developments occurred before the beginning of written history. Over the centuries dairying has developed from the pastoral stage into an intricate, highly commercialized industry.

In the United States dairying produces 19 per cent of the gross national income from agriculture and 15 per cent of the total retail food sales, according to the National Milk Producers Federation (1). In 1957 the farm value of all dairy products was 4.3 billion dollars; the retail value, 9.4 billion dollars; and the marketing bill, 5.1 billion dollars, as reported by the United States Dairy Association (7). Calculations from United States Dairy Association data also show that of the food supply available for human consumption in the United States, dairy products furnish approximately 16 per cent of the calories, 25 per cent of the protein, 76 per cent of the calcium, 48 per cent of the riboflavin, 18 per cent of the vitamin A, 12 per cent of the thiamin, and significant contributions of other minerals and vitamins, notably phosphorus.

The evolution of the dairy industry has been the result of many causes, some of which I wish to discuss, with particular attention to the last hundred years during which developments have been greatly accelerated. First, there is palatability. Early man must have liked milk or he would not have kept milk-producing animals. This liking persisted as urban civilizations developed. Today dairy products are classed among our most palatable foods and the demand for them is accordingly high.

Secondly, present consumer demand results from the comparatively recent knowledge of the outstanding nutritive value of milk and its products. Perhaps primitive man knew that milk was good for him and for his children, but he did not know why. Knowledge of this fact came in later centuries. In the literature one finds many comments on the health value of milk, but the specific knowledge of its nutritive qualities remained unknown until the present time. The landmarks in the development of this knowledge are well known: the discovery of vitamin A in butter, in 1913, with the consequent ushering in of the vitamin era; the recognition of the amino acid basis of protein nutrition and of the high quality of milk protein; the developments in the field of mineral nutrition with respect both to major and trace elements; the discovery that foods could be enriched in vitamin D; and others. Today milk and its products are recognized to be of special importance in the diet as a source of high-quality protein; calcium and phosphorus; riboflavin, vitamin A, and to a lesser degree, other B vitamins; and, through enrichment, vitamin D. These modern nutritional discoveries have contributed greatly to the demand for dairy products and thus to the present status of the dairy industry.

Another essential factor in the development of the industry has been the advances in breeding, feeding, and management which have enabled milk production to keep pace with market demand and lessened the cost of production. These advances have come through research and, in turn, technological advances which have greatly increased the effectiveness of the research results in practice.

Genetic principles have been employed to develop cows of high productive capacity. Artificial insemination is a recent research and technological development which has revolutionized breeding practices. First used on a large scale by the Russians in 1931, artificial breeding is now practiced on nearly 80 per cent of the cows in Denmark, over 50 per cent in England, and around 25 per cent in the United States. The United States figures for 1955 show that 2,210 cows were thus bred artificially per bull, compared with 50, the number a bull can ordinarily breed per year by natural service.

Feeding practices with dairy cows have been greatly improved as a result of the nutrition discoveries of the past 50 years. The recent studies of the physiology of the rumen have been of outstanding significance in showing how more effective advantage can be taken of the roles of rumen microorganisms in breaking down the complex polysaccharides that other species cannot digest, and in synthesizing protein, notably those amino acids which are dietary essentials for other species.

A correlated industrial development of large importance has been the commercial production of urea which is now widely used in ruminant rations as a source of nitrogen for bacterial synthesis into protein. The feed industry, an industrial development of the present century, has played a large role in the extension of improved feeding practices and thus in more economical milk production. The industry which markets various by-product feeds, also supplies the dairy farmer with mixtures compounded to be complete in terms of the nutrients needed to supplement the available home-grown roughage and grain. Many advances in technology have occurred in the production of these manufactured feeds designed to take advantage of the latest findings in nutrition research.

The industrial revolution during the past 50 years has made outstanding contributions to the efficiency of dairy-farm practice by saving labor and speeding up operations through the use of power-driven mechanical equipment. A part of this development has been concerned with general farm machinery, e.g., tractors, tractor-drawn equipment for plowing, seeding, harvesting, threshing, and other operations, silo-filling and emptying devices, barn ventilating systems, hay driers, and many others. In addition, many pieces of specific barn equipment have been developed and come into common use.

The milking machine, invented at the turn of the century, has largely replaced hand-milking. The old system of cooling milk by setting cans in a tank containing ice has been replaced by mechanical coolers and by refrigerated tanks which can hold milk in bulk. In many barns milk drawn from the udder by machine-milking flows via pipeline through filters and coolers directly into the holding tank. In fact, a very recent modification carries the milk directly from the cow, through filters and coolers, to delivery truck tanks for transport to market. These advances have been accompanied by the development of the improved cleaning procedures required to produce milk of appropriate market quality in this pipeline operation.

One of the developments which has proved of outstanding importance to the dairy industry was the invention of the centrifugal cream separator by the Swedish engineer, De Laval. A hand-operated machine was first used on farms in 1890. Today power-driven equipment is found on every farm marketing cream, as well as in commercial creameries and butter plants.

There have been, too, many other improvements in dairy barn operation resulting from the use of mechanical equipment. One particularly welcomed by the farmer is the device which cleans the manure from the stall gutters in one fifth of the time required by the messy hand operation with shovel and wheelbarrow. Prior to the middle of this century, most of the power for dairy barn operations was furnished by internal combustion engines; today they have been replaced in most areas by electricity from centrally stationed generating plants. Electricity both lights the barn and runs its various mechanical devices.

Quantitatively, the most important developments in the dairy industry have been in the marketing field, including the manufacture and marketing of new dairy products. Early records indicate that the first delivery of milk to urban consumers was accomplished by driving the cow through the streets and milking it at each buyer's house. Then came the pushcarts, which gave way to horse-drawn wagons and later to automotive equipment. Distribution in glass bottles first began in 1890; paper containers were introduced in 1929.

The transportation, from far-distant production points, of

an adequate, acceptable, and safe milk supply at a reasonable price has involved many technological developments. It is recorded that milk was first shipped by rail in the United States from Orange County to New York City (60 miles) in a big wooden churn, in 1842. Then, 40-quart cans were used for some 80 years, followed by the refrigerated railroad tank car. In the meantime, automotive transport was developing for milk in cans and later the railroad tank car design was adapted to truck bodies. Today milk rolls from farm to market in refrigerated tank trailers or in bulk tanks loaded into trailers at the farm.

An outstanding landmark in this development of the large-scale, long-distance marketing of milk has been pasteurization. It first came into use in Germany around 1880 for commercial rather than health reasons. At this time, however, the need for a safe milk supply was recognized by public health authorities in the United States and "certified milk," first produced in 1893 in New Jersey, was the initial development. A few milk distributors began offering pasteurized milk in 1902. At this time there was some debate among medical men as to the safety of the product and there was lack of interest or opposition among producers. The question of possible harm to nutritive properties was raised, a question which became much more of an issue in later years as the previously unappreciated special nutritive values of milk were discovered. In 1908 New York City's Sanitary Code was amended to include regulations for pasteurization. The pasteurization of all milk not coming from tuberculin-tested cows was required in Chicago in 1909. As a result of this start, today's milk, marketed in practically all cities and villages, is pasteurized in accordance with regulations set up for the purpose. This development has involved much research on the design and production of equipment and on methods of operation.

Homogenized milk, which was described as early as 1904, was introduced commercially in the United States in 1932, following the solution of many processing problems. Since then its production has continued to grow, particularly as a parallel development with vitamin D fortification and the resultant marketing of vitamin D homogenized milk.

Today approximately 50 per cent of the milk produced in this country is marketed in other forms and in other products than as whole, fluid milk. The arts of butter-and-cheese-making which are more than 5,000 years old, had their industrial beginnings in the United States within the last hundred years. Outstanding among the developments resulting in the present status of the butter industry was the invention of the centrifugal cream separator mentioned above. Another early contribution (1890) of great importance to the industry, and to the production and marketing of milk as well, was the Babcock test for fat—a simple procedure employed routinely in many dairy operations. The machinery and processes used in the large-scale production of butter today, and the many varieties of cheese on the market reflect manifold technological developments which were based on a long series of chemical, bacteriological, and engineering researches.

As milk production centers grew increasingly distant from the market areas, it was natural that attention should be given to the possibility of removing water from milk, to cut down the cost of shipment, and, by appropriate treatment, to provide a better-keeping product. Gail Borden made the primary contribution in inventing a procedure for producing a sweetened condensed milk which was marketed in cans. The product first appeared in 1856 and was widely used during the Civil War. Much research in the field of food engineering, bacteriology, chemistry, and physics, and resulting improvements in technology, are responsible for the product now marketed.

Evaporated milk became available somewhat later and was based on John Meyenberg's process, patented in 1844, of steam-sterilizing unsweetened, condensed milk in cans. Much research was required to overcome certain objectionable features of the early product, and the improvement of equipment and processes has made large contributions to the reduction of costs of production as well. Vitamin D fortifications were instituted by some companies as sources of the vitamin became available. Today practically all the evaporated milk on the market is thus enriched. This is recognized as an important nutritional development for infants and children.

The dry milk industry is a product of the last 50 years, based on machinery invented around the turn of the century and modified later. Many processing and packaging problems were met and overcome in the interest of providing acceptable products of satisfactory keeping quality. The developments have been of greatest significance in the case of the non-fat product, officially termed "dry, non-fat milk." This product has found an increasing market, both as a constituent of other foods and for use by itself, as it became known that it contained the principal nutritive values of the whole product. Its use in bread is a case in point. The introduction of household-size packages inaugurated a home use which is a substantial one. Great impetus has been given to this use by a development of a product which is instantly soluble in water. The production of an equally satisfactory product from whole milk has presented greater problems due to its fat content. Rapid progress is now being made in overcoming these problems.

The story of the ice-cream industry from the hand-cranked freezer of 1846 to the present large-scale, continuous-process freezer represents another triumph in engineering technology and in product development based on physical, biochemical, and bacteriological studies.

I cannot conclude without noting the large contributions made by public health authorities. Their leadership in the adoption of pasteurization has been mentioned. It is interesting to note that the investigations by The New York Academy of Medicine of the now unbelievably bad sanitary conditions in "slop dairies" (dairies where cows were fed distillery refuse) supplying milk to the city sparked the beginning of the sanitary control of milk production and marketing. Today's public health regulations with respect to milk have not only protected the consuming public, but they have resulted in a much larger market for milk. The developments in production, processing, and marketing which I have discussed have been greatly aided thereby.

REFERENCES

1. *Dairy Producer Highlights.* Washington, D. C.: National Milk Federation, 1958.
2. Dillon, John J.: *Seven Decades of Milk.* New York: Orange Judd Publishing Co., 1941.
3. *Journal of Dairy Science.* Golden Jubilee Issue. American Dairy Science Association, June, 1956.

4. O'Reilly, Maurice J.: A Century of Milk. *Borden's Rev. of Nutr. Res., 18:*45-67, 1957.
5. Pirtle, T. R.: *History of the Dairy Industry.* Chicago: Mojonnier Bros., 1926.
6. Shaftel, Norman: A History of the Purification of Milk in New York, or How Now Brown Cow. *N. Y. State J. Med., 58:*911-928, 1958.
7. Supplement for 1957 to *Agriculture Handbook, 62.* Washington, D. C.: United States Dairy Association, 1958.

NUTRITION AND POPULATION PRESSURES

Fairfield Osborn, D.Sc.

I CONFESS AT once that I am hesitant to deal with this subject because I feel that diet and levels of nutrition are not necessarily related to population pressures at all. It is only too evident that what people eat—or, what they would eat if they could afford it—depends upon a number of different circumstances—upon tradition and general culture, upon deep-seated prejudices, upon religious taboos, upon the physical characteristics of a region in which a people lives, and, of course, upon economics. I might interpolate that the word, "economics," as used here, may refer to the economy of any given country or, more specifically, to the economic status of an individual. By and large, the basic cause of hunger (or of the "hidden hunger" of inadequate nutrition) is poverty, and only through the raising of a country's general economic level can it be anticipated that improved nutrition will be gained for an entire population.

Having "cleared the decks," so to speak, through early recognition of the many factors influencing human diet, I now feel free to express the conviction that by far the greatest barrier to the goal of adequate nutrition throughout the world is that of rapid population growth.

Let us go back a minute. Good nutrition is obviously a matter both of the quality and the quantity of food supply. Quality as such is not attainable without quantity. This sounds like a paradox; however, without sufficient quantities and varieties of foods, truly satisfactory levels of nutrition are impossible. The theorist can conjure, if he will, with a fantasy such as the establishment of a series of "world diet banks," from which there would be distributed, through some plan of international pooling of skills and credits, sufficient amounts of *quality* essences to vitaminize the world's undernourished peoples. If only bulk and quantity were not essential to good body health! However, we human beings are forever *animal,* and bulk is an essential to our diet.

Hidden behind the absurdity of such an idea as "world diet banks" and, I might add, the contemporary craze in our country for vitamin pills as a cure for many of our ills, is the inescapable fact that good nutrition will always require an adequate quantity of food supply. For as far as it is sensible to look into the future, we can depend upon only two sources of food—that which can be produced from the land or can be drawn from the oceans.

A tremendous effort, world-wide in scope, has been made since the end of World War II to step up food production. Remarkable results have been achieved, especially in those countries that are sufficiently strong economically to make the necessary investments of capital for equipment, chemical additives, irrigation, etc. Some of the achievements in our own country, for instance, have exceeded the most sanguine expectations, and, no doubt, others will occur in the future. However, the advances made in more fortunate countries, such as our own, are of relatively small importance as far as the world picture is concerned; for it is throughout the world as a whole that the impact of population pressures upon nutrition bears most heavily.

The goal of better distribution of food surpluses from overproducing countries is, of course, one to aim at. Presumably, more effective plans for such distribution can be worked out. In a recent official bulletin of the United Nations Food and Agriculture Organization (October 27, 1958), a significant proposal was launched for a "Free the World from Hunger" year, and the tentative date suggested was 1963. (By the way, present indications are that there will be 200 million *more* people to feed in that year!) One item within the proposed agenda was that of improving distribution between countries having a food surplus and those with a shortage. This idea is all to the good, of course, but we should not be *too* impressed by its possibilities. Every now and then we hear loose talk that our country, with its huge food surpluses, can be the stop-gap to prevent famine elsewhere. To a certain extent, it can. But let us take a specific case—India, for example. In a recent year of shortage India endeavoured to import six million tons of grain. This amount was computed to be enough to feed about 30 million people, or approximately 8 per cent of her total population. As a practical matter, the transport of this amount of grain would require 600 large ships, at least 500 feet in length, with the dispatch of two such ships per day during an entire year. Then there arises the question of who pays—and how. I merely cite these figures to indicate that the distribution of food surpluses is far from a simple matter and that, in any case, existing surpluses in certain countries are at best a minor factor in the world food problem as a whole.

For a time, when the initial reports of the Food and Agriculture Organization were being issued annually, it appeared that the effort to increase food production was more than sufficient to meet the needs of ever-increasing populations. But of late it is becoming evident that the race is not being won and the prospects of winning it are becoming more and more illusory. On November 7th, 1958, B. R. Sen, General Director of the Food and Agriculture Organization, made the following public statement:

> I left Rome last night at the close of the twenty-ninth session of the F.A.O. Council. Before the Council were reports on the world agricultural position up to the end of September. These reports showed that in 1957/58 world agricultural production slipped back and that it would probably move on upward again in 1958/59. I mention these reports in order to say how unsatisfactory is the situation they describe. In the past few years, world agricultural production has increased by about 2 per cent per year. It is certainly better that food production should increase than decrease but the actual rate of increase is quite insignificant. With world population increasing at about 1.6 per cent per year we are merely providing enough food for the increase in population with less than one half per cent extra food each year to improve the diets of hundreds of millions of people who are grossly underfed.
>
> This is the world food problem on its most elemental level. On other levels there is equally little reason for satisfaction.

He concluded by saying that the attainment of reasonably adequate levels of nutrition for hundreds of millions of people remains a distant if not a receding prospect. I might add that when Mr. Sen uses the phrase, "hundreds of millions of people," he is speaking cautiously because it is generally recognized, I think, that at least half of the world's people are definitely undernourished, and this means more than a billion human beings.

"For the record," I would like to point out that the increase in world populations of more than 800 million people since 1900 represents a figure greater than the combined populations of Europe, Africa, and the Western Hemisphere in that year. During the last few years the rate of increase was so great that there are approximately 8 million additional people on the earth every 75 days. The last United Nations official report indicates an even higher rate, citing a current increase of approximately 47 million a year. The truth is, we are witnessing a fantastic evolution in human society and one that, if long continued, will prove intolerable for social and political welfare in general and for nutritional standards in particular.

There is another relevant aspect of this situation which cannot be overlooked. Let us assume that, despite the formidable obstacles in the way, nutritional standards as such are slowly and steadily being improved throughout the world. This may indeed be happening because of the far-flung work of such organizations as the United Nations World Health Organization, the Food and Agriculture Organization, independent groups and foundations, and the gradual education of people concerning the relationship of diet to health. Yet, the consequence of such an improvement in dietary standards would be reflected in a reduction of infant and childhood mortality and in increase in life span or, alternately expressed, a reduction of the death rate. If it be granted that rapid population growth and the pressures it engenders are actually a major obstacle to better nutrition, the net effect of all our efforts would be to compound the problem and make the ultimate goal more remote. Here indeed the nutritionist faces a dilemma.

Are these facts and considerations of a kind that can be evaded by those engaged in the movement for better nutrition? The question is not a theoretical one. Even though there may be a variance of opinion as to the degree to which nutrition and population pressures are related, surely it cannot be denied that the relationship exists.

No purpose is single. One's mind turns to the remarkable series of achievements in the medical world, all of which were "single-purpose" in their aim, such as the eradication of yellow fever and the control of malaria, tuberculosis, and other ravaging diseases. Each achievement in itself added immeasurably to human welfare. Yet the fact remains that these and other public health measures have proven to be the root cause of new problems resulting from the explosive increase in populations. Such a sequence of events is illustrative of the irony of many of our efforts, but human society has passed the point where it can shrug its shoulders and claim it is not responsible for the ultimate consequences of its actions. The final question still remains: If we gain the benefits derived from constant improvements in public health measures, including better nutrition, must we not take adequate steps to prevent the ultimately disastrous consequences of ever-increasing populations? No scientist or professional man has any justification for being solely "single-purpose"—which is next akin to working in a vacuum—nor can he, with any real satisfaction to himself, escape a social responsibility for the results of his actions.

HEALTH IN THE PERSPECTIVE
OF NUTRITION

W. Henry Sebrell, Jr., M.D.

ONE OF the greatest events in the history of man was his change from food gatherer and hunter to food cultivator and producer. As long as man had to spend most of his time seeking food as he needed it, with alternate periods of gluttony and fasting, he had no opportunity to become civilized. Many primitive peoples today still undergo these alternate periods. A successful hunt requires that the kill be eaten at once, followed by fasting until the conclusion of another successful hunt.

It must have been a woman, probably some mother, who first stored some roots, nuts, or seeds to prevent her family from starving. Some of these seeds or tubers probably sprouted in the cave and provided the clue to the cultivation of crops for food. Man's reliance on the cultivation of the seeds from the grasses for his survival has not changed from that day to this.

Man has engaged in war and conflict since the dawn of history, much of it related to his need for food or for land on which to produce food. Repeated cultivation of grain crops exhausts the soil which in primitive societies is likely to be more rapidly depleted by the practice of burning the fields, and the failure to use fertilizer. This means that in a few years the family or the tribe must move to new land. If the land is already in use, conflict is apt to result.

War, in spite of its frequent origin in the need for food, always produces famine. The thought of war usually calls to mind St. John's vision of the Four Horsemen of the Apocalypse. Most of us think only of the horse and the figure of war carrying a bow, or of the pale horse with its figure of death. We should also remember that there was a black horse with a figure which carried a balance. This is the figure of famine, and the voice said to St. John in connection with this figure, "A measure of wheat for a penny, and three measures of barley for a penny, and see thou hurt not the oil and wine." There have been many interpretations of the meaning of these words. However, to a nutritionist they suggest, among other things, that the higher price for wheat may be a recognition of its greater nutritive value.

This relation between war and famine was most forcefully brought out in World War II when famine probably affected more people than at any other time in the world's history. A large part of the world's population lived under a system of food rationing. Thousands died of starvation and at the end of the war it required careful distribution of the available food in the world in order to prevent a public health catastrophe greater than any of the great plagues.

In ancient wars, and in the sieges of the fortified cities of the Middle Ages, it was famine and probably scurvy as well as other deficiency diseases which often led to capitulation. Deficiency diseases no doubt occurred during the long marches of the Roman armies and among the Crusaders, just as scurvy appeared among sailors as soon as prolonged ocean voyages began after Columbus.

In spite of the folklore which accumulated through the centuries, for example, the people's knowledge in Scotland of the value of cods' heads in rickets, and medical observations such as Casal's description of pellagra or Lind's discovery of the value of citrus fruit juice in scurvy, there was no knowledge of the use of food in the body until Lavoisier and Laplace showed that respiration was a kind of combustion. Nor was there general understanding of the relation of the chemistry of the body to food and nutrition except for famine and starvation until the discovery of the accessory food factors.

The deficiency disease concept of beriberi was proposed by Grijns in 1901 in his interpretation of Eijkman's studies on experimental beriberi. In 1887, Takaki in the Japanese navy had demonstrated that beriberi could be prevented by unpolished rice.

Man has pounded and ground his grain since earliest times primarily to enable him to store it successfully but also to make it more edible and of wider usefulness. In ancient Rome dark bread was regarded as food fit only for slaves and the preference for refined cereal grains such as polished rice and white flour persists throughout the world today. Thus unpolished rice, although it will prevent beriberi, has never been willingly accepted, and Takaki's demonstration and the findings of Eijkman and Grijns failed to solve the beriberi problem.

The great plagues of the Middle Ages in which sickness and death were spread by contagion focused medical attention on fumigation, quarantine, and isolation. The development of bacteriology after Pasteur with its microscopic organisms, its vaccines, and immunizations so firmly established the idea in the medical mind that all diseases were caused by positive agents of some kind that even Hopkins' work did not bring medical attention to the point that disease might be caused by an absence of something. This idea was not widely appreciated until Funk wrote his book in 1912 and coined the word, "vitamine" which started the era of the deficiency diseases. We have now reached the point where it is unlikely that we will find many more vitamins, as we define them today, essential for man's health. Nutrition research has already turned to new fields, seeking the details of the metabolic processes by which foods are converted into energy and tissues. This has brought forth a new concept, new, that is, to today's world—that too much food produces a form of malnutrition that can have serious consequences. Hippocrates and Galen cautioned against overeating and it has been repeatedly stated since the earliest times that gluttony is unhealthy. Even Shakespeare *(Love's Labour's Lost)* says, "Fat paunches have lean pates and dainty bits make rich the ribs, but bankrupt quite the wits."

Our present public health efforts to prevent and control obesity upset one of the basic social concepts of our civilization—that a well-filled stomach is a manifestation of success in the world, good health, and good fellowship. If I may again refer to Shakespeare *(Julius Caesar)*, he says: "Would he were fatter (but I fear him not:—yet) if my name were liable to fear I do not know the man I should avoid so soon as that spare Cassius." It is interesting to see the psychological struggle going on today as everyone tries to avoid accepting the facts.

Today the health of most of the world is affected by malnutrition. More than half the world's population suffers from a deficiency in nutrients of one kind or another; much of the remainder is affected by gluttony and obesity.

The rapidly increasing world's population makes malnutrition the most urgent of all the world's health problems. In 1900 the world's population was 1600 million; in 1958 it was 2,500 million, an increase of 900 million. This increase is more than the population of Europe, Africa, and the Western hemisphere together in 1900. The rate of increase today is 4,000 per hour or 8 million each 75 days. The United States will add 100 million by 1980 if the present rate continues. If the world's population continues to increase at this rate, it is obvious that nutritional problems will become increasingly important and more difficult to solve. However, if we would make good use of the nutritional knowledge we have today, we could make the earth support a very great many more people in adequate nutrition. We must supply the best nutrition to as many people as we can for as long as we can.

At the present time we are making relatively little effort to make the best use of the food the world produces. In many technically underdeveloped areas with serious and widespread malnutrition much food is lost through lack of knowledge and facilities for canning, dehydrating, and preserving food and more is lost through lack of proper storage resulting in rodent and insect damage and spoilage from the weather. Land is not fertilized, irrigation facilities are lacking, and primitive methods of planting, cultivating, and harvesting result in low yields; in this country, with its malnutrition from overeating, we have increasing crop surpluses and large quantities of food we cannot use. It was the hope of Lord John Boyd Orr, the first director of the Food and Agriculture Organization, that this organization would be able to assist in achieving a better distribution of the world's food supply, but his hopes have not been realized. If it is ever accomplished through the United Nations, that organization must be strengthened considerably. The distribution of surplus food from this country to an underdeveloped country is only a temporary relief measure and is no permanent answer to the problem. What malnourished people really need is friendly, competent, technical help to show them how to help themselves. They want to learn how to feed themselves and how to maintain their health within their own economic and agricultural resources. They want health and nutrition education and this is what we must give them if we are to develop a practical, successful public health nutrition program for the world. It can be done. However, there is no general solution. Each country must be studied in the light of its agricultural resources, its food habits, its nutritional problems, its cultural background, and its economic problems in order to determine what changes in the food supply are needed and what can be done both for immediate relief and for long-range development. It is only by such methods that the best solutions can be found.

Although we still have widespread deficiency diseases such as beriberi, pellagra, rickets, xerophthalmia, and goiter in many areas, the really important killer of children is kwashiorkor or protein malnutrition, and much research on the many problems in connection with this disease is underway. The greatest real progress is being made with the assistance of a grant from the Rockefeller Foundation to the National Research Council for the purpose of supporting an international research program designed to secure the fundamental knowledge necessary to find practical ways of meeting the protein needs of the large areas of the world where the production of food animals and milk is impracticable. This program, by its international nature, has resulted in improved programs in the United Nations agencies and in better exchange of information and ideas between research workers in widely separated areas. The research has shown that it is possible to obtain protein adequacy in children and recovery from kwashiorkor with mixtures of foods entirely from plant sources. These studies are being continued with a variety of mixtures of readily available foods suited to those parts of the world where the problem is greatest.

Senator Lister Hill has introduced a bill with a proposed appropriation of 50 million dollars to support international medical research. This proposal has received much favorable comment and, if enacted into law, could be a very potent factor in improving nutrition and health throughout the world.

Senator Hubert Humphrey recently suggested that we should have an International Health Year; this also could have important results in nutrition. However, plans such as these must include a consideration of the economic and social factors which govern the production and distribution of food as related to health and recognize that malnutrition is also rooted in ignorance and illiteracy.

If any program is to succeed, one of the most urgent needs is for technically trained personnel who can understand the problems and guide the programs locally. There is a world-wide shortage of such people.

In the newly active Institute of Nutrition Sciences at Columbia University we are initiating a program designed especially for physicians from underdeveloped areas. They are to be given a broad understanding of food production, food distribution, food technology, the nutritive values of food, malnutrition, and public health nutrition so that they can return home and be teachers and leaders of national programs along the best and most practical lines.

What does the trend toward studies of well-being and the growth of physiology indicate for the future? We are now in an era of research popularity for enzyme systems, inherited metabolic defects, and the details of the hormone control of the utilization of nutrients and fat metabolism. In this country, medical research on lipid metabolism and the effects of gluttony is popular. It appears that an area of increasing popularity will be that of the study of the balance of nutrients for optimum health. It is already evident that the interrelationship between nutrients is going to be a very complex and difficult area of research. It will require many years of hard work to work out the optimum relations between the various amino acids, the mineral elements, the control of alternate metabolic pathways, and varying quantities of the vitamins and hormones.

There will be no lack of nutritional problems in these fundamental areas, while the practical problems of making the best use of the world's food supply for health will be just as complex and perhaps even more important to our welfare.

Schools and theories in public health and health education are already well on the road to placing public health on a physiological rather than a morbidity basis. We now talk about the prevention of accidents of heart disease and of cancer, but we still think of obesity in terms of reducing diets after it has occurred, rather than the prevention of obesity. We talk about correcting bad food habits in children rather than instilling good ones. In spite of the foundations of good health being laid in our increasing knowledge of the chemistry of the body and its relation to nutrition, most of our medical schools are still turning out doctors who have had little or no instruction in nutrition. We still have a long way to go.

IMPLEMENTING NUTRITION CONCEPTS IN MEDICINE AND PUBLIC HEALTH

Fredrick J. Stare, M.D., Ph.D.

IN CONSIDERING the problems of teaching nutrition in schools of medicine and public health, we must begin by asking two questions: How does one motivate students in these professions to become interested in nutrition? and, before that can be done, how does one motivate deans and other administrative officials to provide the time and, of course, the funds to attempt the motivation?

Before I discuss the implementation of nutrition in these professional schools, I should like to state that I also think it important to implement nutrition concepts in many non-scientific areas of which I will simply suggest three.

1. *The early elementary grades.* Why not introduce sound nutritional concepts into reading, writing and arithmetic and hence help formulate better food habits? We have done some research in this area, and currently Dr. Jacobson at Teachers College, Columbia University, is doing similar studies.

2. *Schoolteachers.* Schoolteachers are responsible for teaching schoolchildren and they, too, should know some nutrition. My associates, Dr. Jean Mayer and Miss Patricia Stef-

anik, currently have some experimental studies in this field under way at Sargent College in Boston, a teacher-training institution.

3. *Technical assistance programs of our government.* It is shameful the way such programs have avoided nutrition, one of the most important global health problems.

In the past ten or twelve years three papers have come from the Department of Nutrition at Harvard University on the general subject of teaching nutrition in medicine and public health (1, 2, 3). These papers have been quite specific, and the principles presented in them still stand. Most of what I shall discuss here has been taken from them.

Nutrition is such a broad and important subject in health that all physicians should have some awareness of the subject (1). Professional training in nutrition for the physician is important and should include some or all of the following:

1. Basic and historical information on the science of nutrition, in perspective to the other sciences.

2. Applications of nutrition to medical and health problems.

3. An account of recent research in nutrition as it applies to medicine and public health with some evaluation of present and future problems.

4. The economic, social, and psychologic aspects of nutrition.

Professional training in nutrition should be given by each of the following general procedures:

1. Instruction in nutrition should be included in each of the years of medical education.

2. Most of this instruction should be incorporated in standard courses of the curriculum.

3. Special courses in various phases of nutrition should

be available for those students desiring to know more about nutrition.

The same general principles apply to students in schools of public health (2) except that, usually, these students are older, they have been out of medical or nursing school for a variable period, and they may have forgotten what little they had learned about nutrition. Thus, special courses are needed to teach the basic principles of modern nutrition in schools of public health, for without an accurate understanding of principles and facts it is a little hard to have intelligent applications. This only applies to those who are nutritionists. Administrative personnel in public health and those in ancillary sciences must learn the many ways that modern nutrition enters into public health problems and what they can expect from a trained nutritionist.

Three years ago Dr. Van Itallie and I prepared a paper (3) in which we pointed out that the teaching of nutrition to students in the health sciences, namely, medicine, dental medicine, and public health, should still be a matter of concern to educators in these fields. Although interest in this problem undoubtedly reflects awareness of the increasing importance of nutrition in medicine and related fields, the lack of action suggests that there remains considerable uncertainty about the place nutrition should occupy in the curriculum.

Much of the uncertainty about nutrition appears to result from lack of a clear conception of what it encompasses and of the precise relevance of this subject to the health professions. In a way, it is not surprising that such an indeterminate picture has evolved; nutrition as a subject is not readily categorized.

A useful way of approaching the problem of characterizing

nutrition is to examine its orientation. Just as microbiology has principally to do with microorganisms, particularly as they affect health, so is nutrition concerned with food and its constituents, the nutrients—water, protein, fat, carbohydrate, vitamins, and minerals—as they relate to health. Thus, all considerations which are relevant to nutrients are, by extension, relevant to nutrition.

Because of its orientation to the nutrients in a very broad sense, the territory of nutrition seems on casual inspection to be almost limitless. However, this is only an appearance. If a distinction is made between the core of nutrition and its many ramifications, the subject is not unwieldy.

Like other sciences, nutrition can be divided into two general areas: "basic" nutrition and "applied" nutrition. Basic nutrition is concerned primarily with the metabolic facts of nutrition and constitutes the core of the subject; applied nutrition has to do with the use of nutritional knowledge in dietetics, medicine, dental medicine, and public health.

For some reason, the identity of basic nutrition has remained obscure. While everyone knows that a bacteriologist is not necessarily a clinician, no satisfactory term exists to distinguish the investigator doing nutritional research from the public health nutritionist whose knowledge of nutrition is limited to certain concepts of applied nutrition. Both may be called nutritionists. It does not seem to be generally appreciated that there is a body of knowledge about nutrition which can be readily identified as its foundation, and upon which are based many of the principles which guide the practice of nutrition. Thus, while the distinction between the basic and applied aspects of most other sciences appears to have been clearly defined, this has not been the case in nutrition. Nutrition has not yet found a home among the basic medical sciences.

When we consider the basic sciences which the medical and dental curriculums share, it is immediately evident that such subjects as biochemistry, bacteriology, pharmacology, and physiology—to mention a few—all have important nutritional aspects. For example, nutrition and biochemistry are so intimately related that it is frequently difficult to distinguish one from the other. The nutritional characteristics of bacteria are of enormous interest to microbiologists; nutritional disorders form a significant fraction of the subject matter of pathology; pharmacology textbooks contain extensive discussions about the use of vitamins, other nutrients, and anti-nutrients in therapeutics. Recital of the many relationships between nutrition and the basic medical sciences could be an endless affair.

In the clinical subjects it is much the same story. One cannot discuss such subjects as diabetes, atherosclerosis, or liver disease without becoming involved in nutritional considerations.

In the clinic a problem involving treatment of a cardiac arrhythmia has potential continuity with physiology and pharmacology. On the other hand, a difficult problem in parenteral nutrition, or nutritional considerations in coronary disease, frequently cannot be related to any preclinical course, since basic nutrition currently is not taught as a formal preclinical subject.

A misconception that exists among many who guide the educational destinies of our medical and health schools should be examined. Because of the wide publicity which vitamins have received, and because of the dramatic nature of full-blown scurvy, beriberi, pellagra, and rickets, nutrition has become identified in the minds of many physicians and health leaders primarily with the classic deficiency states—states which have largely disappeared from this country.

We all know that much more is involved, but it has not been sufficiently appreciated that nutrition is concerned with atherosclerosis, obesity, hypertension, liver disease, problems of supportive care, and a list of other disorders too long to mention.

In thinking about nutrition and its relationship to medicine, one finds it useful to distinguish between disorders in whch the nutritional environment (usually the diet) is at fault, and disorders in which the environment is not at fault, that is, the individual has become malnourished because of a disease which prevents nutrients from getting to the cells in effective amounts. This second type of malnutrition is often called "conditioned malnutrition."

Upon reflection it will be realized that any disorder which interferes with the ingestion, digestion, assimilation, transport, storage, utilization, or excretion of a nutrient may be responsible for a form of conditioned malnutrition. Since a disordered state of nutrition occurs to a varying degree in almost all forms of disease, the importance of nutrition in medicine and public health would be difficult to exaggerate.

At the risk of being a little brash, I am tempted to say that lack of funds is the main reason we have so little teaching of nutrition today in most of our medical schools and schools of public health. If there were a few endowed "chairs of nutrition," and if sums were available so good people could be employed at good salaries with the specific understanding that their main teaching job was to teach nutrition, I think the deans and other administrative officials would suddenly become very co-operative.

Fredrick J. Stare

The new teaching grants of the National Institutes of Health in the general medical sciences may prove to be a catalytic step in that direction.

REFERENCES

1. Stare, F. J.: Teaching nutrition to medical students. *J. Amer. Dietetic Assoc., 25*:7, 585, 1949.
2. Stare, F. J.: Training physicians in public health nutrition. *Amer. J. Public Health, 39*:5, 1949.
3. Van Itallie, T. B. and Stare, F. J.: Nutrition and the curriculum. *J. Dental Ed., 20*:292-301, 1956.

TOWARD A PHILOSOPHY
FOR NUTRITION

Howard A. Schneider, Ph.D.

THE SCIENCE of nutrition has neighbors on all sides—anthropology, history, medical theory and industrial technology. Recognition of nutrition's setting enlarges our ideas and whets our ambition. Much has been accomplished; much is being done; and now, with whetted hopes, what can we expect from the future?

Sophisticated scientists realize that we have no tea leaves to read, nor any crystal ball, clouded or clear, in which to peer. However, an examination of the philosophical foundations of the science can give us some clue to how well we have built, and how much more weight the foundation is prepared to bear. In a word, we need a philosophy.

I intend to present such a philosophy, one which I believe can carry us to new efforts. In constructing it, I propose to take full advantage of our historical position and appropriate what I need from what has gone before. Like any philosophy, this one will reflect some of my own prejudices and must come under some criticism. In fact, I am only opening a discussion that I hope will continue in a lively fashion for some time to come and in which the whole nutritional community will participate.

Howard A. Schneider

The science of nutrition, I believe, can aspire to accomplishments greater than the enterprises which now engage us. Anyone who lived through the exciting days (for nutrition) of the 1930's and early 1940's knows that those were days when nutrition answered loudly and clearly some of the questions asked of it. Those questions—how to cure and prevent scurvy, rickets, pellagra, beriberi, and some of the anemias—have been answered, and answered forever! Historians of medicine will not overlook the fact that those answers have proved to be uniquely "nibble-proof"; they have not been nibbled away by subsequent doubt, nor have they entered into any cycle of popularity, disfavor, and restoration. But, I submit, the questions have changed. Now we are asked, "What is the relation of nutrition to arteriosclerosis, to mental health, to cancer, to hypertension, and resistance to disease?" These are questions of a different kind and I think all of us are staggered by their weight and complexity. There is much to suggest that nutrition has a great deal to do with these matters, and many of us feel that in these concerns nutrition is confronted with fresh unknowns and questions of considerable theoretical consequence.

How has all this come about? The answer is to be found in the metaphysical foundations of our science. There is nothing wrong with our metaphysical base, but I do believe we have never really analyzed it or understood its consequences.

The question now arises, "Why was the period of revolutionary advance (1915-1945) attended by such remarkable accomplishments?" Before we can understand the present situation, we must answer that question. Fortunately for us, one man who had a philosophic grasp of this earlier period and who was one of its most important leaders, Dr. E. V. McCollum, is also a contributor to this volume. In his essay (3) he tells us what happened in those years. I should like to analyze those events a bit further.

I have mentioned above a metaphysic underlying nutrition. By a metaphysic I mean, in Collingwood's definition, the analysis, in an historical context, of the absolute presuppositions which are made in the course of a piece of thinking. What were the absolute presuppositions which were at the base of the science of modern nutrition? I believe there was only one in 1915 that needs our present attention. It was the unique presupposition that current problems would find their solution by an appeal to the natural world for new and unknown *qualitative* entities rather than to chemical analysis for more precise *quantitative* relations between known entities. The consequences that flowed from this presupposition are well known and need not be repeated here. The nutritional discoveries of the 1930's and early 1940's can be regarded as the climax of the logical efficacy of the McCollum metaphysic of a quarter of a century earlier.

There is one other consequence I wish to examine before we ask whether the earlier presupposition is efficacious today, in 1959. This other consequence, I believe, sheds some light on the proper place of nutrition among the life sciences. Does this seem a trivial objective? One might say, "What does 'place' matter? Content is what's important!" Obviously, the content of a science is important. But I suggest that content reflects the place a science occupies with respect to other sciences as they, in turn, are influenced by it. To be specific, by an historical development based on an early mutual concern with energetics, nutrition laboratories are usually found in biochemistry departments. This association was undoubtedly fruitful and, I think, was cemented and perhaps made unduly rigid by the finding that some vitamins were functional as coenzymes. The continued expansion and development of biochemistry has, however, begun to restrict the science of nutrition, and there is good prospect that nutrition may lose its identity and wind up as a side show in the biochemical circus. This, I believe, would be bad for nutrition, bad for biochemistry, and bad for science.

Where then do we belong? To answer that I must go back about 100 years.

The last great synthesis in biology came from the mind of Charles Darwin in his *On the Origin of Species by Means of Natural Selection,* published in November, 1859. Ever since then we have had to account for the biological world in terms of the process of change. As biologists we learn to live with change. In the first edition Darwin began the first chapter with the heading, "Variation under Domestication." It is not without significance, I think, that in the third sentence on this opening page Darwin spoke of food, ". . . variability may be partly connected with excess of food" (1). How intimately then is nutrition enmeshed with the great overriding problem of biology, the evolution of species!

It would be an interesting task of scholarship to go on through *The Origin* and examine the role Darwin assigns to food, but this would lead us away from the question, "Where do we belong?" It seems to me that a clear answer can be found in the historical consequences of Darwinism. Of these there were two: A science of genetics which had its birth in 1900 with the rediscovery of Mendel's work, and a science of ecology, the study of the mutual interactions of organisms and their environment. The word, "ecology" was coined by the German biologist Ernst Haeckel, Darwin's friend, in 1869. However, as a distinct field of biology, its history, too, begins about 1900.

Food is one of the fundamental preoccupations of modern ecology, and it is here that I believe we can find the answer to our question. Nutrition, I believe, finds its place in the life sciences in the grand design of ecology, for ecology will find in nutrition the science *par excellence.* Our work as nutritionists is to delineate, in all its details, that part of the environment which is consumed. Operationally, we must busy ourselves with all that goes into the mouth and is swallowed, and technically we must be prepared to continue to probe the natural world of the eatable. We must look in two directions: toward the outer world whence comes nutrient, and toward the inner world wherein we measure nurture. Our primary task as nutritional scientists should be the delineation of the structure of the outer nutritional environment. I think we can expect that it will have, like all structure, both gross and fine aspects. But, I must temporarily defer discussion of our approach to that structure until I have dealt once more with the historical record of nutrition and its metaphysical lesson for us.

Every student of nutrition will be eternally grateful to McCollum for his fascinating book, *A History of Nutrition* (2). Here is a mine to be worked for years to come. I hope I do him no injustice if I set forth here a synopsis of what I think are the three important eras in the history of nutrition: (a) the naturalistic era of 400 B.C. to 1750 A.D.; (b) the

229

chemicoanalytical era, 1750 to 1900; and (c) the biological era, 1900 to present. These three eras had three different sets of absolute presuppositions. The naturalistic era supposed that the material basis of nutrition rested on one item, the "nutrient." Foods varied in their content and capacity to supply this nutrient. The chemicoanalytical era supposed something less simple and presupposed that there were four items worth talking about: fat, protein, carbohydrate, and minerals. The biological era, under the leadership of Mc-Collum, introduced an amplified metaphysic by supposing that there were, beyond the four above, additional and qualitatively new items which had to be considered. This led to the recognition of the vitamins and some of the minerals required in minute amounts. The McCollum metaphysic is still the basis of our present understanding.

In the three eras of historical nutrition it is evident that the absolute presuppositions have gone from one, to four, to many. And with this progression the focus on dimensions of structure of the nutritional environment has gone from macro to micro, from gross to fine. The historical and metaphysical trend is thus so evident that I need not labor it. By its insight, I believe we can better understand our task and mission.

Clearly, our approach to nutritional investigation must now be addressed to the problem of the ever finer structure of the nutritional environment. This trend toward finer structure is clearly evident in many other fields of science, e.g., physics, genetics, and morphology. To do this we need not change the McCollum metaphysic. It will serve us for a long time to come. But, it seems to me, its returns have slowed. Why? Clearly because it has run into the demand for increased powers of resolution. Just as the electron microscope advanced the study of fine structure in morphology over that comprehended by the light microscope, just so do we need to advance our study of the fine structure of the nutritional environment. Our limitations here are not biochemical. Biochemistry has improved its processes of chemical resolution to a fantastic degree, and if we are frustrated it is not for biochemical techniques. We can better appreciate our difficulties if we remember that nutrition is logically and systematically a part of ecology. In ecology we recognize that environmental effects are operative within the limits of a genetic framework. *Here* is where our solution lies. Our problems in the fine structure of the nutritional environment are soluble in terms of a rapprochement with the science of genetics. The details of how this rapprochement should and can be effected need not concern us here. The important point to recognize is that by a more sophisticated use of genetics we will be able to increase the sensitivity and plasticity of our nutritional models, in terms of the specific characters with which we are now interested in dealing, and thereby be enabled to continue that unending probing of the natural nutritional environment which is our mission, our task, and our goal.

In brief, then, a philosophy for nutrition in my view should look toward a science of, not physiology or biochemistry, but ecology. And in that ecological context its metaphysic still resides in the presupposition of an ever-increasing list of qualitatively new and distinct entities which are part of the rich fabric of the nutritional environment. To detect these new items I have argued that we must, through use of modern genetics, improve the sensitivity of our biological

Howard A. Schneider

models. This will increase our powers of resolution and we can continue our historical task and mission: the delineation of the fine structure of the environment.

REFERENCES

1. Darwin, Charles: *On the Origin of Species by Means of Natural Selection*. London: Watts & Co., 1859.
2. McCollum, Elmer V.: *A History of Nutrition*. Boston: Houghton Mifflin, 1957.
3. McCollum, Elmer V.: From Hopkins to the Present. *This Volume*, pp. 111-142.

THE INFLUENCE OF HORMONES
ON METABOLIC DEMANDS
AND SUBSEQUENT
ALTERATIONS
IN NUTRITIONAL REQUIREMENTS

Herbert Pollack, M.D.

IT IS easier in clinical medicine to measure the total effect of hormones rather than their function or their mode of action. The mode of action remains a mystery in many cases; the function is inferred by measuring the specific effects and by other associated phenomena in the intact human or the experimental animal.

Hormones are the secretions of the endocrine glands. They vary in type and function in the body. As a group, they have many things in common, particularly from the physiological point of view. Their probable functions are to maintain, or help to maintain the homeostatic mechanisms of the body. They may do this by their ability to help organs and cells to function in a co-ordinated manner. The hormones may serve as the trigger mechanism which sets off a reaction in the direction, or at the rate, which is most economical for the body's functioning.

The gross relationships of hormones to nutrition are matters of everyday experience in clinical medicine. The most striking is the immediate effect of insulin on the utilization of food. Another is the well-known influence of thyroxin—the secretion of the thyroid gland—on speeding up the burning of food and the less well-known one, the lowering of blood cholesterol.

In the matter of the much-debated subject of calcium requirements and utilization, the complex interrelationship of vitamins, hormones, and nutrition can be demonstrated. Parathyroid hormone is an important substance in the maintenance of normal serum calcium concentration. When there is a deficiency of this hormone, the state of hypoparathyroidism, the serum calcium-raising effect can be achieved by the administration of substances with vitamin D activity. In older people, particularly in women after the menopause, a condition known as osteoporosis may develop. This is a loss of calcium from the bones, and it cannot be cured by feeding calcium salts. It is related to the changes in sex hormones. These probably mediate their action on calcium metabolism through their influence on protein metabolism. Thus the nutritionist who attempts to define calcium dietary requirements in the adult will have a difficult problem. The effective amount of calcium in the diet will depend on sex hormone activity, muscular activity, adequacy of protein nutrition, amount of sunlight, state of the kidney function, and activity of the parathyroid gland.

The amount and type of food one eats can influence the hormone activities as well as the converse. This hormone activity can influence the state of nutrition. Meals containing disproportionately large amounts of free sugars can cause an oversecretion of insulin. This in turn can bring about a reactive hypoglycemia which results in increased appetite and, eventually, a form of obesity.

The state of nutrition has a profound influence on hormone secretions and activities. Thus, in emaciation syndromes, there are these manifestations: sterility in the male, amenorrhea in the female, and hypopituitarism in general.

From a metabolic point of view, the hormones can be divided into two categories: the anabolic and the catabolic. Total metabolism of the body is the difference between the anabolic, or building-up processes, and the catabolic, or breaking-down processes. Insulin is probably the most powerful of the anabolic hormones known. Thyroxin, the secretion of the thyroid gland, is a catabolic hormone, or one that speeds up the burning up or destruction of tissues. It is known that insulin is secreted by the pancreas. The removal of the pancreas results in a metabolic disorder known as diabetes mellitus. Practically all the changes in metabolism that occur in diabetes are related to the consequent impaired ability of the body to burn or store sugar. It can be shown definitely that while insulin is not absolutely essential, the sugar disposal is facilitated by the presence of insulin. There is a secondary effect of carbohydrate metabolism on protein metabolism which is extremely important. The interrelationships of these physiological functions is the basis for an understanding of the homeostatic mechanisms.

It is almost impossible to discuss one phase of metabolism without simultaneously considering other phases. A failure of glucose disposal by oxidation or storage leads to an increased catabolism, or breakdown, of body proteins which, in turn, leads to certain disturbances in the vitamin and mineral balances. Not only does this disturbance in carbohydrate metabolism influence proteins, but it is also related directly to fat metabolism. It has been demonstrated many times that fat is formed directly and quantitatively from glucose. The most important path of utilization of sugar is through fat synthesis. Therefore the lack of insulin interferes with lipogenesis, and the administration of insulin speeds up fat formation from carbohydrate. The hormone insulin enables sugar to enter into the tissues freely, but without necessarily having any influence on the subsequent enzymatic activities. This outflow of glucose can explain the decreased concentration of sugar in the blood resulting in increases in the manufacture of glycogen, the burning of sugars, and the formation of fats, and in the so-called sparing of the proteins, the decrease in the phosphorous content of the blood, and, subsequently, of urine, and in changes in the potassium concentration of the blood. All of these are related to the intermediary glucose metabolic factors.

Each hormone has its counterhormone, or the slowing-up hormone. One finds an interrelationship between insulin and the hormones of the anterior pituitary. Since the anterior pituitary controls the thyroid and the adrenal cortex, then, obviously there are interrelationships between these opposing hormones and insulin. These have at times been called antagonists. However they are not, strictly speaking, antagonistic; they are merely opposite in action. Removal of the primary effect, or primary location, of the hormonal activity. results in an extreme sensitivity to insulin. The opposing actions do not necessarily take place at the point of the primary effect, or primary location, of the hormonal activity. One can separate this type of activity, particularly in the case of the pituitary and the adrenal-cortical secretions. The latter prevent, to some extent, the uptake of glucose by the muscles, but they do not depress the rate of glucose oxidation in the body (a separation of the effects of the hormone and the counterhormone).

An interesting hypothesis has been presented along this line to which the feedback principle applies. If, for example, the release of some of the pituitary hormones were controlled by the amount of glucose which enters the cells of the pituitary gland, certain effects would be possible. When the inflow of glucose is large, this might prevent the release of the hormones. If the inflow of glucose were reduced, this would lead to the liberation of the hormone. Thus insulin would be said to control the amount of the opposing-action hormones by its own activity at the site of the production of the opposing hormone. This type of explanation can be used to account for a great many changes that occur in a complex system such as the mammalian organism.

Hypersensitivity to a hormone is just as dangerous to the economy of the body as resistance or insensitivity to the hormone, or absence of the hormone. Studies of the pathway through which these hypersensitivities occur are based in large part upon the concepts which have just been discussed. *Counterhormones can act in the same place as the hormone acts, or they can exert their effect by indirect mechanisms, by acting on the metabolic processes differently from those catabolized, or those actually catalyzed by the primary hormone.* It must be remembered that the blood sugar content at any time is the result of the difference in the rate between glucose leaving and entering the bloodstream. In-between meals, the liver is the main source of glucose entering the blood. When the glucose concentration remains constant, it must be presumed that the glucose replacement is equal to the rate of glucose removal. Thus, if one uses blood-sugar levels as an indication of insulin and the counterinsulin hormone activities, one must differentiate between the routes of glucose utilization. Glucose can be burned, i.e., oxidized, to carbon dioxide and water, which are excreted; it can be deposited in the liver as glycogen; it can be deposited in the other tissues, particularly the muscle, as glycogen; or it can be used for the formation of fat.

We have been discussing carbohydrate as the primary nutrient. The same approach can be applied to the study of protein metabolism.

The adrenal cortex has been implicated in carbohydrate metabolism since the earliest work on the derivative hormones. It was shown quite early, after the introduction of cortisone, that it was capable of producing hyperglycemia and glycosuria in well-fed rats. Clinically, patients with Cushing's disease not infrequently show an impaired carbohydrate tolerance or a frank diabetes. This was related to the excessive production of the adrenal steroid hormones. The contrary effect, that is, the sensitivity of Addison's patients to insulin, was also known. It was a simple step to show that the administration of cortisone to patients with Addison's disease and diabetes changed the sensitivity to insulin. In the human, the administration of cortisone or ACTH brought about the development of a diabetic state, usually temporary, if the dosage was sufficiently large. The extension of this was demonstrated when the administration of cortisone or ACTH to patients with existent diabetes produced an intensification of the diabetic syndrome. I have seen patients with diabetes who were treated with cortisone or cortisone derivatives, whose daily insulin requirements changed from 10 to 15 units to up to 3000 units. One such patient became so insulin-resistant that she was kept out of ketosis only with a dosage of 3000 to 5000 units a day, over a period of several months, before she expired.

Large doses of cortisone and ACTH also affect alterations in nitrogen metabolism. When temporary diabetes is produced by the administration of cortisone or ACTH, there is a pronounced increase in urinary nitrogen. Clinically, this is seen quite frequently in a variety of conditions, and negative nitrogen balances have been reported in many of these patients. The simultaneous administration of the androgens can prevent this large excretion of nitrogen. This had been shown when testosterone brought about a retention of nitrogen in patients with Cushing's syndrome.

Chronic emaciation, due to caloric insufficiency, is a stress situation for the human being. Adaptation mechanisms to it have been observed which are probably a readjustment of many endocrine factors. It has been reported that during chronic emaciation episodes many changes take place which are directly attributable to endocrine alterations; aspermatogenesis in males; amenorrhea, but not sterility, in females; markedly decreased basal metabolic rates; development of pigmentation of the skin; and other phenomena. Autopsies have shown definite involutionary changes, particularly in the testicles, thyroids, and adrenals of patients who have been exposed to these stresses of chronic starvation. The ability to remain alive when the caloric intake is 800 calories daily indicates new equilibrium or homeostatic mechanisms. In contrast to the chronic emaciation syndrome, there is acute starvation. Here the effects are more dramatic and are quite different. In acute starvation episodes, that is, with a sudden withdrawal of all calories, there is at first a markedly increased excretion of nitrogen in the urine which gradually subsides and levels off until there is a terminal nitrogen increase. The initial phase is, of course, dependent upon the presence of the steroid hormones creating an increased gluconeogenesis from the protein, with resultant discarding of the nitrogen residual.

Sudden withdrawal of insulin in certain types of diabetic patients produces a rapid excretion of nitrogen associated with catabolic phenomena.

The marked changes in nitrogen metabolism associated with trauma and disease again can be attributed to the hormonal response to this type of stress. The associated changes in the inorganic elements of potassium and sodium would tend to indicate that this increased excretion of nitrogen is due to the breakdown of formed proteins in the body.

Olsen (1) reviews this subject very extensively. The effect of the various hormones upon protein metabolism is dependent upon a number of variables which include the diet and the resultant nutritional status, and the intactness of the entire endocrine system. The growth hormone, insulin, the androgens—all are definitely protein-anabolic in an over-all effect, although it appears from the data available that their specific modes of action are entirely different. The androgens appear to be anticatabolic. Growth hormone is actually anabolic, and insulin is anabolic. The corticoid steroid hormones are catabolic, but probably not amino acid-catabolic, since the net effect of corticoid action upon gluconeogenesis and urea formation is quite variable. That dietary protein is important is not questioned. Endocrinology and nutrition are inseparably associated at all levels, and these interrelationships must be understood in order to understand the nutritional problems of the human being.

The influence of the endocrine glands on fatty acid and

ketone metabolism is an important consideration for this whole subject. The chief ketone body observed is acetoacetic acid. From this is derived betahydroxybutyric acid and acetone. Acetoacetic acid is a normal intermediary product in fat metabolism. Ordinarily it exists in a transitory state as the acetoacetyl proenzyme A, occurring both in the anabolic and catabolic pathways of the fats. The precursor of acetoacetyl-coA is acetyl-coA. This is derived from a number of sources, but particularly from the catabolism of fatty acids. The Krebs cycle in the metabolism of carbohydrates may also supply the coA. Thus, in the final analysis, ketone metabolism is a reflection of the metabolism of acetyl-coA which may, in turn, be looked upon as the hub of intermediary metabolism. The acetyl-coA may be derived from the carbohydrate metabolism through the pyruvate, from fat catabolism by the successive beta oxidation of fatty acids, and from protein through the various possible pathways, as discussed. First, acetyl-coA may be oxidized to completion in the Krebs cycle after condensation with oxalacetate to form citrate. With each turn of the cycle, a molecule of acetyl-coA is burned completely, oxalacetate is regenerated, and a considerable amount of energy is made available. The acetyl-coA depends upon a continuing metabolism of glucose to follow the synthetic path to a longer-chain fatty acid, and eventually the neutral-fat and the phospholipids, etc. Acetylo-coA is an intermediary in the synthesis of cholesterol, hormones, purines, and prophyrins, and is utilized in steroid acetylation reactions. The liver produces ketones normally, but the rate of production is a balance between the rate of production of acetyl-coA from fat catabolism, on the one hand, and of disposal by oxidation by way of the Krebs cycle, or by reduction and synthesis to fat, on the other hand.

There are many reasons to believe that some features of this metabolic reaction might be moderated by the endocrine secretions. As pointed out earlier, cortisone has diabetogenic action, but the bulk of evidence indicates that it causes a type of diabetes which is primarily due to overproduction of carbohydrate. This is in contrast to the predominantly underutilization diabetes of insulin deficiency.

It is well-known that certain pituitary extracts not only induce ketosis, but also have other interesting metabolic effects. These include mobilization of fat to the liver, hyperlipemia, depression of the respiratory quotient, hypoglycemia in the fasted animal, an anti-insulin activity. Most of these activities are associated with the fraction possessing growth activity. The growth hormone causes a fat accumulation in the liver which is preceded by an increase in the blood's neutral fat content. The same extract, under various experimental conditions, has been shown to lower the respiratory quotient, inhibit glucose utilization for fat synthesis and oxidation, stimulate fat catabolism, block insulin action, and promote protein anabolism.

One must consider the possibility of the influence of dietary factors on the production of the hormones, in addition to the hormones' effect on nutrition. One of the first observations that related a dietary component to the adrenal cortex and hormone secretion was the demonstration that vitamin C is present in high concentrations in the adrenal cortex. It was further shown that the adrenal cortex responds to ACTH by secreting its hormones, with a concomitant fall in the ascorbic acid content of the gland. However, subsequent experiments have demonstrated fairly conclusively that ascorbic acid is not directly concerned with the synthesis and release of adrenal cortical hormones, but that vitamin C deficiency may function as a non-specific stress and as such results in increased steroid secretions by the adrenal cortex.

Pantothenic acid deficiencies in the experimental animals result in adrenal hypertrophy, hemorrhage, and necrosis. Further studies have shown that pantothenic acid-deficient animals have a diminished ability to synthesize the adrenal steroids, and that this vitamin is necessary to maintain the functional integrity of the adrenal cortex.

Restrictions of salt intake have been shown to produce alterations in the adrenal cortex of animals and man. They are followed by an increased urinary excretion of aldosterone and impaired glucose tolerance.

Growth hormones derived from the pituitary gland must be able, in some manner, to take an active part in determining the nitrogen balance in the animal body. Houssay said some time ago that "the normal role of the pituitary in metabolism cannot be to produce diabetes." The diabetogenetic effect, and other similar pathologic effects, must be considered as manifestations either of a large excess of the hormone or of a moderate excess acting under conditions which exaggerate the results of its actions.

First, let us analyze the question of nitrogen retention and nitrogen balance. It has been shown experimentally that the recently hypothysectomized animal is unable to conserve nitrogen to a normal degree when the amount of nitrogen consumed is limited. It may be able to maintain nitrogen balance, or nearly so, when the amount of food ingested is adequate. An interpretation of this may be that the growth hormone enhances the rate of some phase of protein synthesis. If the hormone were to act otherwise, by inhibiting either the breakdown of protein to amino acids or the catabolism of amino acids, then its effect on nitrogen retention should be equally evident regardless of the kind or quantity of protein or amino acids present. A usual requirement for nitrogen balance in normal people and animals, besides the protein intake, is a necessary amount of carbohydrate. Substitution of fat for carbohydrate in the diet, or presentation of the carbohydrate at a different time of the day from the protein, may, under certain conditions, result in a negative nitrogen balance. With respect to the carbohydrate metabolism, it has been demonstrated repeatedly that in the absence of the hypophysis, the animal is unable to conserve carbohydrate during fasting. The respiratory quotient is high. Not only do the blood glucose and liver glycogen fall much more rapidly than in normal fasting animals, but the muscle glycogen, the major site of carbohydrate storage, because of its mass, also tends to be diminished. When carbohydrate is fed, it too disappears at a very rapid rate.

Hormones may function by exerting their influence on the rates of enzymatic reactions. Many such enzymes require some nutritional factor as part of their coenzyme, e.g., nicotinic acid in coenzyme 1 and coenzyme 2, which function as hydrogen acceptors in more than fifty metabolic reactions. Pantothenic acid is a component of coenzyme A which functions in the enzymatic acetylation of fat, protein, and carbohydrate metabolism, and phospholipid and steroid synthesis. Pyridoxin, which functions biochemically in the form of the pyridoxal phosphate, is the coenzyme for transaminase and cocarboxylase systems. One of its important functions is its action in the conversion of tryptophan to niacin. Riboflavin acts as a prosthetic group for various proteins functioning as enzyme hydrogen carriers. Thiamin is an important group in cocarboxylase, and as such participates in the decarboxylations, oxidations, dismutations, and condensations which lead to carbon dioxide formation in metabolism.

The symptoms of malnutrition are very similar to the clinical manifestations observed in many endocrine disturbances. In World War II, in the concentration camps, it was observed that women and men who had been subjected to long periods of chronic starvation, and who evidenced what was called the emaciation syndrome, had sexual disturbances. In the female, amenorrhea would occur within six weeks of food deprivation; in the male, impotence and a complete suppression of spermatogenesis. A decrease in the basal metabolic rate, frequently to levels as low as -40 and -50 was also observed. Gynecomastia was found to be very common among males in the Far Eastern prison camps. The autopsy work paralleled the clinical observations and indicated very definite atrophic changes in the endocrine glands. The amenorrhea and atrophy of the breasts which occurred in the women did not interfere with their ability to bear children. Ovulation continued in the face of these other endocrine changes. This was manifested by the impregnation of many of the women by the guards and the birth of an occasional viable child.

Zubirán (2) in Mexico, measured the gonadotropin and urinary estrogen increase and return to normal with re-feeding. In the case of the male, the testicles were atrophied and the histology of the testicles shows no spermatogenesis. The urines had a very low 17-ketosteroid excretion. The adrenal glands at post mortem were shown to be atrophic with lipid depletions. In addition, in lifetime, the low 17-ketosteroid excretion failed to return to normal and showed a poor response to ACTH. Clinically, of course, the patients with

Herbert Pollack

chronic emaciation resemble Symond's disease, known as panhypopituitarism.

REFERENCES

1. Olson, Robert E.: Role of Hormones in Protein Metabolism. *J. Am. Med. Assoc., 164*:1758-1765, 1957.
2. Zubirán, Salvador and Gómez-Mont, Francisco: Endocrine Disturbances in Chronic Human Malnutrition. *Vitamins and Hormones, 11*:97-132, 1953.

NUTRITIONAL FACTORS
IN THE REGULATION
OF FAT METABOLISM

Jules Hirsch, M.D. and Malcolm L. Peterson, M.D.

IN RECENT years numerous studies have explored the relationship between dietary fats and the concentration of serum lipids both in man and animals. Much of this effort has been prompted by a desire to examine the hypothesis that dietary fat and atherosclerosis are causally related through the intermediate agency of serum lipids. In its simplest form, this idea states that the ingestion of excess fat or of certain types of fat is a cause of serum lipid elevation and, furthermore, such increase in serum lipids over many years will lead ultimately to atherosclerosis and its various dire complications. Although there is as yet neither absolute proof nor disproof of this hypothesis, these investigations have led to many interesting observations which bear on the nature of serum lipids and their function in the organism. It is our purpose to elaborate briefly on some of these observations. As will be evident, much of what is said is both tentative and highly conjectural, even though the data to be used as grist for this mill of fancy are established beyond doubt. These data are the efforts of a number of investigators.

An excellent summary of their work can be found in *Chemistry of Lipides as Related to Atherosclerosis—A Symposium* (1). Before proceeding to specific considerations concerning serum lipids, it may be useful to review some more general concepts relative to the chemical nature of all lipids. However trite and elementary these observations are, the authors have found them to be useful, yet sometimes overlooked, generalizations.

The Chemical Nature and Functions of Lipids

To begin, it should be noted that the covalent bonds creating the special characteristics of lipids are an extreme case of those same covalent bonds which are the hallmark of all organic materials. Those forces which bind atoms into the complex molecules of biological significance are of two fundamental types, ionic and covalent. In terms of the classical Bohr model of the atom, these bonds have been described as follows: When electrons are transferred from the outer orbit of one atom to another, and then the atoms are electrostatically joined, an ionic bond is said to be present. In contrast, the sharing of electrons, without producing an electrical field, which is so typical of carbon-containing compounds, produces covalent bonds. The terms polar and nonpolar are used as a designation for these compounds held together by primarily ionic or primarily covalent bonds. Such polar and nonpolar compounds tend to be mutually unreactive, immiscible, and in nearly all ways unlike each other. Of course, there exists a spectrum of polarity rather than any clear division into two separate categories. Some compounds may even "resonate" between covalent and ionic forms, yielding a "hybrid" mixture of polar and nonpolar possibilities.

In this spectrum of polarity the lipids occupy a significant position as the most nonpolar of all compounds found either in foodstuff or the structural components of living cells. But not all the lipids have equal degrees of polarity. Thus, the lipid compounds found in greatest abundance in man can be listed in order of polarity from the most nonpolar hydrocarbons, such as squalene and carotene, to the slightly more polar cholesterol esters, thence to triglycerides and unesterified cholesterol, and finally to the quite polar and thus somewhat unlipid-like phospholipids. A considerable range in solubility characteristics is thus displayed from hydrocarbons almost totally insoluble in aqueous media to the water-soluble phospholipids. The common building block of lipids, the long-chain carboxylic or fatty acid, is predominantly a nonpolar compound but with a polar end fixing it to alcohols, sterols or sugars.

This extreme nonpolarity which is so much a characteristic of lipids enables them to function as a barrier for the enclosure of more polar systems. Enzymes residing in aqueous media can be sequestered and put into orderly sequence by "walls" of nonreactive lipid. Where a more polar "foot" is required, phospholipid can serve as a bridge between polar and nonpolar molecules, thus anchoring polar materials in place on the lipid wall. In reciprocal fashion, the lipid portions recently found in some enzyme systems may be a bridge to some lipid structure. This makes for the possibility of organization at a molecular level beyond the range of the cell components commonly described and separated. It is of interest that the chief structural lipids found within cellular structures are cholesterol, its esters and the phospholipids. In the sense of this discussion, these comprise a balanced mixture, for they contain an exceedingly polar lipid (phospholipid), a very nonpolar lipid (cholesterol ester) and a substance of intermediate polarity (cholesterol).

Another function of lipid, distinct from its structural function, is the significant role it has in the provision and storage of energy. That lipids may have some special chemical advantage as fuel is evident by our selection of hydrocarbons for combustion engines rather than solutions of sugar or protein. Likewise, the body stores calories for potential fuel as the lipid, triglyceride. The pathways of intermediary metabolism lead inevitably to triglyceride when the organism is surfeited with calories. Even in normal isocaloric states there is continuous conversion of carbohydrate to fatty acids and triglycerides prior to eventual burning of these important fuels. Acetylcoenzyme A, which arises from the oxidative decarboxylation of pyruvate as well as from ingested fat, is either burned or built back into fatty acids. Since the oxidative decarboxylation of pyruvate is not reversible it would be difficult to imagine any mechanism whereby excess acetate would be built into carbohydrate. Hence any excess intake of calories finding its way to the acetate pool will be reconstructed into fat rather than carbohydrate for storage. Finally, in terms of energy yield per unit weight, there is a more than twofold advantage of triglyceride over carbohydrate and protein.

Practically all of man's dietary fat is triglyceride. This is, of course, a result of the fact that our food supplies are rich in the energy stores of other organisms, both plant and animal. However, the structural lipids such as cholesterol and the phospholipids are more generally of endogenous origin. It is noteworthy that these structural lipids are built in a precise, genetically determined way and hence are not subject to dietary vagaries. Furthermore, one cannot change the cholesterol in nervous tissue to phytosterol by subsisting on a diet of vegetables. On the other hand, the energy function of lipids seems to be less dependent on such chemical specificity. Thus, the adipose tissue can slowly change to resemble the fats of dietary origin, with no adverse effects on the organism.

Serum Lipids

Can these two separate functions of structure and energy be seen in the serum lipids? The lipid of human serum is an extraordinarily complex mixture of compounds of different polarity joined with protein to form the macromolecular lipoproteins. There are undoubtedly dozens of different serum lipoproteins which can be separated to some extent by the techniques of electrophoresis, ultracentrifugation and, more recently, column chromatography. Further and more precise chemical definition of each lipoprotein class can then be effected by the use of gas-liquid and silicic acid chromatography.

The lightest group of serum lipids by centrifugal analysis is the large chylomicron, visible in the dark field of an ordinary microscope. These are known to be rich in the triglyceride of recently ingested fat, but they have a low content of other lipids and of protein. This class of lipoproteins is very evidently involved with energy metabolism and is of far less or even negligible importance in the transfer of structural components. In this respect the chylomicrons and closely related low density lipoproteins resemble that small fraction of serum lipids, the nonesterified fatty acids, which serves as an immediately available source of energy. The more dense lipoproteins, which tend toward increasing concentrations of protein, cholesterol and phospholipid, have ever-diminishing amounts of triglyceride. Unlike the chylomicrons, the concentration of these dense macromolecules is less subject to variation with food intake or other metabolic alterations. Those changes which do occur are much lower, as though these heavy lipoproteins were in much slower turnover than the lipoproteins rich in triglyceride.

There are notable deficiencies in such gross oversimplification of the morphology of serum lipids. Seemingly in wanton disregard of the authors' desire for a classification, the very lightest of lipoproteins, the chylomicroms, contain a small quantity of protein very much like that in the most dense of the lipoprotein classes. Furthermore, there are no sharp distinctions between some of these classes: there are subclasses, intermediates and variations depending on the techniques used for separation. However, it is to be hoped that such simplifications may give insight into the functions and dynamic relations of the various lipoproteins. Thus, the serum contains a multitude of different lipid types, coming and going from major sites of active metabolism. Some are in rapid-fire transport feeding the cellular furnaces with fuel; others would appear to be a more slowly moving effluvium or cast-off of cell membranes and intracellular structures, changed very little by metabolic alterations. The causes of variation in the concentrations of serum lipids are very much subject to genetic and humoral influences, as yet only poorly understood. There are, however, dietary effects on serum lipids which are more accessible to study via controlled dietary manipulation.

Dietary Effects on the Serum Lipids

A fundamental tool of nutritional research is to be found in the use of synthetic fluid formulas of precisely determined composition. By feeding such formulas as the sole sources of calories, in lieu of diets of mixed solid foods, it becomes possible to control the dietary intake of fat and other foods with unusual precision and a minimum of food analysis. If this feeding is combined with careful observation of hospitalized patients it becomes possible to evaluate the effects of dietary fat on the level of serum lipids. For example, a formula with 40 per cent of calories from corn oil and the remainder from dextrose and milk protein, lowers the level of cholesterol and phospholipid in nearly all subjects, whether the initial level of these lipids was elevated or normal. This lipid-lowering effect is quite slow, requiring several weeks to reach a fixed baseline. The level remains lowered as long as no other dietary changes are made; but if, for example, lard is substituted isocalorically for the corn oil, there is a slow rise in cholesterol and phospholipid levels. Within several weeks, a new, higher equilibrium is reached. Throughout such manipulations the serum triglyceride levels are unchanged; hence, these changes involve the relatively triglyceride-free or dense lipoproteins.

After many studies of this type it has been concluded that this cholesterol-lowering effect is shared by many dietary fatty acids and is related to the mean unsaturation and also to the chain length of its constituent fatty acids. The more unsaturated the fed fat, the lower are the levels of serum cholesterol. On the other hand, short-chain fatty acids produce higher levels than would be expected on the basis of unsaturation alone. But these dietary effects rarely lower the serum cholesterol below the 100 mg. to 150 mg. per cent mark. This is of some interest in the light of recent population surveys which demonstrate that individuals in some parts of the world have even lower levels. Interestingly, the feeding of protein-free formulas and simultaneous treatment of the subject with hormones which increase the need for protein bring about a dramatic decrease in serum cholesterol to those low levels seen in malnourished populations. It would seem as though the β-lipoprotein cholesterol is sensitive to the type of dietary fat as already discussed, but both β- and α-lipoprotein concentrations decrease when protein malnutrition threatens.

The mechanism whereby unsaturation of dietary fats lowers serum lipid levels is not known. It has been shown that in some individuals there is an increase in the fecal excretion of sterol at the same time that there is lowering of lipids by unsaturated fat, but whether or not the gut is the chief locus of action of unsaturated dietary fat is not clear. Since it is dense β-lipoprotein or "structural" lipid which is reactive in this particular dietary response, one is led to the following speculation: The structures which these dense lipoproteins represent, either as precursors or end products, are very likely specially constituted cellular organelles. The short-range physical forces which modify these lipid-protein "packages" may depend in part upon the fatty acid structure of their constituents, i.e., number of double bonds and length of fatty acid chain. Thus, the lipid-protein combination may be assembled differently as the component fatty acids vary. Very likely, there are specific requirements for these lipoproteins, in terms of some physical characteristic or precise detail of structure. If a cellular partition must have specified numbers of foci with polarity of constant intensity, any variation in fatty acids could be compensated by changes in the physical dimensions of such a partition. Those changes which are observed in serum concentrations of these lipoproteins when dietary fatty acids are altered may well be the most easily observed evidence of the changing transport of structural lipids needed for the maintenance of such precise structures. The mechanism whereby these important controls might be effected is completely unknown.

Another dietary maneuver which can produce interesting changes in the serum lipids is by no means so predictable and uniform as those which have already been described. This is a variation of serum triglyceride concentration produced by altering the quantity rather than the type of ingested fat. The change is made at the expense of carbohydrate, so that total caloric intake remains constant. If a formula is fed as previously described, with 40 per cent of calories from corn oil, 45 per cent from dextrose, and the remaining 15 per cent from milk protein, and then this formula is replaced isocalorically by one containing only 10 per cent of calories from corn oil, but with 75 per cent of calories from dextrose, there will be a startling increase in the serum triglycerides of some individuals. The cholesterol and phospholipid show very little change, certainly not significant in comparison to the changing triglyceride levels. As the ratio of dietary fat to carbohydrate increases, the triglycerides fall. Unlike the changes in cholesterol brought about by the saturation-unsaturation manipulation, these changes occur within several days of the formula shift. Here, then, the changes are exclusively in those low-density lipoproteins rich in triglycerides. It is now well known that the serum triglycerides are in rapid turnover and intimately related to the other members of the energy-providing system: carbohydrate, adipose tissue and serum nonesterified fatty acids. The detailed functioning of this system is not yet completely charted, but it is yielding rapidly to the probing of isotope experiments and the new methods of fatty acid analysis. In any event, there seems little doubt that the triglycerides are an *energy* lipid and that the dietary change just described is an *energy* alteration, in contrast to the *structural* lipid changes previously noted.

Thus, two separate functions of the serum lipids are discernible. A dissection of these functions is demonstrable by the use of formula-feeding experiments in man, as described. Dietary studies of this type have not yet provided the long-awaited, certain answer to the riddle of atherogenesis, but it is the essence of nutritional science to make predictable and reproducible observations on diet and its effects. It is gratifying that this step is finally being taken in the lipid division of human nutrition.

REFERENCE

1. Page, Irvine H., ed.: *Chemistry of Lipides as Related to Atherosclerosis—A Symposium.* Springfield, Ill.: Charles C Thomas, 1958.

EPIDEMIOLOGY OF PROTEIN MALNUTRITION

Moisés Béhar, M.D. and Nevin S. Scrimshaw, Ph.D.

PROTEIN MALNUTRITION is at present one of the most serious nutritional problems encountered in tropical and subtropical areas. Its effects are well recognized when its manifestations are severe, as in the case of small children in the postweaning period suffering from kwashiorkor. Less dramatic, and consequently less apparent, manifestations of protein malnutrition can be found at all ages. From the point of view of public health these less recognized forms are much more important because of their greater prevalence and because of their impact on health, capacity for work, and mental well-being.

The prevalence of kwashiorkor is an index of the much more widespread problem of protein malnutrition, and will be used in this sense here. Therefore, when we discuss the epidemiology of kwashiorkor, we include the magnitude of the more generalized condition.

The areas of the world in which, to our knowledge, kwashiorkor has been reported, are:

1. *Africa:* Algeria, Angola, Basutoland, Belgian Congo, Cameroons, Egypt, French Equatorial Africa, French West Africa, Gambia, Gold Coast, Kenya, Morocco, Mozambique, Nigeria, Nyasaland, Rhodesia, Ruanda-Urundi, Tanganyika, Tunisia, Uganda, Union of South Africa.

257

2. *America:* Argentina, Bolivia, Brazil, British Guiana, Chile, Colombia, Costa Rica, Cuba, Ecuador, El Salvador, Guatemala, Haiti, Honduras, Jamaica, Mexico, Netherlands Antilles, Nicaragua, Panama, Peru, Puerto Rico, Trinidad, Uruguay, Venezuela.

3. *Asia:* Ceylon, China, India, Indochina, Indonesia, Iraq, Japan, Jordan, Lebanon, Malaya, Philippines, Thailand.

4. *Europe*[1]*:* France, Greece, Hungary, Italy, Spain.

5. *Oceania:* Fiji, New Caledonia, Papua.

It has not been possible, however, to establish even approximately the prevalence of the syndrome for any region, since all reports are based almost exclusively on hospital cases and there is no way of estimating the number of children dying without medical attention and, therefore, not reported as kwashiorkor cases. In addition, it should be mentioned that, even in hospitals, the death certificates or clinical diagnoses often emphasize intercurrent diseases such as pneumonia or gastrointestinal disturbances, ignoring the state of malnutrition.

Recently the Institute of Nutrition of Central America and Panama (INCAP) has investigated, through visits to the home and interviews with the parents, all deaths that occurred during a two-year period in children up to 15 years of age in four rural communities of the Guatemalan highlands (3). It was found that of a total of 109 children who died between the ages of one to four years, 40 presented the signs and symptoms of kwashiorkor. This would indicate that the syndrome occurs in a fatal form in about 3 per cent of the estimated one-to-four-year-old child population in the communities studied. It should be added that these villages were not among those with the worst medical and social conditions or the most serious nutritional problems.

[1] Sporadic cases.

In Haiti, Jelliffe (17) has recently reported that in children one to three years of age "The prevalence of kwashiorkor . . . varied from 3.0 to 16.4 per cent, with an average for the whole survey of 6.5 per cent." His observations were not limited to fatal cases as in the INCAP studies.

Variations and Similarities in Clinical Descriptions

Almost all workers who are familiar with the problem agree at present on the fundamental characteristics of kwashiorkor (31), and the definition given by the third Joint FAO/WHO Expert Committee on Nutrition is in accord with the generally accepted criteria (18). Their description is as follows:

> Kwashiorkor commonly occurs in infants and young children who have been fed on a diet low in protein and composed mainly of foods rich in carbohydrate. The main clinical features are failure of growth, retarded development, wasting of muscles, loss of appetite, mental apathy, oedema, dyspigmentation of hair and skin, diarrhoea, and the presence of undigested food in the stools. Subcutaneous fat is often well retained. There may be signs of associated vitamin deficiency. In the blood there is a reduction in the concentration of albumen and of certain enzymes. The characteristic pathological features are fatty infiltration of the liver and atrophy of the pancreas and of other glands concerned with exocrine secretion, together with a diminution in the amount of pancreatic enzymes in the duodenal juice. The disease responds well to treatment with skim milk.

It should be recognized that no one of the characteristics mentioned can be considered pathognomonic, that the absence of any one characteristic does not prevent making the diagnosis, and that all may be present in varying degrees or combinations. As Brock (4) has stated, the condition is really a disease spectrum rather than a specific disease. There are, accordingly, marked variations in the clinical picture from one region to another and even within the same region. Some of the factors responsible for these differences are considered below.

Although it is generally agreed that the primary cause of kwashiorkor is a lack of protein, it is recognized that this deficiency may be accompanied by a variable degree of caloric deficiency. In some cases, e.g., those described in Jamaica, the marked protein deficiency is found in children with an adequate or even excessive caloric intake (16). In the latter case the children present the characteristic alterations of kwashiorkor: edema, skin lesions, hair changes, apathy, gastrointestinal disorders, fatty liver, hypoproteinemia, and a marked deficiency of their digestive enzymes. They do retain, however, a considerable amount of adipose tissue and may even be obese. This is known as the "sugar baby" type of kwashiorkor and can be considered the purest form of protein malnutrition.

At the other extreme is the child with such a marked caloric deficiency that proteins no longer constitute the limiting factor in the diet; in other words, the diet is balanced in its calorie-protein relation but is not quantitatively adequate. This is often the case with children fed primarily or entirely with very small quantities of milk. Even though there is a marked protein deficiency, the clinical picture of kwashiorkor is not present; instead, such a child shows a severe height-weight deficit, extreme thinness, and no subcutaneous fat. Muscular wasting is evident, but the child is generally alert and has a good appetite. Fatty liver does not develop and serum proteins and digestive enzymes are not markedly reduced and may be within normal values: this is the clinical picture of marasmus.

The great majority of children diagnosed as having kwashiorkor in Africa, India, or Central America represents intermediate forms between the two extremes of the sugar baby type and marasmus. They present characteristics of both and are the result of a diet with a more or less severe caloric deficit but with a still greater reduction in protein intake.

Differences in the clinical picture observed in different localities may be due also to the variability of superimposed vitamin or mineral deficiencies. In Indonesia, for example, it is common to observe severe ocular lesions of vitamin A deficiency in kwashiorkor (20). In some regions of India a megaloblastic anemia due to a vitamin B_{12} deficiency complicates the picture of kwashiorkor (19). In areas where hookworm exists or where there are other conditions that may result in a loss of iron, the anemia is predominantly of the microcytic hypochromic type. In many cases the causes for the regional variations have not been sufficiently studied to identify the specific factors involved.

Some of the vitamin deficiencies that are observed in kwashiorkor do not seem to be due to a deficient intake, but seem rather to be secondary to a protein deficiency. For example, blood serum vitamin A values are reduced even in regions in which the vitamin A activity of the diet appears adequate. This seems to be due largely to disturbances in the absorption of fat, probably because of the lowered enzyme activity resulting from the severe protein deficiency (1, 15, 27, 29).

Finally, the clinical picture of kwashiorkor may vary according to the age at which it occurs. Differences in age of occurrence are in turn due to differences in weaning practices and the dietary habits of the preschool child. This is illustrated by the data presented in Figure 1. Of the 34 cases reported by Van der Sar (28) in Curaçao, all were children under two years of age. A similar situation was reported by Gerbasi (14) in Sicily who found that 31 of 36 cases were children under two years of age. In a study of 205 cases, Pretorius et al. (22) in South Africa reported that 20 per cent occurred in children over two years of age, and the majority of these were between two and three years of age. Even among the cases under two years reported by these authors, more occurred in children of one to two years of age, in contrast with the situation in Italy and in Curaçao where the prevalence seems to be about the same for the one- and two-year age groups. This seems to be related to a habitually later weaning in South Africa. According to these authors, the disease generally develops within one to six months after weaning. In Uganda, Davies (9) reports a situation similar to that in South Africa.

FIGURE 1

AGE DISTRIBUTION OF KWASHIORKOR

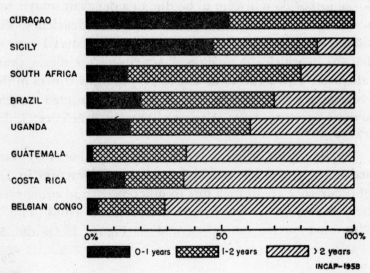

262

In Central America the prevalence is also greater after the age of two. Of 100 cases studied by us in Guatemala, 68 occurred in children over two years of age, while only 2 cases occurred in children under one. Peña Chavarría et al. (21) analyzed 236 cases in Costa Rica and found that 64 per cent occurred in children over two years of age. They reported that the percentage of cases found in children under one (14 per cent) was much greater than that observed in a previous study, a difference which they attribute principally to an increase in early weaning. Another important epidemiological fact in Guatemala is the relatively high prevalence of cases in children over five years of age.

In the Belgian Congo the majority, 56 of 79 cases reported by DeMaeyer (10), also occurred in children over two years old. The situation seems to be similar in India. Although we were unable to obtain complete information, Venkatachalam et al. (30) report that 48 per cent of their cases occurred in children over three years of age. This would seem to indicate that the majority occurred in children over two.

The situation in Brazil seems to be more nearly like that of Africa than of Central America. Waterlow and Vergara (32) studied 50 cases of which 35 occurred in children under two years of age. The reports by other authors in the same area are in agreement with this observation which indicates that, in general, nearly two thirds of the cases occur at this age. The dietary habits in Brazil, with a great consumption of cassava and weaning usually before one year of age, follow the African pattern more closely than that of Central America.

Basic Epidemiology

An analysis of the usual weight curve of children in the areas where kwashiorkor occurs and of the conditions that precipitate the appearance of clinical cases of marasmus or kwashiorkor helps in understanding the main points in the epidemiology of protein malnutrition, at least as far as young children are concerned. In Central America, as in most other kwashiorkor regions, the average weight of children at birth does not differ greatly from that considered normal in areas where the problem of protein malnutrition does not exist. The children are usually breast-fed, without any adequate supplementary feeding, at least during the first year of life. They progress quite satisfactorily for the first six months, but at this time their growth begins to lag behind that of well-nourished children. After the first year the rate of growth is reduced even further, remaining practically stationary until four or five years of age when they start once again to grow at the same rate as well-nourished children. After about five years of age their growth curve runs parallel to that of well-nourished controls, with a retardation of two to four years. Although the supplementary food the child receives toward the end of lactation varies from one region to another, it tends to be mainly of vegetable origin, rich in carbohydrates and very poor in proteins, and frequently deficient in various other nutrients. The small amounts of proteins in these diets are usually of low biological value and difficult to digest. In Central America the child does not participate in the usual family diet until he is four or five years old; at this time his protein intake improves.

The reasons for keeping preschool children on the diets described are not primarily economic or the result of limited availability of food. They are rather the consequence of ignorance of the nutritional needs of the child and the ways of satisfying them, conditioned by prejudices and taboos concerning the use of certain foods for the small child.

If for some reason the mother is unable to breast-feed her child during the first months of life, it is common practice to feed him very diluted milk or simply "rice water" or some other very thin starchy gruel. The child then loses weight rapidly, consuming his own tissues, and finally reaches the marasmic stage of caloric deficiency. If the child receives highly starchy foods, and especially if infection is also present, kwashiorkor may be produced as the result of an imbalance between the caloric and protein intake.

The children who do not have these problems and who survive the first year of life appear apathetic and small but not necessarily thin, because the reduction of weight is more or less proportional to that of height. Some in whom the condition is more serious may show slight changes in their hair, which becomes dry, breakable, falls out easily, and may also be depigmented. Later the apathy is accentuated; the child loses his appetite, frequently suffers diarrheal episodes, and may present discrete maleolar edema. This condition, found in a large proportion of children between one and four years of age living in areas where protein malnutrition is prevalent, has been called prekwashiorkor by some investigators. From the point of view of public health, this condition constitutes a very grave problem which in general has not received enough attention either because it goes unnoticed or because it lacks the drama of kwashiorkor. Among these children, infection takes a heavy toll.

Interrelation of Protein Malnutrition with Infection

In tropical and subtropical areas where protein malnutrition is prevalent, infections are particularly likely to constitute a serious problem. Unfortunately, public health programs designed to reduce parasitic and other infectious diseases frequently concentrate entirely on environmental sanitation measures without taking the nutritional factors into consideration.

There is a large number of studies in experimental animals, some of them very carefully controlled, which leaves no doubt that protein malnutrition *is* of significance in increasing the severity of protozoan, helminth, and most bacterial and rickettsial infections (2, 5, 6, 7, 12, 24). This does not seem to hold true for viral infections. Since the most likely cause of death in many viral infections is a secondary bacterial complication, malnutrition may still be of significance in determining mortality associated with viral invasions.

There are surprisingly few direct experimental studies in humans of the effect of protein malnutrition on the consequences of infections and manifestations, but suggestive epidemiological evidence is abundant. For example, in every area in which malnutrition is common, a considerable number of children die as a consequence of respiratory infections, infectious diarrhea, whooping cough, measles, amebiasis, hookworm infestation, and many other diseases that certainly would not, in most instances, be fatal to well-nourished children. Improving the nutritional status of these populations, even without a marked change in sanitary practices, would reduce the tragically high mortality that prevails today among young children in technically underdeveloped areas. Of course, both environmental sanitation and nutrition are likely to improve simultaneously, and this should be the objective of public health efforts. The natural experiment is thus confounded but the interests of the population in question are best served.

The frequency and severity of infectious processes in kwashiorkor can be mentioned as a specific example of the interrelationship between protein malnutrition and infection. Like many other investigators, we have observed that the most common cause of death in children with kwashiorkor is a severe bronchopneumonia unaccompanied by the usual manifestations of defense reactions to the infection (26).

On the other hand, a vicious circle is closed when infections maintain or aggravate the precarious nutritional status of these badly nourished individuals. It is known that fever increases metabolic demands and that organisms already in a deficient nutritional state have more difficulty recovering in a satisfactory manner. Simultaneously with this increase in nutritional demands there may be a decrease in absorption, particularly when diarrhea occurs. Furthermore, there is generally a significant increase in urinary nitrogen excretion, presumably as a result of tissue destruction (25). If, in addition, we recall that there is a reduction in the intake as a consequence of anorexia, without taking into consideration the reductions to which the sick are frequently submitted through dietary-therapeutic errors, we will have a more complete idea of the damage these infectious processes may cause in populations already basically malnourished. This is why most authors recognize infectious processes as precipitating factors in kwashiorkor or in children who are in the state of chronic protein malnutrition already described. In our experience we have found that even banal respiratory infections may interfere with the nutritional recovery of kwashiorkor cases.

Role of Diarrheal Diseases in Precipitating Kwashiorkor

Special emphasis needs to be placed on the role of diarrhea as a factor responsible for protein malnutrition. This condition is very common in the areas in which kwashiorkor occurs. Studies done by INCAP in two rural villages of the Guatemalan highlands have shown that 70 per cent of the children under five years of age suffered from one or more episodes of diarrhea during a one-year period and that for these children the average number of episodes for that year was about three.

In the majority of instances these diarrheal processes have the characteristics of an infectious diarrhea. By stool cultures a prevalence of 6 per cent of Shigella in children has been found in several Guatemalan towns, including the two mentioned above. Comparative studies in children with and without diarrhea, however, do not show a marked difference in the positivity of stool examinations for either Shigella or other organisms considered pathogenic, and for intestinal parasites. Ramos-Alvarez and Sabin (23) have recently reported isolating a large variety of enteroviruses (ECHO, coxsackie A and B, polioviruses) and a small number of adenoviruses in 50 per cent of diarrheal cases in Cincinnati, Ohio and found shigella and salmonella in only 9 per cent of the cases. If a similar situation prevails in Guatemala, the failure to find a better correlation between the isolation of pathogenic bacteria and the occurrence of diarrhea can thus be accounted for and a marked effect on net nitrogen retention can be predicted. It is of interest to note that apart from diarrheal disease, the other infection most often associated with the precipitation of kwashiorkor is another virus disease, measles (11).

In addition to its physiological effects on nitrogen absorption and excretion, diarrheal and other infections play an important direct role since it is precisely these cases in which the greatest dietetic errors are committed as intended therapy. Through fear of the diarrhea, these children are often completely deprived of the scant sources of protein they have been receiving and are submitted to drastic diets based exclusively on starches. This was the major etiologic factor in the development of "starchy food dystrophy" as first recognized by Czerny and Keller (8) in Germany.

Besides contributing to a state of chronic protein malnutrition, diarrhea frequently constitutes the precipitating factor of the severe forms. In our experience in Central America at least three fourths of the cases of kwashiorkor seem to have started with an acute episode of diarrhea of an apparently infectious nature. When a severe deficiency is established, however, the diarrhea constitutes a symptom in the clinical picture and disappears rapidly with adequate dietetic treatment. Although several authors report similar experiences in different areas, Gerbasi's (13) observations in Italy are particularly striking. He considers that an inadequate protein intake plays a secondary etiopathogenic role in comparison to that of infectious diarrhea. In a series of 20 cases Gerbasi found that only 7 children could be considered to have been on an inadequate protein diet, but that 18 had a history of infectious diarrhea. One cannot help but wonder if, as a consequence of the diarrhea, the protein intake was not reduced, leaving a preponderantly starchy diet. In our experience—similar to the majority of cases reported by Gerbasi—if a child, especially under two years of age, suffers from a prolonged diarrheal process but continues to receive a diet with an adequate protein/calorie relation, he develops the clinical picture of marasmus rather than that of kwashiorkor.

Summary

The factors responsible for protein malnutrition in the majority of the tropical and subtropical areas are:

1. Scarcity of protein-rich foods of high biological value.

2. Ignorance of the mothers regarding the nutritional needs of their children and the ways of satisfying those needs.

3. Prejudices or faulty habits in dietary practices especially in regard to small children.

4. Very low purchasing power.

5. Poor sanitary conditions and hygiene leading to heavy infestation with parasites and frequent infections.

6. Insufficient productive capacity of a population due both to the failure to employ modern agricultural techniques, and often also to weakness and apathy associated with endemic disease.

All these factors are intimately related and each in turn contributes to the maintenance of the others. The suppression of any one factor would benefit the others as in a chain reaction, but only when substantial progress is made in correcting all these problems will the great majority of the world's population be able to share in the technical and health gains of the more highly developed nations, and thus rise above the poverty, ignorance, disease, and early death which now befall them.

REFERENCES

1. Arroyave, G.; Viteri, F.; Béhar, M.; and Scrimshaw, N. S.: Impairment of Intestinal Absorption of Vitamin A Palmitate in Severe Protein Malnutrition (Kwashiorkor). *Amer. J. Clin. Nutrition,* 7:185-190, 1959.

2. Aycock, W. L. and Lutman, G. E.: Vitamin Deficiency as an Epidemiologic Principle. *Amer. J. Med. Sci., 208:*389-406, 1944.

3. Béhar, M.; Ascoli, W.; and Scrimshaw, N. S.: An Investigation into the Causes of Death in Four Rural Communities

in Guatemala. *Bull. World Health Org., 19*:1093-1102, 1958.
4. Brock, J. F.: In: *Malnutrition in African Mothers, Infants and Young Children.* Report of Second Inter-African (C.C.T.A.) Conference on Nutrition (Gambia, 1952). London: Her Majesty's Stationery Office, 1954, p. 104.
5. Chandler, A. C. Interrelations between Nutrition and Infectious Disease in the Tropics. *Amer. J. Trop. Med. Hyg., 6*:195-208, 1957.
6. Clark, P. F.; McClung, L. S.; Pinkerton, H.; Price, W. H.; Schneider, H. A.; and Traker, W.: Influence of Nutrition in Experimental Infections. *Bacteriol. Rev., 13*:99-134, 1949.
7. Clausen, S. W.: The Influence of Nutrition upon Resistance to Infection. *Physiol. Rev., 14*:309-350, 1934.
8. Czerny, A. D. and Keller, A.: *Des Kindes Ernährung, Ernährungsstörungen und Ernährungstherapie.* Vienna: F. Deuticke, 1906, pp. 62-81.
9. Davies, J. N. P.: Analysis of Morbidity and Mortality in Children at Mulago Hospital 1950-51. In: *Malnutrition in African Mothers, Infants and Young Children.* Report of Second Inter-African (C.C.T.A.) Conference on Nutrition (Gambia 1952). London: Her Majesty's Stationery Office, 1954, pp. 84-91.
10. DeMaeyer, E. M. and Vanderborght, H.: Evolution de la Courbe Pondérale et de Certains Constituants Biochimiques et Hématologiques du Sang dans le Kwashiorkor. *Annales de la Société Belge de Médecine Tropicale, 34*:417-432, 1954.
11. Dupin, H.: *Etude des Carences Protidiques Observées Chez l'Enfant en Pays Tropical (Kwashiorkor).* Paris: Librairie Arnette, 1958.
12. Frye, W. W.: Nutrition and Intestinal Parasitism. *Ann. N. Y. Acad. Sci., 63*:175-185, 1955.
13. Gerbasi, M.: Il Kwashiorkor in Sicilia (Distrofia Pluricarenziale Edemigena). *La Pediatria, 64*:941-1004, 1956.
14. Gerbasi, M.: *Il Kwashiorkor.* Atti del XXV Congresso della Societá Italiana di Pediatria, Palermo, October, 1957.
15. Gómez, F.; Ramos-Galván, R.; Cravioto, J.; Frenk, S.; Vásquez Santaella, J.; and de la Peña, C.: Fat Absorption in Chronic Severe Malnutrition. *Lancet, 2*:121-122, 1956.
16. Jelliffe, D. B.; Bras, G.; and Stuart, K. L.: Kwashiorkor and Marasmus in Jamaican Infants. *West Indian Med. J., 3*:43-55, 1954.

17. Jelliffe, D. B., personal communication.
18. Joint FAO/WHO Expert Committee on Nutrition, Third Report. World Health Organization Technical Report Series, No. 72, 1953.
19. Mehta, G. and Gopalan, C. Haematological Changes in Nutritional Oedema Syndrome (Kwashiorkor). *Ind. J. Med. Res., 44:*727-735, 1956.
20. Oomen, H. A. P. C. Xerophthalmia in the Presence of Kwashiorkor. *Brit. J. Nutrition, 8:*307-318, 1954.
21. Peña Chavarría, A.; Saenz Herrera, C.; and Cordero Carvajal, E.: Síndrome Policarencial de la Infancia. *Revista Medica de Costa Rica, 170,* 1948.
22. Pretorius, P. J.; Davel, J. G. A.; and Coetzee, J. N.: Some Observations on the Development of Kwashiorkor. A Study of 205 Cases. *So. Afric. Med. J., 30:*396-399, 1956.
23. Ramos-Alvarez, M. and Sabin, A. B.: Enteropathogenic Viruses and Bacteria. Role in Summer Diarrheal Diseases of Infancy and Early Childhood. *J. Amer. Med. Assoc., 167:*147-156, 1958.
24. Robertson, E. C. The Vitamins and Resistance to Infection. *Medicine, 13:*123-206, 1934.
25. Robinson, U.; Béhar, M.; Viteri, F.; Arroyave, G.; and Scrimshaw, N. S.: Protein and Fat Balance Studies in Children Recovering from Kwashiorkor. *J. Trop. Pediat., 2:*217-223, 1956-57.
26. Tejada, C.; Béhar, M.; and Cofiño, E.: Estudio Clínico-Patológico de las Bronconeumonías del Niño Desnutrido. *Rev. Col. Med. Guatemala, 7:*134-139, 1956.
27. Thompson, M. D. and Trowell, H. C.: Pancreatic Enzyme Activity in Duodenal Contents of Children with a Type of Kwashiorkor. *Lancet, 1:*1031-1035, 1952.
28. Van der Sar, A.: Incidence and Treatment of Kwashiorkor in Curaçao. *Documenta Neerlandica et Indonesica de Morbis Tropicis, 3:*25-44, 1951.
29. Véghelyi, P. V.: Activité Pancréatique et Carence des Protides. *Acta Chirg. Belg. Supp. 2:*374-377, 1948.
30. Venkatachalam, P. S.; Srikantia, S. G.; and Gopalan, C.: Clinical Features of Nutritional Oedema Syndrome in Children. *Ind. J. Med. Res., 42:*555-568, 1954.
31. Waterlow, J. C. and Scrimshaw, N. S.: The Concept of

Kwashiorkor from a Public Health Point of View. *Bull. World Health Organization, 16:*458-464, 1957.
32. Waterlow, J. and Vergara, A.: *Protein Malnutrition in Brazil.* Rome: Food and Agriculture Organization of the United Nations, 1956.

NUTRITION IN THE EARLY DEVELOPMENT PHASE

Paul György, M.D.

THAT WE need to clarify controversial points, which require new approaches to research, is best illustrated by the last edition of *Recommended Dietary Allowances* published by the Food and Nutrition Board of the National Research Council (30). In a table which contains recommendations for calories and various nutrients, no figures are given for the young infant in his first month of life and no "allowances" for protein are indicated for the first year. Human milk is emphasized as desirable food for the first month of life, although in general the impracticability of this recommendation under present prevailing conditions is obvious. How did we reach such an impasse?

Since the turn of the century, with the firm establishment and progressive growth of pediatrics as a medical specialty, infant nutrition has been greatly influenced by the existing and fluctuating trends of nutritional and clinical research. Consequently, as part of pediatric practice, infant nutrition is not, and never has been, based on static and well-established rules and methods. It has undergone in the past half-century many important changes and modifications. In general, how-

274

ever, progress in infant nutrition, especially in its broad prospects, remained through all these years a shining example of a purely clinical and empirical approach. Apart from the accessories, by no means unimportant, of the infant diet— e.g., vitamins and minerals—the basic rules in the nutrition of the infant which should determine the requirement for calories, protein, carbohydrates, and fat, were formulated through observations in the clinic and not through animal experimentation.

Animals differ from human infants in their growth rate and, consequently, also in their requirements for calories and body-building food constituents, especially protein. Furthermore, there is no animal known or available for experimentation with the long sucking period of the human infant. Thus, it is understandable that human milk, certainly *the* physiological complete food for the human infant, received no particular attention by experimental nutritionists working with animals. From a purely teleologic point of view, human milk must be considered superior to cow's milk as the initial food for the human infant. In teleologic language: human milk is for the human infant and cow's milk is for the calf.

For the human infant, cow's milk or any other food different from human milk remains a substitute food. However, human milk is not always available nor is breast-feeding always possible. In countries of the West, especially in the United States, certain cultural-anthropological factors plus lack of proper educational preparation of the mother makes breast-feeding, even when possible, a difficult goal to achieve. It is certainly discouraging that in many of the "highly developed" countries society subordinates breast-feeding to a secondary position in infant feeding. According to a recent statistical study (29) never more than 25 per cent and as few as 12 per cent of the newborn infants leaving the hospital nursery were exclusively breast-fed in various parts of the United States in 1956 (Table 1).

TABLE 1

Per Cent Infants Leaving the Hospital Nursery
With Different Types of Feeding in the United States

Region	Breast only 1946-56		Breast and Artificial 1946-56		Artificial only 1946-56	
Northeast	23	12	12	6	67	82
East & Central	36	20	30	15	34	65
Mountains & Plains	44	26	28	17	28	57
Southeast	55	27	27	16	18	57
Pacific	31	25	29	19	40	56
Southwest	47	27	35	23	18	50

Even in the earliest developmental phase of scientific pediatrics, 50 to 60 years ago, there were teleologic considerations which furnished the foundation and leading principle for artificial feeding of infants. In comparing the crude chemical composition of human milk with that of cow's milk (Table 2), it is not surprising that the higher content of cow's milk in protein and salts, which are the specific body-

TABLE 2

Composition of Human Milk and Cow's Milk

	Human Milk Per Cent	Cow's Milk Per Cent
Protein	1.2	3.5
Lactose	6.6	4.0
Fat	3.5	3.5
Ash	0.2	0.7
Calories	65	65

building constituents, compared with the corresponding average analytical data for human milk, has been related by the pioneers of modern pediatrics at its inception to the more rapid growth and greater apposition of tissue in the calf than in the human infant. The additional assumption, not supported by scientific facts but only by clinical observations and "impressions," has been made that too much protein and salt as present in undiluted cow's milk, may be harmful to the young infant. Czerny's *Milchnährschaden* (milk dystrophy) was looked upon as the result of overfeeding with milk, mainly protein and salts. Today it is customary, perhaps with unwarranted superficiality, to see in this disease entity the result of a qualitatively incorrect dietary regime, such as lack of iron, vitamins, supplementary feeding (vegetables, meat, etc.). Of course, this possibility, the result of consecutive nutritional research, would not even have been considered at the beginning of the century; at that time dilution of cow's milk as initial formula for the young infant was strongly favored and widely accepted. One part of cow's milk diluted with two parts of water represented the first step in adaptation of cow's milk to human milk, at least with regard to protein and salts. The reduced caloric density of this formula was compensated in part with the addition of carbohydrate. But still it was often difficult to cover the caloric requirement of the infant with such diluted formula, necessitating much higher intake in volume than the infant could cope with. This initial step in artificial feeding—the mixture of milk, water, and sugar—has undergone gradual changes in the consecutive decades up to the present time. The danger of undernutrition with the one-third milk formula has led to the use of the more concentrated one half milk-water-sugar mixture, with satisfactory caloric density.

With the increasing intrusion of cow's milk formulas in pediatric practice, some difficulties have arisen such as diarrhea, vomiting, "colic," unsatisfactory gain in weight, etc. Acidulated milk, introduced in Holland, then used in Germany in the form of buttermilk, has been considered by prominent pediatricians as the answer to better artificial feeding. Such acidulated formulas were widely acclaimed in the United States ten or twenty years ago, but at present they are given sparingly. In warm and tropical countries, and in regions with less well-developed hygienic conditions and a dearth of refrigeration facilities, acidulated milk may be still advisable. The high acidity acts as a preservative and may counteract, certainly to some extent, secondary bacterial contamination. In reverse, it may be stated that the greatest benefit in successful artificial infant feeding has been achieved by following proper aseptic rules: pasteurization, autoclaving, and other related procedures. One is even justified in stating that with good aseptic care it is difficult to cause clinically demonstrable harm to a normal infant kept on any feeding regimen, providing the regimen covers the minimum requirements for all essential nutrients.

The trend in modern pediatric practice is toward maximal growth. Even half-diluted cow's milk contains more protein and salt than human milk. It is claimed that the increased supply of protein and salts leads to increased rate of growth through higher retention of nitrogen and salts. More concentrated milk formulas, two thirds or whole cow's milk—both widely used in early infancy—should have an even greater growth-promoting effect. Should it be concluded, however, from such observations that cow's milk is superior to human milk? Or, conversely, that better weight gain and steeper weight curves are to be preferred under all circumstances to the average obtained with human milk? Can physicians be sure that accelerated weight gain and overfeeding in infants are only temporary interludes and will have no lasting effect which might manifest itself perhaps years or even decades later in adult life? There is no reason to believe that maximal weight gain and accelerated maturation in infancy should be *the* optimal nutritional goal.

Based on short-term clinical observations, artificial feeding as it is used today under strict rules of hygiene yields good results. A quotation from a recent report of the Committee on Nutrition of the Academy of Pediatrics summarizes the present status very well: "The practice produces neither beneficial nor harmful results but rather attests the adaptability of the baby to the whim of his caretakers."

All these developments and tendencies, supported by the increased use and distribution of canned evaporated milk and of proprietary concentrated milk preparations, determined the wide popularity of concentrated milk formulas. The large selection of other commercially available baby food (cereals, vegetables, meat products, etc.) opened the way to the early use of supplementary food in the infant diet. In the United States the great majority of artificially fed infants is kept on feeding schedules, implying a high intake of protein, salts, and in many instances also of calories. Nowadays even very young infants are receiving milk-water-sugar mixtures which furnish a daily intake equivalent to 100 calories and 3.5 grams (or more), of protein per kilogram. This figure (3.5 grams) was the previously (1953) recommended daily allowance of the Food and Nutrition Board of the National Research Council for infants. Premature infants are receiving even higher amounts of protein—4.0 to 6.0 grams per kilogram and more—daily.

If one would adhere strictly to the term, "allowances" as the Report of the Food and Nutrition Board uses it, one could perhaps acquiesce in the acceptance of the present-day feeding scheme for infants: "Allowances are designed to maintain good nutrition in healthy persons in the United States under current conditions of living and to cover nearly all variations of requirements for nutrients in the population at large" (30). This conditional acceptance, however, would imply that the allowances as stated are based on scientific facts and are not prompted in the first place by convenience or by recognition of existing customs and practice. It appears, however, and this is the origin of the present controversy, that (a) convincing scientific support for the recommended daily allowance of 3.5 grams of protein in infancy is not available; and (b) "allowances" are often mistaken for "requirements." There is a frighteningly widespread shortage of protein over a large part of the inhabited globe, especially in the tropical belt. Protein malnutrition is rampant in these areas, particularly affecting infants in the postweaning period. From a general, world-wide, socioeconomic point of view it is imperative to remain staunch and exact in our dietary standards and to avoid exaggerated claims. One should guard against even a semblance of a "double standard," allowing for the maintenance of good nutrition in the United States, high protein intake, when such a goal is beyond the reach of the majority of the world's population and may not necessarily be desirable.

The most telling argument against the figure of 3.5 grams of protein per kilogram a day for infants is the fact that with such an allowance breast milk will be considered "substandard," since infants fed only on breast milk can practically never have a daily intake of 3.5 grams of protein. Or else they must be grossly overfed, with an intake of over 200 calories per kilogram a day (instead of the normal 100 to 120 calories). Obviously, this dilemma could have been solved by giving separate allowance figures for breast-fed and artificially fed infants (2.0 versus 3.5 grams of protein.) But here again formidable difficulties presented themselves. Is the biological value of cow's milk protein so much inferior to that of protein in human milk to warrant this differentiation? Or is the over-all nutritional value of a given food—i.e., milk—as a source of protein perhaps also modified by other characteristics of the food in question? Is it possible to give figures for protein as we do for carbohydrates, vitamins, or minerals (even for these, with some reservation) without referring to the quality of the protein (vegetable versus animal, amino acid pattern, imbalance, etc.) and to the protein-containing food itself?

This brings us back to our question: whether human milk has special nutritional qualities for the human infant not fully shared by cow's milk. In the past two to three decades a generation of pediatricians has grown up which has never experienced the results of controlled feeding with human milk in hospitals. It is not surprising that they are unfamiliar with the advantages of breast-feeding. Those of us, like myself, whose pediatric practice dates back many decades, will not hesitate to testify in favor of breast-feeding in the prevention of infectious diseases, and, at that time, the best therapeutic diet for infants with chronic and often even very severe acute pyogenic infections. Similar observations were made in chronic intestinal disorders or in severe malnutrition combined with chronic infection. In general, this effect of human milk in a variety of infections was ascribed not so much to the presence of specific antibodies but to the action of unspecific factors of unknown origin. Transfer of immune bodies from ingested human milk through the intestine into the blood is a negligible factor in resistance to disease if it occurs at all.

Improved general hygiene and the use of antimicrobial agents have of late obscured the superiority of human milk over cow's milk in regard to the figures of morbidity and mortality. Recent statistical studies, however, published from by no means underdeveloped countries like the United Kingdom and Sweden indicate that these differences may be demonstrated not only under poor but also under good hygienic conditions.

Table 3 summarizes for Manchester, England, the rather impressive number of observations regarding morbidity and mortality in infants exclusively or partially breast-fed or bottle-fed (32).

TABLE 3

Relation Between Feeding and Mortality and Morbidity

Feeding	No. of infants	Mortality (per 1000)	Morbidity (per 1000)	Case mortality (Per Cent)
Breast-fed	971	10.2	223.4	4.6
Partly bottle-fed	1441	25.7	464.2	5.5
Bottle-fed	854	57.3	573.7	10.0
Total	3266	29.3	421.3	6.9

The significantly lower figures for mortality and morbidity in breast-fed, even partially breast-fed, infants are of interest. This conclusion applies not only to gastrointestinal but also to respiratory infections, including otitis. In Table 4—de-

TABLE 4

The Effect of Breast Milk and Artificial Food on the Incidence
of Infections in Infants 0-9 Months of Age

Age groups, months (3-month periods)	0-2	1-3	2-4	3-5	4-6	5-7	6-8	7-9
Breast Milk								
Total days of observation	1,377	1,709	1,578	1,248	923	665	430	235
Days with fever 38.1° and above	3	5	6	8	7	6	2	4
Days with subfebr. temp. 37.6°-38.0°	26	45	59	86	85	66	23	4
Total days with rise in temp. 37.6° and above	29	50	65	94	92	72	25	8
Artificial Food								
Total days of observation	1,151	1,664	1,853	1,771	1,547	1,219	952	630
Days with fever 38.1° and above	1	10	12	20	29	34	37	24
Days with subfebr. temp. 37.6°-38.0°	52	99	146	158	165	129	94	45
Total days with rise in temp. 37.6° and above	53	109	158	178	194	163	131	69

scribing a study carried out in Sweden—the much larger number of days with elevated temperature in bottle-fed infants of all age classes, especially around four to eight months of life, when compared with breast-fed infants, is certainly impressive (36). In more recent observations, again from Sweden, these conclusions have been confirmed (26, 28).

The second distinctive feature regarding infants fed human milk as compared to those fed cow's milk refers to the intestinal flora and the reaction of the feces. In contrast to the acid reaction of the feces of normal breast-fed infants, the pH of the feces in infants given the usual cow's milk formulas falls in the neutral or alkaline range. Unlike the mixed intestinal flora of infants on cow's milk formulas, the intestinal flora of healthy breast-fed infants is characterized by the prevalence of a particular species of Lactobacillus, namely, Lactobacillus bifidus.

In the course of investigations on the metabolic requirement of various strains of Lactobacillus bifidus isolated from the feces of young infants, we encountered in our laboratory an apparently specific variant of it (15). On our regular medium, this newly isolated strain has shown at primary isolation only scant or no growth. Further propagation of this new variant of Lactobacillus bifidus, which was named Lactobacillus bifidus var. pennsylvanicus (19), was achieved in consecutive subcultures when human milk was added to the medium (15). With increased supplements of human milk to the original liquid medium, acid production as an index of bacterial growth increased exponentially toward a maximum, indicating that a constituent of human milk must be an essential growth factor for Lactobacillus bifidus var. pennsylvanicus (Figure 1). With average samples of human

FIGURE 1

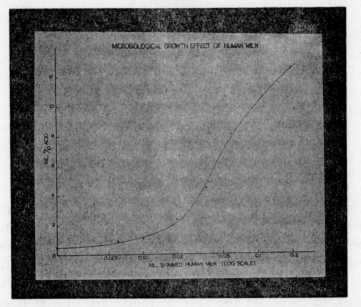

milk half the maximal growth was reached with about 0.06 ml. of whole or skimmed milk added to 10 ml. of the basal liquid medium. In contrast, cow's milk was practically inactive. In the first example, shown in Table 5, the ratio of activity of cow's milk to human milk was about 1:50. A similar ratio of activity, with an average of 1:40, was found with other samples of human milk and cow's milk. Thus with regard to this microbiological growth factor, the activity of cow's milk is definitely of a lower order of magnitude than that of human milk.

The "bifidus factor" in human milk is not destroyed or altered in its activity by autoclaving. Human milk ash was inactive.

TABLE 5

Assay of Human and Cow's Milk

Supplement (per 10 ml. of medium)		Titration Ml. n/10 NAOH
None		0.4
Human Milk	0.02 ml.	2.2
(Skimmed)	0.06	7.9
	0.2	12.5
Cow's Milk	0.1 ml.	0.6
(Skimmed)	0.3	0.8
	1.0	2.3

In further studies the activity of human milk was compared with that of the milk of other species (Table 6). The average relative activity was the highest for human colostrum, closely followed by rat colostrum, then by human milk, rat milk, cow's and sow's colostrum. All the other milks tested, in particular the milk of ruminants, such as cows, sheep, and goats, have shown only very slight activity (17). The highest titre of the bifidus factor in early milk, not only in cow's colostrum, but in human colostrum, rat colostrum, and sow's colostrum may have a special significance. Chemically, the bifidus factor belongs to the group of N— containing carbohydrates. In human milk the presence of a great variety of such oligo- and polysaccharides has been demonstrated (12). Their total quantity in fresh human milk may be estimated to be around 0.7 per cent, which is by no means a negligible amount with respect to total solids.

Skepticism about the overestimation of the differences in the intestinal flora between breast-fed and artificially-fed infants is best countered or at least shaken, by reference to the very interesting, little-known disease entity, familiarly named

TABLE 6

Activity of Human Milk as Compared
with Milk from Other Species

Species	Activity	One Unit in	Relative Activity
Guinea Pig	0	....	....
Cow	(+)	2.5 ml.	2.5
Sheep	(+)	2.5	2.5
Goat	(+)	2.5	2.5
Mare	+	0.5	12
Sow	+	0.4	15
Cow colostrum	++	0.15	40
Rat	++	0.13	45
Rat colostrum	++	0.03	200
Human	++	0.06 (0.02 to 0.15)	100
Human colostrum	++	0.02 (0.01 to 0.03)	300

Acrodermatitis enteropathica. The disease is characterized by vesicular dermatitis around the body orifices and the distal parts of the extremities, with multiple paronychia on hands and feet, diarrheal attacks, and other digestive dysfunction.

The disease usually appears after weaning, and without treatment is usually fatal. Recently we observed the condition in a very young infant, only a few weeks old, who had been fed cow's milk formula since birth. Brandt, in 1936, stated that "among all the therapeutic experiments that have been instituted the treatment with mother's milk is the only one that has any demonstrable effect. After addition of mother's milk to the diet, there has been an increase of the body weight from a previously almost arrest of growth, and in particular the general condition has shown a distinct improvement. . . . Diet free from cow's milk or addition of goat's milk were ineffective" (5).

From our own observation human milk has also shown beneficial effect, but unfortunately the supply was exhausted before complete remission was obtained. More recently, the intestinal antiseptic, Diodoquin, has proved to be a very effective remedy in the treatment of Acrodermatitis enteropathica (10). The nature of this condition is unknown; it is probably based on an inborn metabolic error.

The newborn, especially the prematurely born, infant is at birth not fully endowed with all metabolic enzymatic equipment which characterizes later age periods. The renal function reaches its maturity at the age of four or even six months. In its immature state, especially in the newborn period, it shows impairment of concentrating power. In consequence, it handles with difficulty abnormal loads as represented by electrolytes and metabolic products of protein.

Cow's milk, with its high content of salt and protein, will be handled with difficulty in concentrated form, as will any other form of food with higher protein content than the more diluted foods.

Figure 2 summarizes observations on adults (6). With 2000 calories and no protein in the diet, the nitrogen balance is extremely negative. The loss of water, expressed by the obligatory urine volume, is about 300 cc.

With 7.5 per cent of calories in form of protein, which, interestingly enough, is the same as that present in human milk, and with still 2000 total calories, we can improve considerably on the nitrogen losses; at the same time, the urinary volume does not increase very much. These observations were made during World War II and the conclusions have been used for the preparation of life-raft rations. If 15 per cent of the total calories are used in the form of protein, the improvement in nitrogen balance is negligible but the water loss doubles; thus the life span of the person on the life raft is reduced by 50 per cent because of thirst and water losses.

FIGURE 2

RELATION OF CALORIES AND PROTEIN TO OBLIGATORY URINE VOLUME

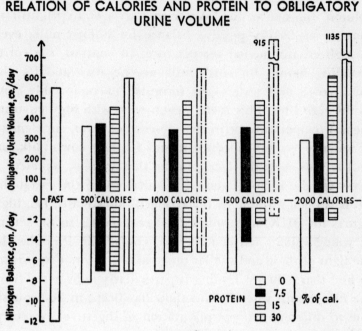

TABLE 7

Osmolar Load and Water Balance in Young Infants

	Supply of Water				Expenditures of Water				Water Excess of Expenditures	
	Preformed Water *	*Water of Oxidation*	*Total Water*	*Renal*	*Extrarenal at 21° C*	*Extrarenal at 34° C*	*Total at 21° C*	*Total at 34° C*	*At 21° C*	*At 34° C*
Human milk	200	13	213	20	80	147	100	167	113	46
Cow's milk	200	13	213	87	80	147	167	234	46	—21
Cow's milk plus carbo- hydrate **	200	13	213	61	80	147	141	208	72	5

* For concentration of 150 ml./100 cal. (20 cal./oz.).

** Two thirds of the calories from cow's milk and one third from added carbohydrate.

Table 7 is taken from a statement of the Committee on Nutrition of the Academy of Pediatrics (7). In the last column, the figures for "Water in Excess of Expenditures" show a satisfactory positive balance for human milk, even at high environmental temperature. In contrast, the corresponding figures for cow's milk are negative and for the usual cow's milk-water-sugar formulas, uncomfortably close to the zero line. This is the reason why, with high environmental temperature or in the presence of fever, supplement of water is recommended for infants fed such cow's milk formulas. However, the fact remains that it must represent a stress for the infant. Even with added water, the metabolic stress is demonstrable in the changed homeostasis, i.e., high figures for BUN, inorganic P, and reduced Ca in the serum of young infants fed concentrated cow's milk formulas. In the light of these and similar observations it is not surprising to find that: "Breast feeding is particularly indicated during the first month when infants show handicaps in homeostasis due to different rates of maturation of digestive, excretory, and endocrine function" (30).

More and more data are accumulating to testify to the immaturity of the newborn infant, especially of the premature infant. About 20 years ago Levine, Marples, and Gordon (24, 25) found that premature infants who had been fed their recommended high-protein formula excreted in the urine large amounts of parahydroxy phenyllactic and para-hydroxyphenyl pyruvic acid. They also reported that, with the addition of ascorbic acid, this excretion was reduced to practically zero. They related this finding to a disturbance or immaturity of the tyrosine-oxidase system.

Kretchmer and his associates (22, 23) showed that the catabolism of phenylalanine may also be impaired at birth.

In particular, they found that the activity of phenylalanine hydroxylase is negligible in the livers of rats late in gestation and in the early neonatal period (31). This immaturity of the tyrosine system is reminiscent of the injury of the same system observed as sequence of tourniquet shock and may have a similar or closely related foundation (3, 27).

Even more interesting are studies on the immaturity of red blood cells in newborn infants, especially in premature infants. Recently Gross and Hurwitz (14) have found high values for glucose-6-phosphate dehydrogenase, aldolase, and 6-phosphogluconic dehydrogenase. The increased metabolic activity of red blood cells in newborn infants, and for a longer period of time in premature infants, may be linked to glycolysis and to the "pentose-shunt," with gradual decline to values found for adult subjects, in the second six months of life. The reduced glutathione is not lowered in amount but it is unstable in the red blood cells of the newborn infant. This instability of reduced glutathione is found as a genetic attribute in persons with hemolytic tendency after administration of plasmaquine, naphthaline, furadantoin, and related substances (9, 11, 39).

The hemolysis by vitamin K is also of interest. Analogues such as Synkayvite occasionally caused hemolytic anemia in premature infants whose only medication had been prophylactic daily injections of Synkayvite in large doses (10 mg. per day) (1). It was shown previously that red blood cells taken from rats deficient in vitamin E are unduly sensitive to hemolysis in vivo, and in vitro to substances such as dialuric acid, H_2O_2 (16, 18, 20, 33, 34). Newborn infants, and again especially premature infants, have a physiological vitamin E deficiency detectable by the increased susceptibility of red blood cells—even in vitro—to H_2O_2 (16, 33). Allison and his

collaborators (2) have clearly demonstrated that the hemolysis observed in rats after injection of Synkayvite and a few
other vitamin K analogues was seen only in animals with vitamin E deficiency. Hemolysis was prevented by previous administration of vitamin E. It may be assumed that these
observations on animals are applicable to newborn infants.

The over-all problem of man's protein requirement is at
present in the forefront of interest and is one of the "emo-
tional" problems in American pediatrics. One may distinguish two groups: high protein and low protein groups. As
emotions go, they are often not based on clearly scientific
evidence. In this particular instance the question arises: "Is
human milk good for a human infant?" And it is; it must be.

The chemical composition of human milk and cow's milk
indicates (Table 2) that the protein content of human milk
is only about one third of that of cow's milk. If we give
enough calories—and we know how many calories we should
give—then we would give 2 to 2.5 grams of protein in the
form of human milk to a young human infant. This should
represent the necessary and probably optimal requirement,
although "optimal" is difficult to define.

In cow's milk formulas, often 5 to 8 grams of protein per
kilogram and day are given, especially to premature infants.
This contrasts sharply with the 2 to 2.5 grams of protein
breast-fed infants receive. The questions arise: Is the protein
of cow's milk a poor protein? Can it be utilized and assimilated in a manner comparable to the protein of human milk?
Professor Platt of London, in recent unpublished studies,
established in experiments on rats the biological value, or,
perhaps more exactly, the net protein utilization—the proportion of ingested protein and protein retained for human

milk and cow's milk—and found the difference not remarkable—94.5 for human milk and 81.5 for cow's milk.

Tomarelli et al. (37) found no difference of statistical significance in rats in the nutritional indexes of protein efficiency ration, protein retention efficiency, net protein utilization (by carcass N analysis), biological value, true digestibility and net protein utilization.

In our own studies on infants, in number perhaps insufficient for a definite conclusion, no significant difference was found in the utilization of protein offered in form of human milk or cow's milk (39). Even in premature infants kept on low protein rations (about 2.5 grams of protein in the form of cow's milk per kilogram and day), the results were perfectly satisfactory and statistically not different from those seen and observed on a high-protein diet (6 to 8 grams of protein per kilogram and day, again in form of cow's milk), at least not with regard to weight gain, total serum protein, serum protein fractions, Hb, and Erythrocytes. The reduced concentrating power of the kidneys in these young premature infants manifested itself in higher figures for serum phosphate and BUN compared with those found in infants on a low-protein formula. Continuation of high-protein feeding to infants beyond the usual limit of five pounds of body weight, has, if anything, a less beneficial effect, at least on weight gain, than observed in infants on a lower protein formula.

Late effects of early nutrition, including high- or low-calorie and high- or low-protein feeding, are a distinct possibility and as such would be of special and far-reaching interest. In the absence of longitudinal studies from infancy to adult life in man, this crucial question cannot be answered at the present time.

Paul György

The most impressive example of a lasting and apparently fixed effect of nutritional deficiency on growth and development has been furnished through experimental studies on rats in the Cambridge (England) laboratory of R. A. McCance (38). Several newborn litters of rats of identical genetic strain were mixed and divided among the lactating dams, only a few to some and large numbers to others. After weaning (for the same duration) all rats were put on an identical commercial ration. Those rats which were nursed in large numbers (up to 12) by one mother were small at time of weaning; the controls, which were kept with the mother in small number (about 4) were large. This difference in size was not corrected by postweaning *ad libitum* feeding of a regular commercial ration; the animals originally underfed remained small throughout the extended period of observation. Whether this late effect was due solely to the original caloric deficiency or to some other more qualitative deficiency must remain unanswered for the time being.

The specific aftereffect of early dietary deficiency on the development of particular pathologic conditions is well documented by the interesting experimental studies of Hartroft and Best (21) who have found severe hypertension developing late in life, in a group of rats kept only one week in early life on a diet deficient in choline. To what extent the promotion of degenerative diseases and malignancy seen in rats fed a high-calorie diet and, at least under special conditions, the enhancing effect of protein on the same group of diseases, should be considered as sequelae of early harmful influence or as a continuous process, is still an open question (35). These experiments on animals may have no bearing on human nutrition, but at least they make desirable long-extended, follow-up studies on the conceivable late consequence of infant feeding in its present form. It would be of special interest for pediatricians to know more about the possible late effects of breast-milk versus artificial feeding.

In view of all these open questions and scarcity of sufficient clinical and experimental material pertaining to these defects in our knowledge, intensive research is required to study the following things:

1. The cultural-anthropological reasons and their possible remedies, if desirable and obtainable, for the progressive reduction in breast-feeding in the United States and other highly developed countries.

2. The nutritive value of human milk with special reference not only to its specifically different composition but also to its biological value for over-all life processes.

3. The chemical maturation of the growing infant, exemplified by various enzyme systems (glycolysis, pentose-shunt, presence of promoters or inhibitors, etc.).

4. Long-term, follow-up studies, not only on animals, should shed light on the possible late effect of early feeding on life span, degenerative diseases, gerontology, including cancer.

In summary, nutrition in the early developmental phase may be viewed in two ways. For present practical purposes it has achieved substantial progress over the last 50 years. However, applying the methods, indirect as they are, of modern biochemistry and nutrition, it may be safely stated that infant nutrition is not a closed chapter.

REFERENCES

1. Allison, A. C.: Danger of Vitamin K to Newborn. *Lancet,* *1*:669, 1955.
2. Allison, A. C.; Moore, T.; and Sharman, I. M.: Haemolysis

Paul György

and Haemoglobinuria in Vitamin-E Deficient Rats after Injections of Vitamin-K Substitutes. *Brit. J. Haemat., 2:*197-204, 1956.

3. Anderson, P. R.; McElroy, O. E.; and Gray, I.: Physical Properties of Tyrosine Oxidizing System Following Tourniquet Injury. *Arch. Biochem. Biophys., 75:*78-86, 1958.

4. Barness, L. A.; Baker, D.; Guilbert, P.; Torres, F. E.; and György, P.: Nitrogen Metabolism of Infants Fed Human and Cow's Milk. *J. Pediat., 51:*29-39, 1957.

5. Brandt, T.: Dermatitis in Children with Disturbances of the General Condition and the Absorption of Food Elements. *Acta Dermato-Venereol., 17:*513-546, 1936.

6. Calloway, D. H. and Spector, H.: Nitrogen Balance as Related to Caloric and Protein Intake in Active Young Men. *Amer. J. Clin. Nutr., 2:*405-411, 1954.

7. Committee on Nutrition, Amer. Acad. Pediatrics: Water Requirement in Relation to Osmolar Load as it Applies to Infant Feeding. *Pediatrics, 19:*339-341, 1957.

8. Committee on Nutrition, Amer. Acad. Pediatrics: On the Feeding of Solid Foods to Infants. *Pediatrics, 21:*685-692, 1958.

9. Dern, R. J.; Weinstein, I. M.; LeRoy, G. V.; Talmage, D. W.; and Alving, A. S.: The Hemolytic Effect of Primaquine. *J. Lab. Clin. Med., 43:*303-309, 1954.

10. Dillaha, C. J. and Lorincz, A. L.: Enteropathic Acrodermatitis (Danbolt): Successful Treatment with Diodoquin ® (Diiodohydroxyquinoline). *A.M.A. Arch. Derm. Syph., 67:*324-326, 1953.

11. Flanagan, C. L.; Schrier, S. L.; Carson, P. E.; and Alving, A. S.: The Hemolytic Effect of Primaquine. *J. Lab. Clin. Med., 51:*600-608, 1958.

12. Gauhe, A.; György, P.; Hoover, J. R. E.; Kuhn, R.; Rose, C. S.; Ruelius, H. W.; and Zilliken, F.: Bifidus Factor. IV. Preparations Obtained from Human Milk. *Arch. Biochem. Biophys., 48:*214-224, 1954.

13. Gordon, H. H. and de Metry, J. P.: Hemolysis in Hydrogen Peroxide of Erythrocytes of Premature Infants. Effect of Alpha-tocopherol. *Proc. Soc. Exp. Biol. & Med., 79:*446-450, 1952.

14. Gross, R. T. and Hurwitz, R. E.: The Pentose Phosphate

Pathway in Human Erythrocytes. *Pediatrics, 22:453-459,* 1958.

15. György, P.: A Hitherto Unrecognized Biochemical Difference Between Human Milk and Cow's Milk. *Pediatrics, 11:98-107,* 1953.

16. György, P.; Cogan, G. M.; and Rose, C. S.: Availability of Vitamin E in the Newborn Infant. *Proc. Soc. Exp. Biol. & Med., 81:536-538,* 1952.

17. György, P.; Kuhn, R.; Rose, C. S.; and Zilliken, F.: Bifidus Factor. II. Its Occurrence in Milk from Different Species and in Other Natural Products. *Arch. Biochem. Biophys., 48:202-208,* 1954.

18. György, P. and Rose, C. S.: Tocopherol and Hemolysis in Vivo and in Vitro. *Ann. N. Y. Acad. Sci., 52:231-239,* 1949.

19. György, P. and Rose, C. S.: Further Observations on the Metabolic Requirements of Lactobacillus Bifidus Var. Pennsylvanicus. *J. Bacteriol., 69:483-490,* 1955.

20. György, P. and Rose, C. S.: Effect of Dietary Factors on Early Mortality and Hemoglobinuria in Rats Following Administration of Alloxan. *Science, 108:716-718,* 1948.

21. Hartroft, W. S. and Best, C. H.: Hypertension of Renal Origin in Rats Following Less Than One Week of Choline Deficiency in Early Life. *Brit. Med. J., 1:423-426,* 1949.

22. Kretchmer, N.; Levine, S. Z.; McNamara, H.; and Barnett, H. L.: Certain Aspects of Tyrosine Metabolism in the Young. I. The Development of the Tyrosine Oxidizing System in Human Liver. *J. Clin. Invest., 35:236-244,* 1956.

23. Kretchmer, N.; McNamara, H.; Barnett, H. L.; and Levine, S. Z.: The Development of Tyrosine Oxidase Activity in Liver. *A.M.A. Amer. J. Dis. Childr., 90:576,* 1955.

24. Levine, S. Z.; Gordon, H. H.; and Marples, E.: A Defect in the Metabolism of Tyrosine and Phenylalanine in Premature Infants. II. Spontaneous Occurrence and Eradication by Vitamin C. *J. Clin. Invest., 20:209-219,* 1941.

25. Levine, S. Z.; Marples, E.; and Gordon, H. H.: A Defect in the Metabolism of Tyrosine and Phenylalanine in Premature Infants. I. Identification and Assay of Intermediary Products. *J. Clin. Invest., 20:199-207,* 1941.

26. Mannheimer, E.: Mortality of Breast Fed and Bottle Fed Infants. *Acta Genet., 5:134-163,* 1955.

27. McElroy, O. E.; Anderson, P. R.; and Gray, I.: Effect of Tourniquet Injury on the Tyrosine Oxidizing System of Liver of Rats. *Arch. Biochem. Biophys. 75:69-77*, 1958.

28. Mellander, O.: Vahlquist, B.; Mellbin, T.: Breast Feeding and Artificial Feeding. The Norrbotten Study. *Acta Paediat., 48:* Suppl. 116, 1959.

29. Meyer, H. F.: Breast Feeding in the United States: Extent and Possible Trend. *Pediatrics, 22:116-121*, 1958.

30. National Research Council: *Recommended Dietary Allowances.* Washington, D. C.: National Academy of Sciences, 1958.

31. Reem, G. H. and Kretchmer, N.: Development of Phenylalanine Hydroxylase in Liver of the Rat. *Proc. Soc. Exp. Biol. & Med., 96:458-460*, 1957.

32. Robinson, M.: Infant Morbidity and Mortality. *Lancet, 1:788-794*, 1951.

33. Rose, C. S. and György, P.: Hemolysis with Alloxan and Alloxan-like Compounds, and the Protective Action of Tocopherol. *Blood, 5:1062-1074*, 1950.

34. Rose, C. S. and György, P.: Specificity of Hemolytic Reaction in Vitamin E-Deficient Erythrocytes. *Amer. J. Physiol., 168:414-420*, 1952.

35. Ross, M.: *Federation Proceedings,* in press.

36. Sydow, G. v. and Faxén, N.: Breast or Cow's Milk as Infant Food. *Acta Paediat., 43:362-367*, 1954.

37. Tomarelli, R. M.; Minnick, N.; d'Amato, E.; and Bernhart, F. W.: Bioassay of the Nutritional Quality of the Protein of Human and Cow's Milk by Rat Growth Procedures. *J. Nutr., 68:265-279,* 1959.

38. Widdowson, E.: Personal communication.

39. Zinkham, W. H. and Childs, B.: A Defect of Glutathione Metabolism in Erythrocytes from Patients with a Naphthalene-Induced Hemolytic Anemia. *Pediatrics, 22:467-471*, 1958.

RESEARCH PROSPECTIVES
IN NUTRITION:
THE NUCLEUS OF THE PROBLEM

Max A. Lauffer, Ph.D.

THE SCIENCE of nutrition is the study of one important aspect of the interaction between an organism and its environment. The capacity to respond to environment is obviously largely determined by heredity. This is true not only of the nutritional responses of different species but even of the variation in response between individuals of the same species. Galactosemia, a children's disease characterized by inability to utilize galactose, phenyl pyruvate, oligophrenia, and glycogen storage disease are all described as inherited abnormalities.

Since these abnormalities appear to be hereditary, complete understanding of them is possible only in terms of genetics. Much evidence indicates that at the root of genetic mechanisms is nucleic acid. Chromosomes were early found in the nuclei of cells undergoing division, and a strong case was made for identifying the assortment of genetic traits with the movements of these microscopically visible bodies.

299

Nucleic acid is found in great abundance in cell nuclei. That chromosomes are rich in this substance was early inferred from the fact that they could be stained by chemicals known to combine with deoxyribonucleic acid (DNA).

More detailed knowledge of the intimate connection between genetic information and nucleic acid is derived from studies carried out on viruses. When a bacterial virus infects a bacterium it apparently injects only its DNA into the bacterial cell (9). Because the process of infection leads to the multiplication of bacterial virus, this experiment demonstrated that the genetic information of the bacterial virus is transmitted by the DNA.

Two other phenomena—lysogeny and transduction—discovered in the study of bacterial viruses help to associate genetic information with nucleic acid. Soon after bacteriophages were first recognized, it became evident that there are in nature lysogenic bacteria which possess and transmit to their progeny the potentiality of producing virus if subjected to stress such as treatment with a nitrogen mustard or irradiation with X rays. The phenomenon of lysogeny was described in detail by Lwoff (12). The most probable explanation is that the nucleic acid of the bacteriophage is incorporated into that of the bacterium. This is duplicated and passed on from generation to generation without any apparent harm to the bacterial cell. Upon being subjected to stress, the nucleic acid containing the genetic information of the bacteriophage becomes activated and, thereafter, directs the production of bacterial virus. Occasionally, when a bacterium of the right genetic make-up is infected with a virus, it does not become diseased in the usual sense but becomes lysogenic.

When a bacterium is infected with a virus grown in a different kind of bacterium, some genetic traits of the original bacterium show up in the infected bacterium. This rare event is called transduction. It is obvious that transduction can be demonstrated only in those cases in which the bacterium survives infection in a manner at least superficially similar to that involved in the production of a lysogenic strain. A much-studied example of transduction involves the transfer from one bacterium to another by the bacteriophage lambda of a gene-controlling galactose fermentation. More information concerning this phenomenon can be found in a review by Bertani (1). It is obvious that, if a bacteriophage particle transfers only DNA to a bacterium during the process of infection, then a gene transduced as a byproduct of the infection must also be nucleic acid.

Much additional information about the relationship between nucleic acid and genetic information has come from studies on the inactivation of various viruses by X rays. For many viruses the ability to produce infection decreases exponentially with the dose of X rays (11). This is illustrated (in Figure 1) by data obtained with tobacco mosaic virus (TMV) (2). This result can be interpreted in terms of target theory. From the relationship between dose and biological response, one can calculate the size of the target. The basic idea is that a virus will become inactivated only if an ionization occurs within it. The probability that an ionization will occur within the biologically sensitive target depends on the number of ionizations produced per unit volume, which is directly related to dose, and upon the volume occupied by the target. Since the fractional biological effect is by hypothesis equal to the probability of an ionization occurring

Max A. Lauffer

FIGURE 1
X-IRRADIATION OF 2 PER CENT TOBACCO MOSAIC VIRUS
IN 25 PER CENT BROTH SOLUTION *

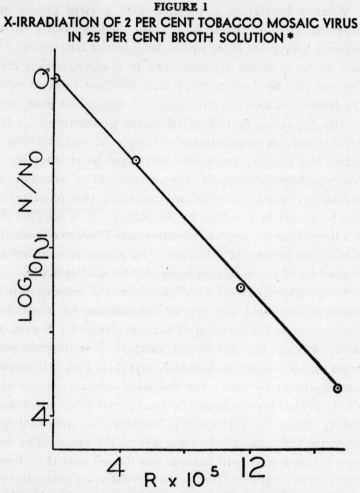

*Based on data reported by Buzzell, Trkula, and Lauffer (2, p. 470)

in a target, one can estimate the target size from the fraction
of virus particles which become inactivated by a known dose.
As is shown in Table 1, there is high correlation between
radiosensitive volume and nucleic acid volume for many
viruses (2, 5).

302

TABLE 1

Virus Volumes (X 10^{18} ml)

Virus	Target Vol.	NA Vol.	Total Vol.
Tobacco Mosaic	4.1	3.0	50
Tobacco Necrosis	1.5	1.5	8.1
Tobacco Ringspot	2.8	3.2	8.1
Tomato Bushy Stunt	2.9	2.7	15.6
T_2 Bacteriophage	52	55	150
T_6 Bacteriophage	52	55	150
T_7 Bacteriophage	17.5	18	47
Shope Papilloma	3.9	4.2	48
PR8 Influenza	18	15	294

If nucleic acid is the radiosensitive seat, then there should be physical damage to nucleic acid as a result of inactivation of viruses by X rays. As illustrated in Table 2, RNA isolated from TMV inactivated with X rays has a lower intrinsic viscosity than RNA isolated from unirradiated virus (10). The most reasonable interpretation of this result is that the nucleic acid thread is broken by the action of X rays. This comes about not by breaking the entire TMV rod, but by damage inflicted internally.

TABLE 2

Intrinsic Viscosity of RNA from X-irradiated TMV

	Dose (r X 10^{-5})		
	0	4.6 ($2D_0$)	18.6 ($8D_0$)
(η)	84	65	37
ml/g	77		40
	74		43
mean	78	65	40

It is consistent with target theory that an occasional virus particle should escape a hit in the nucleic acid and, thereby, survive even when subjected to many times the average lethal dose of radiation. However, it will have been hit many times in the protein coat because the protein of a TMV particle has a much larger volume than the nucleic acid. Such survivors of X ray irradiation, however, were found to have the same thermal stability as unirradiated virus (2) (See Figure 2). All these results led to the conclusion that the biological activity of TMV depends on the physical intactness of the nucleic acid but that a comparable degree of intactness of the protein is not required (10). It has been shown by independent reports that isolated RNA of TMV is infectious (6, 8).

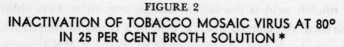

FIGURE 2

INACTIVATION OF TOBACCO MOSAIC VIRUS AT 80°
IN 25 PER CENT BROTH SOLUTION *

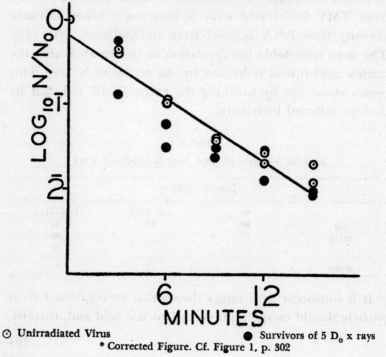

⊙ Unirradiated Virus   ● Survivors of 5 D_0 x rays

* Corrected Figure. Cf. Figure 1, p. 302

More recently, experiments involving the ultracentrifuge have confirmed the relationship between the inactivation of TMV by X rays and the depolymerization of one nucleic acid (4). Isolated nucleic acid is also inactivated by X rays and the inactivation is also accompanied by depolymerization (15).

It is evident from the studies reviewed that genetic information of TMV is carried by the RNA. The facts that the target volume almost equals the RNA volume and that the inactivation is an exponential function of dose are evidence that all of the RNA is necessary for the transfer of genetic information. This result, taken by itself, does not answer the question whether the RNA is all in one piece physically. However, it is very unlikely that an infection could be induced, especially at low concentration, if two independent pieces of RNA had to enter the same cell. Furthermore, biophysical studies carried out both in Schramm's laboratory and in the author's indicate that the molecular weight of the RNA is approximately 2 million, the right value for particles consisting of all of the RNA in the TMV particle. It is, therefore, very likely that the RNA is, indeed, in one physical piece. X-ray diffraction studies (7) can be interpreted to mean that the RNA of TMV is a single thread coiled into a helix, lying near but not at the center of the TMV rod. It somewhat resembles a long coiled spring.

If nucleic acid is able to transmit genetic information, how does it do it? The answer must lie either in its chemical constitution or in its physical structure. Genetic information can be transmitted only by specifically reproducible non-uniformities in structure. A review of the physical and chemical structure of nucleic acid has been presented by Crick (3). There is nothing in the physical structure of either DNA or RNA which would provide the possibilities for the variety of information needed to differentiate between strains of organisms. It is therefore necessary to look to the chemical structure.

Nucleic acid is a polymer made up of phosphoric acid, ribose or deoxyribose, and purine and pyrimidine bases. A small segment of a stretched-out polymer chain of RNA is shown in the formula below (Figure 3). The possibility of carrying genetic information might lie in the sequence in which the bases are arranged along the chain. This, at any rate, is the current dogma of molecular geneticists. How much information could be carried if this is the mechanism in a single RNA particle obtained from TMV? From the molecular weight of the RNA and from the residue weights of purine and pyrimidine bases, of phosphoric acid, and of ribose, one can easily calculate that there are about eight thousand mononucleotide units, or eight thousand bases along a single TMV RNA chain. This particular nucleic acid has the bases, guanine, adenine, cytosine, and uracil. The relative amounts of the four are known; however, the sequence of occurrence could vary. The following sentence shows how genetic information could be carried in a TMV particle: GACUUAGUCAACUGUCUGAAGAUCUAGAG-ACUUGACUGCUGCGAUCUAGGACUUCAGAAGGAC-UUAGCAUCUAGGUCAAUGCUAUCAGAGAUGAUGA-UCU. It contains one hundred letters taken from a four-letter alphabet, GACU, and represents 1/80 of the total information-carrying power of a TMV RNA molecule. The sequence written here is purely imaginary; it is correct only in the relative composition of G's, A's, C's and U's.

Studies on TMV have provided a certain amount of evidence in favor of the hypothesis that genetic information is carried by the sequence of residues along the nucleic acid chain. If this theory is correct, differences in the sequences

FIGURE 3

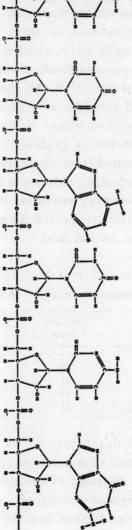

for different strains of TMV must exist. There is some evidence that this is the case (13). Nucleic acid isolated from various strains of TMV was digested with pancreatic ribonuclease. According to present understanding of the action of this enzyme, it can split a chain only at a site where there is a pyrimidine base, cytosine, or uricil. If this is so, in order for the enzyme to split off a monopyrimidine nucleotide, there must be two monopyrimidine nucleotides adjacent to each other in the sequence in the chain. The amount of uridylic acid and of cytodylic acid isolated from digests of nucleic acids from various strains of TMV do, indeed, show some significant differences (Table 3). Furthermore, fragments have been isolated from digests containing two, three, and four bases and showing differences between strains (14). These results provide very important evidence in favor of the currently held view that genetic information is carried by the base sequence in nucleic acid.

TABLE 3

Monopyrimidine Nucleotides in RNA Digests

Strain	Per Cent Total	Per Cent Total
	U.A.	C.A.
TMV	51	46
HR	48	42
YA	49	45
M	71	61

In the course of this paper, it has been assumed that genetics lie at the base of nutritional response of an organism. Evidence from the study of chromosomes in the nuclei of cells and from the study of viruses—infection by nucleic acid, lysogeny and transduction, and the correlation of X-ray inactivation with nucleic acid depolymerization—shows conclusively that genetic information is associated with nucleic acid, deoxyribonucleic acid in the cases of higher organisms, and of bacterial viruses and ribonucleic acid in the case of TMV. The possibility of finding different sequences in the arrangement of the purine and pyrimidine bases along the nucleic acid chain affords a molecular mechanism for recording genetic information within the nucleic acid molecule. Experimental evidence in favor of this view is provided in the demonstration that there are differences in the base sequences of the nucleic acids from various strains of TMV.

Many nutritional responses are based on inherited capacities. Through studies on nucleic acids, we gain knowledge of the physical and chemical basis of heredity, and thus we lay the foundation for fuller understanding of aspects of human nutrition.

REFERENCES

1. Bertani, G.: Lysogeny. *Advances in Virus Research,* 5:151-193, 1958.
2. Buzzell, A.; Trkula, D.; and Lauffer, M. A.: X-Ray Studies on Tobacco Mosaic Virus. *Arch. Biochem. Biophys., 63:*470-476, 1956.
3. Crick, F. H. C.: Nucleic Acids. *Scientific Amer., 197:*188-200, 1957.
4. Englander, S. W.; Buzzell, A.; and Lauffer, M. A.: The Relationship between Inactivation of Tobacco Mosaic Virus by X-rays and Breakage of Nucleic Acid. *Biochim. Biophys. Acta, 40:*385-392, 1960.
5. Epstein, H. T.: Identification of Radiosensitive Volume with Nucleic Acid Volume. *Nature, 171:*394-395, 1953.
6. Fraenkel-Conrat, H.: The Role of the Nucleic Acid in the Reconstitution of Active Tobacco Mosaic Virus. *J. Amer. Chem. Soc., 78:*882-883, 1956.

7. Franklin, R. E.; Klug, A.; and Holmes, K. C.: *Nature of Viruses*. Boston: Little, Brown, 1957, pp. 39-55.
8. Gierer, A. and Schramm, G.: Infectivity of Ribonucleic Acid from Tobacco Mosaic Virus. *Nature, 177:*702-703, 1956.
9. Hershey, A. D. and Chase, M.: Independent Functions of Viral Protein and Nucleic Acid in Growth of Bacteriophage. *J. General Physiol., 36:*39-56, 1952.
10. Lauffer, M. A.; Trkula, D.; and Buzzell, A.: Mechanism of Inactivation of Tobacco Mosaic Virus by X-rays. *Nature, 177:*890, 1956.
11. Lea, D. E.: *Actions of Radiations on Living Cells*. New York: Macmillan, 1953.
12. Lwoff, A.: Lysogeny. *Bacteriol. Rev., 17:*269-337, 1953.
13. Reddi, K. K.: Structural Differences in the Nucleic Acids of Some Tobacco Mosaic Virus Strains. I. Monopyrimidine Nucleotides in Ribonuclease Digests. *Biochimica et Biophysica Acta, 25:*528-531, 1957.
14. Reddi, K. K.: The Arrangement of Purine and Pyrimidine Nucleotides in Tobacco Mosaic Virus Nucleic Acid. *Proc. Nat. Acad. Sci., 45:*293-300, 1959.
15. Wohlhieter, J. A.; Buzzell, A.; and Lauffer, M. A.: Effect of X-rays on Nucleic Acid Isolated from Tobacco Mosaic Virus. *Biochim. Biophys. Acta,* in press.

NEW HORIZONS IN RESEARCH

Charles G. King, Ph.D., D.Sc.

EACH OF us shares with every other living organism the common experience of beginning life with an uncertain background and an uncertain future. Awareness of this element of the unknown can add immeasurably to the zest and satisfaction of living. Furthermore, so far as we know, all life may have had a single beginning from which successive organisms have been reproduced through many millions of years and with many millions of variations.

Each man can assume that most of his characteristics, but not all, are transmitted safely through genetic structures. However, these genetic assurances are subject to undetected changes that can be imposed either physically or chemically from our environment. It follows that each of us has a degree of unpredictable freedom and responsibility to chart our own course, choose our own sense of values, and create our greatest contributions in life.

There are great advantages in being akin to all living things and especially to all mankind. For example, we can have a high degree of confidence that anything we learn about the content or functions within any living cell probably will be pertinent to what happens in the human body, including our own. Of course, every human body differs in some respects from all others.

The above kinds of relationship serve as a challenge to the research scientist and to the physician in approaching any living organism or patient. This sense of necessity to study the individual within the framework of statistical probability affords the greatest growing point, I believe, on the frontier of science.

The implications of this viewpoint appear to be as great in the social sciences as they are in the biological sciences, because they create a fundamental demand for respect of the individual. Hence they apply in our personal relationships and in our political views of government. They give meaning also to Albert Schweitzer's views as expressed in his philosophical treatise on "Reverence for Life."

In the years to come the research areas of most intensive and fruitful study will continue to change as we gain more knowledge. But there are basic patterns that I believe will serve as a guide for several decades.

The first objective is to identify the more significant nutrients so that they can be measured accurately and, on this basis, can be studied and controlled, ultimately, with respect to functions. This is an extremely important point for emphasis because scientists and laymen are often far too cocksure with respect to what is known. Even among scientists there is a tendency to let ignorance of adjacent fields blind them to how little is really understood. Strangely, this situation persists despite the fact that each research scientist or physician takes pride in pointing out the areas where research is needed in the immediate environment of his own special field.

Progress is still rapid in identifying new, essential nutrients, such as selenium, cobalt, and molybdenum. The elements fluorine, bromine, and vanadium are still in a twilight zone, and at least five research groups believe they have evidence for the existence of one to three new vitamins not yet identified. There is still considerable disagreement about which amino acids and fatty acids should be grouped as essential. To be practical, we must include consideration of the nonessential nutrients that have a direct bearing on the functions and requirements of the essential nutrients. Then the number is legion! New substances in this group are reported in almost every issue of the biochemical journals.

The science of biochemistry is most active, however, in discovering how the individual nutrients function. It would be useless and completely illogical to attempt to separate this field from the science of nutrition. In many ways it is the major part of nutrition, because the intakes of nutrients derive their significance from the functional roles to be played inside the organism. In this respect the nutrition scientist might be said to be a biochemist, physiologist, or physician with an alert appreciation of the significance of the initial stages of the reactions that characterize a cell or organism.

The following examples will illustrate how slow our progress has been in searching for chemical understanding of how the nutrients function.

1. Of the first five vitamins to be identified, very little is known of the chemical functions of vitamins A, C, D and E.

2. In the best American biochemical research journal, about one fifth of all the papers still deal with the functions of glucose and its direct fragments.

3. The reactions of linoleic acid are just beginning to be identified during the present decade. Although it was one

of the first nutrients to be identified, it has achieved major interest in relation to public health and industrial practices only within the past few years.

4. In most parts of the world where science is least advanced, the task of meeting protein requirements is paramount. Solving this problem efficiently is still contingent on a clearer picture of how the amino acids function.

5. We might go back still further and look at calcium, one of the very early mineral elements to be identified as essential. Yet the functions of this element are still too uncertain to interpret its role in the cardiovascular diseases and in the nutritional problems of pregnancy, lactation, infant feeding, and senescence.

Nutrition is still a young, growing, and vigorous science with increased value to mankind as a result of each discovery. Narrow definitions of nutrition are no longer acceptable. Examples of research that furnishes basic information about the manner in which organisms utilize nutrients from their environment for growth, reproduction, and the maintenance of health might be cited as follows:

George W. Beadle and his associates at the California Institute of Technology have added extensively to our understanding of how each cell transmits, or fails to transmit the chemical mechanisms essential to the succeeding cells. Step by step, the enzymes and the specific atomic and electronic changes will be identified by these workers or others. The insight derived from these studies applies in large measure to all living organisms from the simplest bacteria, molds, and other micro-organisms to man himself. Related to these studies of fundamental principles in genetics are the studies of the cell nucleus in its balanced relationships to other parts of the cell, as illustrated by the work of Alfred Mirsky and his associates at the Rockefeller Institute and by Arthur Pollister's group at Columbia University.

For their fundamental value in working toward an understanding of living organisms, we must cite the studies of biochemists such as Albert Lehninger of Johns Hopkins University, Henry Lardy at the University of Wisconsin, A. Baird Hastings of Harvard University, Carl Cori of Washington University, and Fritz Lipmann of the Rockefeller Institute. These scientists have been identifying the individual catalysts that characterize nearly all living cells in the utilization and transformation of nutrients such as the simplest sugar, fat, or amino acid in furnishing energy and in forming the cell constituents that ultimately explain growth and health.

Of comparable importance to understanding the nature of energy and growth are techniques for identifying and appraising departures from normal balances that would serve to identify risks of disease in advance of actual breaks in health. At this stage the science of nutrition encompasses the identification of nutrients entering each cell or organism and traces them through the intricate mechanisms that characterize life.

The Significance of Quantitative Data

The early stages of medical science and the science of nutrition were concerned primarily with day-to-day comfort and gross departures from health as reflected by obvious sickness or physical injury. With the advent of the microscope and the development of biochemistry, by which invisible changes could be measured quantitatively, a new era in the interpretation of health and disease moved forward rapidly.

Charles G. King

A long period followed during which growth and reproduction became measuring standards for health and nutrition. Experimental animals then became standard tools to accelerate measurements of maturity and aging. These reflected still more sensitive indexes in life-span appraisals of health, and laid the foundation for our present, far more complex concepts of nutrition that include consideration of such factors as mental health, social adjustments, and life-span enjoyment of efficiency instead of mere survival.

The Search for Optimum Nutrition

The transition from primitive practices in the use of foods to a quantitative concept of furnishing all the necessary nutrients in balanced proportions without excess of calories for each individual through the experiences of a lifetime, has brought us to the frontier of facing new problems.

Hence we recognize the significance of long-term studies such as those under way at the University of Colorado where A. H. Washburn is studying the *total development of individuals.* The study of each infant begins with the initial stages of pregnancy when there is a record of genetic or familial background, plus a study of the physical and social environment into which the child is born. The health status of the parents also becomes a matter of importance in forecasting the risks to the child on either a genetic or environmental basis. The professional qualifications of the staff associated with Washburn permit a broad study that is exceedingly rare but commensurate in value. The role of nutrition is recognized in these studies as one of the most fundamental factors in the physical development of the infant and has become increasingly important with the accu-

316

mulation of evidence based upon the nutrition of the mother, the nutritional practices of the infant and growing child, together with accurate records of physical development, maintenance of health, educational advances, and social adjustment in the family and in the community. Although time has not permitted a major evaluation of the processes of aging and the relative risks from many of the diseases of greatest current interest such as coronary heart disease, cerebral strokes, and premature senility, information of this nature will become available and will be unique in value, if the studies can be continued into the years ahead. Second-generation children are being studied already.

Here is an illustration of the value of such long-term studies. When concern was first expressed regarding the advantages or disadvantages of an infant's intake of cow's milk or modified formulas, as compared to the nutrients supplied in mother's milk, it was possible to gain some of the critically needed information promptly by reference to the children for whom Washburn's group had obtained meticulous records. This reference group will be uniquely valuable in supplementing the search for information by more intense studies of infants whose dietary practices can be regulated in short-term tests.

Another approach to long-term studies related to human health has been made possible by the development of standard and controlled colonies of primates of different types. These animals, although handicapped in comparison with smaller animals by their longer life span and greater costs for maintenance, afford many advantages by their closer anatomical and nutritional resemblance to human beings. For example, the primates are the only animals, other than guinea pigs, which, like man, require an intake of vitamin C. At least one type of baboon and one type of monkey (woolly) are subject in their native environment to atherosclerosis and related diseases of the cardiovascular system—thus affording a unique basis for controlled experimentation.

Among the major questions facing the medical profession, public health authorities, and nutrition scientists today is an appraisal of the effect of our rapidly decreasing energy expenditure in physical work. The first obvious impact of decreased work output is a tendency to consume excessive calories and become obese, but this is only a beginning in appraising the problem. According to the trend of present evidence, this new circumstance of living introduces a host of nutrition problems of unknown significance. Theoretically, the basal nutrient requirements, when there is a large energy expenditure, might permit a higher relative content of carbohydrates and fats to furnish the energy needs, beyond a normal intake of protein, minerals, and vitamins. Hence, if this concept is valid, modern dietary practices may need reappraisal in terms of foods characterized by a greater content of protein, minerals, and vitamins per thousand calories.

A third factor that cannot be adequately appraised from present evidence has to do with a cumulative effect of nerve tensions and the conventional stresses of living when there is a less than normal opportunity for the physical work, exercise, or recreation that might be important in maintaining optimal functioning of the nervous system, the cardiovascular system and, in turn, all the tissues of the body.

A fourth area is becoming increasingly important in seeking to evaluate the effects of immunization against common infections, compared with earlier normal experiences with infections at low levels of virulence but with a gradual development of adequate defense mechanisms. A closely associated problem is the indication that good-quality protein intakes, moderately above levels required for normal growth, may be important in the maintenance of protection against infections. On the other hand, it is uncertain how far this trend toward higher and more regular protein intakes can be pushed without incurring a risk of imposing stress on the kidneys and liver as a result of excessive protein. Research such as that developed notably at Notre Dame University in the use of germ-free animals will make an important contribution, and studies of protein intake in relation to defense mechanisms, such as those of Paul Cannon at the University of Chicago and by René Dubos at the Rockefeller Institute, will have value in the most advanced countries as well as in areas where protein deficiencies among children constitute an acute hazard to health and to the national economy.

A new type of risk is obviously going to assume crucial interest to the entire world. Here we speak of the efforts to appraise the significance of injuries to health that may arise from radioactive exposures, either from the external environment or from the internal environment, as a result of contamination of the atmosphere, soil, water supplies, and foodstuffs. Dietary practices may be found to have an important bearing on the body's resistance to injuries from radioactive exposures. There is also an interest in foreseeing the variations that may arise in the effects of radioactive materials on different crops and in different areas. Apparently one of the greatest risks of this nature will be with reference to sea food.

Charles G. King

New Techniques of Identifying Departures from Optimum Nutrition

New techniques for measuring nutrients and intermediate products such as the freely circulating or combined mineral elements, amino acids, vitamins, lipids, and sugars are opening new horizons for evaluating nutritional status without waiting for irreversible injuries to occur. We are in the unhappy but challenging situation of being able to measure a great many intermediate changes of this kind without being able to evaluate the significance of the measurements in terms of health. The predictive element is missing in most instances, but we can be confident that in time this area of nutrition research will lay the foundation for great advances in the medical sciences and in guiding food practices. This is perhaps the most exciting challenge in the science of nutrition today, and I predict that it will continue to be of intense interest and value in the years and centuries ahead.

Micromethods of biochemical analysis, e.g., those used by Oliver Lowry and Linderstrom-Lang and their associates, respectively at Washington University and the University of Copenhagen, and the histochemistry techniques developed by David Glick and his associates at the University of Minnesota, illustrate the rapid trend of research in this direction. Another striking development is under way in measurements of serum lipides, by S. R. Lipsky at Yale University and E. H. Ahrens at the Rockefeller Institute. The sensitivity of analyses now permitted in the use of radioactive and heavy isotopes adds a further chapter in the direction of identifying chemical changes that will revolutionize medicine, agriculture, food technology and the biological sciences beyond our present imagination.

Developments in the science of genetics and in biochemistry will almost certainly become much more useful and increasingly reliable in identifying the genetic pattern of each individual. It is scarcely necessary to mention here the value of such contributions in extending the protective mechanisms that have begun to show on the horizon in dealing with galactosemia, in which milk sugar is a hazard to health; celiac disease, in which one of the protein fragments in wheat and rye can impose a risk to health; cystic fibrosis, in which nearly all of the mucous and secretory cells are impaired; phenylketonuria, in which an essential amino acid becomes toxic at normal levels of intake; and cholesteremia, which currently resembles Pandora's box.

In conclusion, the integration of basic research in biochemistry, genetics, psychology, and, broadly, in all aspects of the biological sciences is almost certain to build the science of nutrition into an increasingly dominant position in agriculture, medicine, public health, food technology, public education, economics, and even such sciences as population control, for the general betterment of mankind. These advances cannot be divorced from our highest concepts of morality, religion, and the values that we most treasure in life.